Jeremy from Grant

THE COMPLETE TALES FROM SHAKESPEARE

All those told by Charles & Mary Lamb
with 12 others newly told
by J. C. Trewin

NEW YORK: FRANKLIN WATTS INC.

LONDON: THE NONESUCH PRESS

TALES FROM SHAKESPEARE
was first published in 1807

This Nonesuch edition, designed by
Sir Francis Meynell, first published 1964
Reprinted 1966

The version of the First Folio portrait is by Leonard Beaumont, and the signature of William Shakespeare is taken from his will, by courtesy of the Public Record Office, London

First American publication 1964 by Franklin Watts Inc.
575 Lexington Avenue, New York 22, N. Y.
Library of Congress Catalog Card Number: 64–23192

Printed and made in Great Britain
by William Clowes and Sons, Limited

OTHER NONESUCH BOOKS
FOR YOUNG PEOPLE

Alice's Adventures in Wonderland
Through the Looking Glass *and*
The Hunting of the Snark
by Lewis Carroll, with the original illustrations to the two 'Alice' books by John Tenniel

At the Back of the North Wind
by George MacDonald, illustrated by Charles Mozley

The Bastables
by E. Nesbit, illustrated by Susan Einzig

Fifty Favorite Fairy Tales
chosen from the Color Fairy Books of Andrew Lang by Kathleen Lines, illustrated by Margery Gill

Memorable Poetry
Chosen by Sir Francis Meynell

Tarka the Otter
by Henry Williamson, illustrated by Barry Driscoll

Treasure Island
by Robert Louis Stevenson, illustrated by Robert Micklewright

The Contents

The Introduction by J. C. Trewin

DURING the spring and summer of the year 1806, when Mary Ann Lamb was forty-one and her brother Charles ten years younger, they would often sit at night in their London home at Mitre Court Buildings, Temple, writing at one table (as Mary said) 'like Hermia and Helena in the *Midsummer Night's Dream*; or rather like an old literary Darby and Joan'.

They were engaged upon *Tales From Shakespeare*, a plan suggested by William Godwin and – particularly no doubt – his wife, who had opened a publishing house that specialised in children's books. Charles was by profession a clerk in the London office of the East India House, and by inclination a writer. Small, stammering, and gay, a man of innumerable friends, he was a brave and affectionate brother, devoted to Mary who suffered intermittently from a desolating mental illness. She, too, was eager to write. Though, when *Tales From Shakespeare* appeared in January 1807, it bore only Charles's name on the title-page, Mary had been responsible in fact for some fourteen of the narratives and Charles for only six.

Mary, who liked happy endings, kept firmly to the comedies and romances, all of which were included except *Love's Labour's Lost* and *The Merry Wives of Windsor*. Certain characters vanished in her compression. Thus in *Twelfth Night* there is no reference by name to Malvolio, Sir Toby, Sir Andrew, Maria, and Feste; and neither Touchstone nor Jaques arrives in *As You Like It*.

Charles proposed to deal with the tragedies. Finally, he did only *King Lear* (probably his best work), *Macbeth*, *Timon of Athens*, *Romeo and Juliet*, *Othello* (his own preference), and *Hamlet*. The Roman tragedies, *Troilus and Cressida*, and the histories were omitted entirely.

In a letter, when about eight of the plays had been done, Charles said hopefully, 'I think it will be popular among the little people.

Besides money. It is to bring in sixty guineas.' At another date Mary wrote of them at their table together, 'I taking snuff and he groaning all the while and saying he can make nothing of it which he always says till he has finished, and then finds that he *has* made something of it.'

Between them – though, because of the publishers' caprice, Charles had the printed credit – they made of it a book that would grow into a classic. There were a few troubles on the way. Mary at one point (said Charles) was complaining of 'having to set forth so many female characters in boy's clothes. She begins to think Shakespeare must have wanted Imagination.' At this stage Mary had 'stuck fast' in *All's Well That Ends Well*; Charles had to help her out.

Finally, in January 1807, the twenty narratives were published together as '*Tales From Shakespeare. Designed For Young Persons.* By Charles Lamb. London, M. J. Godwin.' Sending a copy off to his friend William Wordsworth, the poet, who lived in the Lake District – the book went by coach from the Swan and Two Necks in Lad Lane – Charles objected to the illustrations and added that, besides the six tragedies, he was himself answerable for 'occasionally a tail piece or correction of grammar, for none of the cuts [pictures] and all of the spelling. The rest is my Sister's. We think *Pericles* of hers the best and *Othello* of mine – but I hope all have some good. *As You Like It* we like least.'

A preface, written for the most part by Mary, began with the assurance:

> [Shakespeare's] words are used whenever it seemed possible to bring them in; and in whatever has been added to give them the regular form of a connected story, diligent care has been taken to select such words as might least interrupt the effect of the beautiful English tongue in which he wrote; therefore, words introduced into our language since his time have been as far as possible avoided.

The *Tales* had immediate and continued success, though the authors did not make much from them. Charles died on December 27, 1834, at the age of fifty-nine, and was buried at Edmonton. Mary, who survived him into Queen Victoria's reign – and in all by twelve-and-a-half years – died in London on May 20, 1847, and was buried at Edmonton near her brother. Charles, who became known under the pen-name of Elia, lives on as one of the most graceful essayists in the literature of England; and Mary lives not only because she was Charles's sister in that moving companionship, but also because she has long had her rightful place as the principal author of *Tales From Shakespeare*.

* * *

I came to Shakespeare first by way of the *Tales*. My home was on the extreme tip of the Lizard peninsula in South Cornwall, a house separated by only a garden and a field from Old Lizard Head. My father, a merchant captain, used to take several crates of books with him on a long voyage and leave them with us on his return; always he sailed with a new cabin library. His reading was wide and unexpected: certainly I have never been able to imagine him far up the River Amazon, reading *Lamb's Tales* in the tropical night. But there it was: a copy of the *Tales* was among his books on a South American voyage. Later it stayed on the shelves of Kynance Bay House from which I seized it and read it with enthusiasm in the long winter evenings.

At the time I was only eight, and ready to transfer every scene to a place familiar and local. Even now I cannot hear the names of, say, Illyria or Mantua without flashing up a mental picture that might have surprised the dramatist.

From Lamb it was a natural move to the text of the plays themselves. I can remember the exact moment when I found them. There were books all over the house, including some on an overcrowded shelf high above the sitting-room fireplace. I reached up early one evening to get something like *Ben-Hur* and instead dislodged a Shakespeare which fell upon the rug. It opened as it fell, and I went on for a while from that page. So the Duke of Bedford's speech at Henry the Fifth's funeral in *Henry the Sixth: Part One* – not one of the Lambs' plays – became the first Shakespeare lines I read in the text:

> Hung be the heavens with black, yield day to night!
> Comets, importing change of times and states,
> Brandish your crystal tresses in the sky . . .

Later I would associate the words with the sudden light that entered a chink in the drawn green blinds of my bedroom, hovered upon wall and ceiling, faded, returned, faded, returned, and would do so, I realised, until daybreak dimmed it. That was the reflection from the great beam of the Lizard lighthouse. I have never watched it since without recalling *Henry the Sixth* and 'Brandish your crystal tresses in the sky.' Curiously, the play – *Part One* – would be the last I met in performance.

The first play I read straight through in the original text was *Pericles, Prince of Tyre*, mainly because it came at the end of my book, after the Sonnets: this marked the fact that it was not printed in the first collected edition of Shakespeare in 1623. Without knowing why it was isolated, I took pity on it: some of it mystified me, but it would have done so much more if I had not read Mary Lamb's version (her favourite of all the *Tales*) and made an early acquaintance with the ringing muster of its names. After this, whenever I was in doubt, I would go back to Mary and Charles for help: the gentle pair have been not too far from my elbow ever since, though not in the smudgy green volume with my father's bold signature travelling across the fly-leaf. Shakespeare began for me, I suppose, with Mary's 'There was a certain island in the sea, the only inhabitants of which were an old man, whose name was Prospero, and his daughter Miranda, a very beautiful young lady.'

Now, when I am able to add to the original *Tales* all except two of the plays that Mary and Charles ignored, I can say (in a very slight variation of the Shakespearean line) 'It is an honour that I dreamed not of'. As a young playgoer my hero in the Shakespearean theatre was Sir Frank Benson. When, not long ago, I wrote his biography, it delighted me to discover that, through life, he loved and read *Lamb's Tales*. Though I prize Benson's copy of *The Dramatic Essays of Charles Lamb*, I wish that the *Tales* were there as well.

The present collection adds now to the Lambs' twenty *Tales* another twelve, the Wars of the Roses sequence (*Henry VI* and *Richard III*) given under a single heading. The only plays omitted are the early revenge tragedy of *Titus Andronicus* and the late *Henry the Eighth*, much of it written by John Fletcher. Shakespeare's view of

English history is, of course, his own. We ought not to inquire into it too closely; and certainly we should not ask too many questions about Falstaff's appearance at Windsor in *The Merry Wives*. Legend says that Queen Elizabeth commanded Shakespeare to write it so that she might see Falstaff in love. It is detached entirely from the two parts of *Henry the Fourth*.

Finally, Shakespeare's time schemes are highly individual. In the histories he would condense into a few days or months the progress of years. These are things for which one must now ask pardon in the words of Chorus in *Henry the Fifth*:

> Jumping o'er times,
> Turning the accomplishment of many years
> Into an hour-glass . . .

As always, I must thank my wife for her understanding aid.

J.C.T.

Comedies

THE TEMPEST

THERE was a certain island in the sea, the only inhabitants of which were an old man, whose name was Prospero, and his daughter Miranda, a very beautiful young lady. She came to this island so young, that she had no memory of having seen any other human face than her father's.

They lived in a cave or cell, made out of the rock; it was divided into several apartments, one of which Prospero called his study; there he kept his books, which chiefly treated of magic, a study at that time much affected by all learned men: and the knowledge of this art he found very useful to him; for being thrown by a strange chance upon this island, which had been enchanted by a witch called Sycorax, who died there a short time before his arrival, Prospero, by virtue of his art, released many good spirits that Sycorax had imprisoned in the bodies of large trees, because they had refused to execute her wicked commands. These gentle spirits were ever after obedient to the will of Prospero. Of these Ariel was the chief.

The lively little sprite Ariel had nothing mischievous in his nature, except that he took rather too much pleasure in tormenting an ugly monster called Caliban, for he owed him a grudge because he was the son of his old enemy Sycorax. This Caliban, Prospero found in the woods, a strange misshapen thing, far less human in form than an ape: he took him home to his cell, and taught him to speak; and Prospero would have been very kind to him, but the bad nature which Caliban inherited from his mother Sycorax, would not let him learn anything good or useful: therefore he was employed like a slave, to fetch wood, and do the most laborious offices; and Ariel had the charge of compelling him to these services.

When Caliban was lazy and neglected his work, Ariel (who was invisible to all eyes but Prospero's) would come slily and pinch him, and sometimes tumble him down in the mire; and then Ariel, in the likeness of an ape, would make mouths at him. Then swiftly changing his shape, in the likeness of a hedgehog, he would lie tumbling in Caliban's way, who feared the hedgehog's sharp quills would prick his bare feet. With a variety of such-like vexatious tricks Ariel would often torment him, whenever Caliban neglected the work which Prospero commanded him to do.

Having these powerful spirits obedient to his will, Prospero could by their means command the winds, and the waves of the sea. By his orders they raised a violent storm, in the midst of which, and struggling with the wild sea-waves that every moment threatened to swallow it up, he showed his daughter a fine large ship, which he told her was full of living beings like themselves. 'O my dear father,' said she, 'if by your art you have raised this dreadful storm, have pity on their sad distress. See! the vessel will be dashed to pieces. Poor souls! they will all perish. If I had power, I would sink the sea beneath the earth, rather than the good ship should be destroyed, with all the precious souls within her.'

'Be not so amazed, daughter Miranda,' said Prospero; 'there is no harm done. I have so ordered it, that no person in the ship shall receive any hurt. What I have done has been in care of you, my dear child. You are ignorant who you are, or where you came from, and you know no more of me, but that I am your father, and live in this poor cave. Can you remember a time before you came to this cell? I think you cannot, for you were not then three years of age.'

'Certainly I can, sir,' replied Miranda.

'By what?' asked Prospero; 'by any other house or person? Tell me what you remember, my child.'

Miranda said, 'It seems to me like the recollection of a dream. But had I not once four or five women who attended upon me?'

Prospero answered, 'You had, and more. How is it that this still lives in your mind? Do you remember how you came here?'

'No, sir,' said Miranda, 'I remember nothing more.'

'Twelve years ago, Miranda,' continued Prospero, 'I was Duke of Milan, and you were a princess, and my only heir. I had a younger brother, whose name was Antonio, to whom I trusted everything; and as I was fond of retirement and deep study, I commonly left the management of my state affairs to your uncle, my false brother (for so indeed he proved). I, neglecting all worldly ends, buried among my books, did dedicate my whole time to the bettering of my mind. My brother Antonio being thus in possession of my power, began to think himself the duke indeed. The opportunity I gave him of making himself popular among my subjects awakened in his bad nature a proud ambition to deprive me of my dukedom: this he soon effected with the aid of the King of Naples, a powerful prince, who was my enemy.'

'Wherefore,' said Miranda, 'did they not that hour destroy us?'

'My child,' answered her father, 'they durst not, so dear was the love that my people bore me. Antonio carried us on board a ship, and when we were some leagues out at sea, he forced us into a small boat, without either tackle, sail, or mast: there he left us, as he thought, to perish. But a kind lord of my court, one Gonzalo, who loved me, had privately placed in the boat, water, provisions, apparel, and some books which I prize above my dukedom.'

'O my father,' said Miranda, 'what a trouble I must have been to you then!'

'No, my love,' said Prospero, 'you were a little cherub that did preserve me. Your innocent smiles made me bear up against my misfortunes. Our food lasted till we landed on this desert island, since when my chief delight has been in teaching you, Miranda, and well have you profited by my instructions.'

'Heaven thank you, my dear father,' said Miranda. 'Now pray tell me, sir, your reason for raising this sea-storm?'

'Know then,' said her father, 'that by means of this storm, my enemies, the King of Naples, and my cruel brother, are cast ashore upon this island.'

Having so said, Prospero gently touched his daughter with his magic wand, and she fell fast asleep; for the spirit Ariel just then presented himself before his master, to give an account of the tempest, and how he had disposed of the ship's company, and though the spirits were always invisible to Miranda, Prospero did not choose she should hear him holding converse (as would seem to her) with the empty air.

'Well, my brave spirit,' said Prospero to Ariel, 'how have you performed your task?'

Ariel gave a lively description of the storm, and of the terrors of the mariners; and how the king's son, Ferdinand, was the first who leaped into the sea; and his father thought he saw his dear son swallowed up by the waves and lost. 'But he is safe,' said Ariel, 'in a corner of the isle, sitting with his arms folded, sadly lamenting the loss of the king, his father, whom he concludes drowned. Not a hair of his head is injured, and his princely garments, though drenched in the sea-waves, look fresher than before.'

'That's my delicate Ariel,' said Prospero. 'Bring him hither: my daughter must see this young prince. Where is the king, and my brother?'

'I left them,' answered Ariel, 'searching for Ferdinand, whom they have little hopes of finding, thinking they saw him perish. Of the ship's crew not one is missing; though each one thinks himself the only one saved: and the ship, though invisible to them, is safe in the harbour.'

'Ariel,' said Prospero, 'thy charge is faithfully performed: but there is more work yet.'

'Is there more work?' said Ariel. 'Let me remind you, master, you have promised me my liberty. I pray, remember, I have done you worthy service, told you no lies, made no mistakes, served you without grudge or grumbling.'

'How now!' said Prospero. 'You do not recollect what a torment I freed you from. Have you forgot the wicked witch Sycorax, who with age and envy was almost bent double? Where was she born? Speak; tell me.'

'Sir, in Algiers,' said Ariel.

'Oh, was she so?' said Prospero. 'I must recount what you have been, which I find you do not remember. This bad witch, Sycorax, for her witch-crafts, too terrible to enter human hearing, was banished from Algiers, and here left by the sailors; and because you were a spirit too delicate to execute her wicked commands, she shut you up in a tree, where I found you howling. This torment, remember, I did free you from.'

'Pardon me, dear master,' said Ariel, ashamed to seem ungrateful; 'I will obey your commands.'

'Do so,' said Prospero, 'and I will set you free.' He then gave orders what further he would have him do; and away went Ariel, first to where he had left Ferdinand, and found him still sitting on the grass in the same melancholy posture.

'O my young gentleman,' said Ariel, when he saw him, 'I will soon move you. You must be brought, I find, for the lady Miranda to have a sight of your pretty person. Come, sir, follow me.' He then began singing,

'Full fathom five thy father lies:
   Of his bones are coral made;
Those are pearls that were his eyes:
   Nothing of him that doth fade,
But doth suffer a sea-change
Into something rich and strange.
Sea-nymphs hourly ring his knell:
Hark! now I hear them, – Ding-dong, bell.'

This strange news of his lost father soon roused the prince from the stupid fit into which he had fallen. He followed in amazement the sound of Ariel's voice, till it led him to Prospero and Miranda, who were sitting under the shade of a large tree. Now Miranda had never seen a man before, except her own father.

'Miranda,' said Prospero, 'tell me what you are looking at yonder.'

'O father,' said Miranda, in a strange surprise, 'surely that is a spirit. Lord! how it looks about! Believe me, sir, it is a beautiful creature. Is it not a spirit?'

'No, girl,' answered her father; 'it eats, and sleeps, and has senses such as we have. This young man you see was in the ship. He is somewhat altered by grief, or you might call him a handsome person. He has lost his companions, and is wandering about to find them.'

Miranda, who thought all men had grave faces and grey beards like her father, was delighted with the appearance of this beautiful young prince; and Ferdinand, seeing such a lovely lady in this desert place, and from the strange sounds he had heard, expecting nothing but wonders, thought he was upon an enchanted island, and that Miranda was the goddess of the place, and as such he began to address her.

She timidly answered, she was no goddess, but a simple maid, and was going to give him an account of herself, when Prospero interrupted her. He was well pleased to find they admired each other, for he plainly perceived they had (as we say) fallen in love at first sight: but to try Ferdinand's constancy, he resolved to throw some difficulties in their way: therefore advancing forward, he addressed the prince with a stern air, telling him, he came to the island as a spy, to take it from him who was the lord of it. 'Follow me,' said he, 'I will tie you neck and feet together. You shall drink sea-water; shell-fish, withered roots, and husks of acorns shall be your food.' 'No,' said Ferdinand, 'I will resist such entertainment, till I see a more powerful enemy,' and drew his sword; but Prospero, waving his magic wand, fixed him to the spot where he stood, so that he had no power to move.

Miranda hung upon her father, saying, 'Why are you so ungentle? Have pity, sir; I will be his surety. This is the second man I ever saw, and to me he seems a true one.'

'Silence,' said the father: 'one word more will make me chide you, girl! What! an advocate for an impostor! You think there are no more such fine men, having seen only him and Caliban. I tell you, foolish girl, most men as far excel this, as he does Caliban.' This he said to prove his daughter's constancy; and she replied, 'My affections are most humble. I have no wish to see a goodlier man.'

'Come on, young man,' said Prospero to the Prince; 'you have no power to disobey me.'

'I have not indeed,' answered Ferdinand; and not knowing that it was by magic he was deprived of all power of resistance, he was astonished to find himself so strangely compelled to follow Prospero: looking back on Miranda as long as he could see her, he said, as he went after Prospero into the cave, 'My spirits are all bound up, as if I were in a dream; but this man's threats, and the weakness which I feel, would seem light to me if from my prison I might once a day behold this fair maid.'

Prospero kept Ferdinand not long confined within the cell: he soon brought out his prisoner, and set him a severe task to perform, taking care to let his daughter know the hard labour he had imposed on him, and then pretending to go into his study, he secretly watched them both.

Prospero had commanded Ferdinand to pile up some heavy logs of wood. Kings' sons not being much used to laborious work, Miranda soon after found her lover almost dying with fatigue. 'Alas!' said she, 'do not work so hard; my father is at his studies, he is safe for these three hours; pray rest yourself.'

'O my dear lady,' said Ferdinand, 'I dare not. I must finish my task before I take my rest.'

'If you will sit down,' said Miranda, 'I will carry your logs the while.' But this Ferdinand would by no means agree to. Instead of a help Miranda became a hindrance, for they began a long conversation, so that the business of log-carrying went on very slowly.

Prospero, who had enjoined Ferdinand this task merely as a trial of his love, was not at his books, as his daughter supposed, but was standing by them invisible, to overhear what they said.

Ferdinand inquired her name, which she told, saying it was against her father's express command she did so.

Prospero only smiled at this first instance of his daughter's disobedience, for having by his magic art caused his daughter to fall in love so suddenly, he was not angry that she showed her love by forgetting to obey his commands. And he listened well pleased to a long speech of Ferdinand's, in which he professed to love her above all the ladies he ever saw.

In answer to his praises of her beauty, which he said exceeded all the women in the world, she replied, 'I do not remember the face of any woman, nor have I seen any more men than you, my good friend, and my dear father. How features are abroad, I know not; but, believe me, sir, I would not wish any companion in the world but you, nor can my imagination form any shape but yours that I could like. But, sir, I fear I talk to you too freely, and my father's precepts I forget.'

At this Prospero smiled, and nodded his head, as much as to say, 'This goes on exactly as I could wish; my girl will be Queen of Naples.'

And then Ferdinand, in another fine long speech (for young princes speak in courtly phrases), told the innocent Miranda he was heir to the crown of Naples, and that she should be his queen.

'Ah! sir,' said she, 'I am a fool to weep at what I am glad of. I will answer you in plain and holy innocence. I am your wife if you will marry me.'

Prospero prevented Ferdinand's thanks by appearing visible before them.

'Fear nothing, my child,' said he; 'I have overheard, and approve of all you have said. And, Ferdinand, if I have too severely used you, I will make you rich amends, by giving you my daughter. All your vexations were but trials of your love, and you have nobly stood the test. Then as my gift, which your true love has worthily purchased, take my daughter, and do not smile that I boast she is above all praise.' He then, telling them that he had business which required his presence, desired they would sit down and talk together till he returned; and this command Miranda seemed not at all disposed to disobey.

When Prospero left them, he called his spirit Ariel, who quickly appeared before him, eager to relate what he had done with Prospero's brother and the King of Naples. Ariel said he had left them almost out of their senses with fear, at the strange things he had caused them to see and hear. When fatigued with wandering about, and famished for want of food, he had suddenly set before them a delicious banquet, and then, just as they were going to eat, he appeared visible before them in the shape of a harpy, a voracious monster with wings, and the feast vanished away. Then, to their utter amazement, this seeming harpy spoke to them, reminding them of their cruelty in driving Prospero from his dukedom, and leaving him and his infant daughter to perish in the sea; saying, that for this cause these terrors were suffered to afflict them.

The King of Naples, and Antonio the false brother, repented the injustice they had done to Prospero; and Ariel told his master he was certain their penitence was sincere, and that he, though a spirit, could not but pity them.

'Then bring them hither, Ariel,' said Prospero: 'if you, who are but a spirit, feel for their distress, shall not I, who am a human being like themselves, have compassion on them? Bring them, quickly, my dainty Ariel.'

Ariel soon returned with the king, Antonio, and old Gonzalo in their train, who had followed him, wondering at the wild music he played in the air to draw them on to his master's presence. This Gonzalo was the same who had so kindly provided Prospero formerly with books and provisions, when his wicked brother left him, as he thought, to perish in an open boat in the sea.

Grief and terror had so stupefied their senses, that they did not know Prospero. He first discovered himself to the good old Gonzalo, calling him the preserver of his life; and then his brother and the king knew that he was the injured Prospero.

Antonio with tears, and sad words of sorrow and true repentance, implored his brother's forgiveness, and the king expressed his sincere remorse for having assisted Antonio to depose his brother: and Prospero forgave them; and, upon their engaging to restore his dukedom, he said to the King of Naples, 'I have a gift in store for you too;' and opening a door, showed him his son Ferdinand playing at chess with Miranda.

Nothing could exceed the joy of the father and the son at this unexpected meeting, for they each thought the other drowned in the storm.

'O wonder!' said Miranda, 'what noble creatures these are! It must surely be a brave world that has such people in it.'

The King of Naples was almost as much astonished at the beauty and excellent graces of the young Miranda, as his son had been. 'Who is this maid?' said he; 'she seems the goddess that has parted us, and brought us thus together.' 'No, sir,' answered Ferdinand, smiling to find his father had fallen into the same mistake that he had done when he first saw Miranda, 'she is a mortal, but by immortal Providence she is mine; I chose her when I could not ask you, my father, for your consent, not thinking you were alive. She is the daughter to this Prospero, who is the famous Duke of Milan, of whose renown I have heard so much, but never saw him till now: of him I have received a new life: he has made himself to me a second father, giving me this dear lady.'

'Then I must be her father,' said the king; 'but oh! how oddly will it sound, that I must ask my child forgiveness.'

'No more of that,' said Prospero: 'let us not remember our troubles past, since they so happily have ended.' And then Prospero embraced his brother, and again assured him of his forgiveness; and said that a wise over-ruling Providence had permitted that he should be driven from his poor dukedom of Milan, that his daughter might inherit the crown of Naples, for that by their meeting in this desert island, it had happened that the king's son had loved Miranda.

These kind words which Prospero spoke, meaning to comfort his brother, so filled Antonio with shame and remorse, that he wept and was unable to speak; and the kind old Gonzalo wept to see this joyful reconciliation, and prayed for blessings on the young couple.

Prospero now told them that their ship was safe in the harbour, and the sailors all on board her, and that he and his daughter would accompany them home the next morning. 'In the meantime,' says he, 'partake of such refreshments as my poor cave affords; and for your evening's entertainment I will relate the history of my life from my first landing in this desert island.' He then called for Caliban to prepare some food and set the cave in order; and the company were astonished at the uncouth form and savage appearance of this ugly monster, who (Prospero said) was the only attendant he had to wait upon him.

Before Prospero left the island, he dismissed Ariel from his service, to the great joy of that lively little spirit; who, though he had been a faithful servant to his master, was always longing to enjoy his free liberty, to wander uncontrolled in the air, like a wild bird, under green trees, among pleasant fruits, and sweet-smelling flowers. 'My quaint Ariel,' said Prospero to the little sprite when he made him free, 'I shall miss you; yet you shall have your freedom.' 'Thank you, my dear master,' said Ariel; 'but give me leave to attend your ship home with prosperous gales, before you bid farewell to the assistance of your faithful spirit; and then, master, when I am free, how merrily I shall live!' Here Ariel sang this pretty song:

'Where the bee sucks, there suck I;
In a cowslip's bell I lie:
There I crouch when owls do cry.
On the bat's back I do fly
After summer merrily.
Merrily, merrily shall I live now
Under the blossom that hangs on the bough.'

Prospero then buried deep in the earth his magical books and wand, for he was resolved never more to make use of the magic art. And having thus overcome his enemies, and being reconciled to his brother and the King of Naples, nothing now remained to complete his happiness, but to revisit his native land, to take possession of his dukedom, and to witness the happy nuptials of his daughter and Prince Ferdinand, which the king said should be instantly celebrated with great splendour on their return to Naples. At which place, under the safe convoy of the spirit Ariel, they, after a pleasant voyage, soon arrived.

THE TWO GENTLEMEN OF VERONA

THERE lived in the city of Verona two young gentlemen, whose names were Valentine and Proteus, between whom a firm and uninterrupted friendship had long subsisted. They pursued their studies together, and their hours of leisure were always passed in each other's company, except when Proteus visited a lady he was in love with; and these visits to his mistress, and this passion of Proteus for the fair Julia, were the only topics on which these two friends disagreed; for Valentine, not being himself a lover, was sometimes a little weary of hearing his friend for ever talking of his Julia, and then he would laugh at Proteus, and in pleasant terms ridicule the passion of love, and declare that no such idle fancies should ever enter his head, greatly preferring (as he said) the free and happy life he led, to the anxious hopes and fears of the lover Proteus.

One morning Valentine came to Proteus to tell him that they must for a time be separated, for that he was going to Milan. Proteus, unwilling to part with his friend, used many arguments to prevail upon Valentine not to leave him: but Valentine said, 'Cease to persuade me, my loving Proteus. I will not, like a sluggard, wear out my youth in idleness at home. Home-keeping youths have ever homely wits. If your affection were not chained to the sweet glances of your honoured Julia, I would entreat you to accompany me, to see the wonders of the world abroad; but since you are a lover, love on still, and may your love be prosperous!'

They parted with mutual expressions of unalterable friendship. 'Sweet Valentine, adieu!' said Proteus; 'think on me, when you see some rare object worthy of notice in your travels, and wish me partaker of your happiness.'

Valentine began his journey that same day towards Milan; and when his friend had left him, Proteus sat down to write a letter to Julia, which he gave to her maid Lucetta to deliver to her mistress.

Julia loved Proteus as well as he did her, but she was a lady of a noble spirit, and she thought it did not become her maiden dignity too easily to be won; therefore she affected to be insensible of his passion, and gave him much uneasiness in the prosecution of his suit.

And when Lucetta offered the letter to Julia, she would not receive it, and chid her maid for taking letters from Proteus, and ordered her to leave the room. But she so much wished to see what was written in the letter, that she soon called in her maid again; and when Lucetta returned, she said, 'What o'clock is it?' Lucetta, who knew her mistress more desired to see the letter than to know the time of day, without answering her question, again offered the rejected letter. Julia, angry that her maid should thus take the liberty of seeming to know what she really wanted, tore the letter in pieces, and threw it on the floor, ordering her maid once more out of the room. As Lucetta was retiring she stopped to pick up the fragments of the torn letter; but Julia, who meant not so to part with them, said, in pretended anger, 'Go, get you gone, and let the papers lie; you would be fingering them to anger me.'

Julia then began to piece together as well as she could the torn fragments. She first made out these words, 'Love-wounded Proteus;' and lamenting over these and such like loving words, which she made out though they were all torn asunder, or, she said, *wounded* (the expression 'Love-wounded Proteus' giving her that idea), she talked to these kind words, telling them she would lodge them in her bosom as in a bed, till their wounds were healed, and that she would kiss each several piece, to make amends.

In this manner she went on talking with a pretty lady-like childishness, till finding herself unable to make out the whole, and vexed at her own ingratitude in destroying such sweet and loving words, as she called them, she wrote a much kinder letter to Proteus than she had ever done before.

Proteus was greatly delighted at receiving this favourable answer to his letter; and while he was reading it, he exclaimed, 'Sweet love, sweet lines, sweet life!' In the midst of his raptures he was interrupted by his father. 'How now!' said the old gentleman; 'what letter are you reading there?'

'My lord,' replied Proteus, 'it is a letter from my friend Valentine, at Milan.'

'Lend me the letter,' said his father: 'let me see what news.'

'There are no news, my lord,' said Proteus, greatly alarmed, 'but that he writes how well beloved he is of the Duke of Milan, who daily graces him with favours; and how he wishes me with him, the partner of his fortune.'

'And how stand you affected to his wish?' asked the father.

'As one relying on your lordship's will, and not depending on his friendly wish,' said Proteus.

Now it had happened that Proteus' father had just been talking with a friend on this very subject: his friend had said, he wondered his lordship suffered his son to spend his youth at home, while most men were sending their sons to seek preferment abroad; 'some,' said he, 'to the wars, to try their fortunes there, and some to discover islands far away, and some to study in foreign universities; and there is his companion Valentine, he is gone to the Duke of Milan's court. Your son is fit for any of these things, and it will be a great disadvantage to him in his riper age not to have travelled in his youth.'

Proteus' father thought the advice of his friend was very good, and upon Proteus telling him that Valentine 'wished him with him, the partner of his fortune,' he at once determined to send his son to Milan; and without giving Proteus any reason for his sudden resolution, it being the usual habit of this positive old gentleman to command his son, not reason with him, he said, 'My will is the same as Valentine's wish;' and seeing his son look astonished, he added, 'Look not amazed, that I so suddenly resolve you shall spend some time in the Duke of Milan's court; for what I will I will, and there is an end. To-morrow be in readiness to go. Make no excuses; for I am peremptory.'

Proteus knew it was of no use to make objections to his father, who never suffered him to dispute his will; and he blamed himself for telling his father an untruth about Julia's letter, which had brought upon him the sad necessity of leaving her.

Now that Julia found she was going to lose Proteus for so long a time, she no longer pretended indifference; and they bade each other a mournful farewell, with many vows of love and constancy. Proteus and Julia exchanged rings, which they both promised to keep for ever in remembrance of each other; and thus, taking a sorrowful leave, Proteus set out on his journey to Milan, the abode of his friend Valentine.

Valentine was in reality what Proteus had feigned to his father, in high favour with the Duke of Milan; and another event had happened to him, of which Proteus did not even dream, for Valentine had given up the freedom of which he used so much to boast, and was become as passionate a lover as Proteus.

She who had wrought this wondrous change in Valentine was the Lady Silvia, daughter of the Duke of Milan, and she also loved him; but they concealed their love from the duke, because although he showed much kindness for Valentine, and invited him every day to his palace, yet he designed to marry his daughter to a young courtier whose name was Thurio. Silvia despised this Thurio, for he had none of the fine sense and excellent qualities of Valentine.

These two rivals, Thurio and Valentine, were one day on a visit to Silvia, and Valentine was entertaining Silvia with turning everything Thurio said into ridicule, when the duke himself entered the room, and told Valentine the welcome news of his friend Proteus' arrival. Valentine said, 'If I had wished a thing, it would have been to have seen him here!' And then he highly praised Proteus to the duke, saying, 'My lord, though I have been a truant of my time, yet hath my friend made use and fair advantage of his days, and is complete in person and in mind, in all good grace to grace a gentleman.'

'Welcome him then according to his worth,' said the duke. 'Silvia, I speak to you, and you, Sir Thurio; for Valentine, I need not bid him do so.' They were here interrupted by the entrance of Proteus, and Valentine introduced him to Silvia, saying, 'Sweet lady, entertain him to be my fellow-servant to your ladyship.'

When Valentine and Proteus had ended their visit, and were alone together, Valentine said, 'Now tell me how all does from whence you came? How does your lady, and how thrives your love?' Proteus replied, 'My tales of love used to weary you. I know you joy not in a love discourse.'

'Ay, Proteus,' returned Valentine, 'but that life is altered now. I have done penance for condemning love. For in revenge of my contempt of love, love has chased sleep from my enthralled eyes. O gentle Proteus, Love is a mighty lord, and hath so humbled me, that I confess there is no woe like his correction, nor no such joy on earth as in his service. I now like no discourse except it be of love. Now I can break my fast, dine, sup, and sleep, upon the very name of love.'

This acknowledgment of the change which love had made in the disposition of Valentine was a great triumph to his friend Proteus. But 'friend' Proteus must be called no longer, for the same all-powerful deity Love, of whom they were speaking (yea, even while they were talking of the change he had made in Valentine), was working in the heart of Proteus; and he, who had till this time been a pattern of true love and perfect friendship, was now, in one short interview with Silvia, become a false friend and a faithless lover; for at the first sight of Silvia all his love for Julia vanished away like a dream, nor did his long friendship for Valentine deter him from endeavouring to supplant him in her affections; and although, as it will always be, when people of dispositions naturally good become unjust, he had many scruples before he determined to forsake Julia, and become the rival of Valentine; yet he at length overcame his sense of duty, and yielded himself up, almost without remorse, to his new unhappy passion.

Valentine imparted to him in confidence the whole history of his love, and how carefully they had concealed it from the duke her father, and told him, that, despairing of ever being able to obtain his consent, he had prevailed upon Silvia to leave her father's palace that night, and go with him to Mantua; then he showed Proteus a ladder of ropes, by help of which he meant to assist Silvia to get out of one of the windows of the palace after it was dark.

Upon hearing this faithful recital of his friend's dearest secrets, it is hardly possible to be believed, but so it was, that Proteus resolved to go to the duke, and disclose the whole to him.

This false friend began his tale with many artful speeches to the duke, such as that by the laws of friendship he ought to conceal what he was going to reveal, but that the gracious favour the duke had shown him, and the duty he owed his grace, urged him to tell that which else no worldly good should draw from him. He then told all he had heard from Valentine, not omitting the ladder of ropes, and the manner in which Valentine meant to conceal them under a long cloak.

The duke thought Proteus quite a miracle of integrity, in that he preferred telling his friend's intention rather than he would conceal an unjust action, highly commended him, and promised him not to let Valentine know from whom he had learnt this intelligence, but by some artifice to make Valentine betray the secret himself. For this purpose the duke awaited the coming of Valentine in the evening, whom he soon saw hurrying towards the palace, and he perceived somewhat was wrapped within his cloak, which he concluded was the rope-ladder.

The duke upon this stopped him, saying, 'Whither away so fast, Valentine?' – 'May it please your grace,' said Valentine, 'there is a messenger that stays to bear my letters to my friends, and I am going to deliver them.' Now this falsehood of Valentine's had no better success in the event than the untruth Proteus told his father.

'Be they of much import?' said the duke.

'No more, my lord,' said Valentine, 'than to tell my father I am well and happy at your grace's court.'

'Nay then,' said the duke, 'no matter; stay with me a while. I wish your counsel about some affairs that concern me nearly.' He then told Valentine an artful story, as a prelude to draw his secret from him, saying that Valentine knew he wished to match his daughter with Thurio, but that she was stubborn and disobedient to his commands, 'neither regarding,' said he, 'that she is my child, nor fearing me as if I were her father. And I may say to thee, this pride of hers has drawn my love from her. I had thought my age should have been cherished by her childlike duty. I now am resolved to take a wife, and turn her out to whosoever will take her in. Let her beauty be her wedding dower, for me and my possessions she esteems not.'

Valentine, wondering where all this would end, made answer, 'And what would your grace have me to do in all this?'

'Why,' said the duke, 'the lady I would wish to marry is nice and coy, and does not much esteem my aged eloquence. Besides, the fashion of courtship is much changed since I was young: now I would willingly have you to be my tutor to instruct me how I am to woo.'

Valentine gave him a general idea of the modes of courtship then practised by young men, when they wished to win a fair lady's love, such as presents, frequent visits, and the like.

The duke replied to this, that the lady did refuse a present which he sent her, and that she was so strictly kept by her father, that no man might have access to her by day.

'Why then,' said Valentine, 'you must visit her by night.'

'But at night,' said the artful duke, who was now coming to the drift of his discourse, 'her doors are fast locked.'

Valentine then unfortunately proposed that the duke should get into the lady's chamber at night by means of a ladder of ropes, saying he would procure him one fitting for that purpose; and in conclusion advised him to conceal this ladder of ropes under such a cloak as that which he now wore. 'Lend me your cloak,' said the duke, who had feigned this long story on purpose to have a pretence to get off the cloak; so upon saying these words, he caught hold of Valentine's cloak, and throwing it back, he discovered not only the ladder of ropes, but also a letter of Silvia's, which he instantly opened and read; and this letter contained a full account of their intended elopement. The duke, after upbraiding Valentine for his ingratitude in thus returning the favour he had shown him, by endeavouring to steal away his daughter, banished him from the court and city of Milan for ever; and Valentine was forced to depart that night, without even seeing Silvia.

While Proteus at Milan was thus injuring Valentine, Julia at Verona was regretting the absence of Proteus; and her regard for him at last so far overcame her sense of propriety, that she resolved to leave Verona, and seek her lover at Milan; and to secure herself from danger on the road, she dressed her maiden Lucetta and herself in men's clothes, and they set out in this disguise, and arrived at Milan soon after Valentine was banished from that city through the treachery of Proteus.

Julia entered Milan about noon, and she took up her abode at an inn; and her thoughts being all on her dear Proteus, she entered into conversation with the innkeeper, or host, as he was called, thinking by that means to learn some news of Proteus.

The host was greatly pleased that this handsome young gentleman (as he took her to be), who from his appearance he concluded was of high rank, spoke so familiarly to him; and being a good-natured man, he was sorry to see him look so melancholy; and to amuse his young guest, he offered to take him to hear some fine music, with which, he said, a gentleman that evening was going to serenade his mistress.

The reason Julia looked so very melancholy was, that she did not well know what Proteus would think of the imprudent step she had taken; for she knew he had loved her for her noble maiden pride and dignity of character, and she feared she should lower herself in his esteem: and this it was that made her wear a sad and thoughtful countenance.

She gladly accepted the offer of the host to go with him, and hear the music; for she secretly hoped she might meet Proteus by the way.

But when she came to the palace whither the host conducted her, a very different effect was produced to what the kind host intended; for there, to her heart's sorrow, she beheld her lover, the inconstant Proteus, serenading the Lady Silvia with music, and addressing discourse of love and admiration to her. And Julia overheard Silvia from a window talk with Proteus, and reproach him for forsaking his own true lady, and for his ingratitude to his friend Valentine; and then Silvia left the window, not choosing to listen to his music and his fine speeches; for she was a faithful lady to her banished Valentine, and abhorred the ungenerous conduct of his false friend Proteus.

Though Julia was in despair at what she had just witnessed, yet did she still love the truant Proteus; and hearing that he had lately parted with a servant, she contrived with the assistance of her host, the friendly inn-keeper, to hire herself to Proteus as a page; and Proteus knew not she was Julia, and sent her with letters and presents to her rival Silvia, and he even sent by her the very ring she gave him as a parting gift at Verona.

When she went to that lady with the ring, she was most glad to find that Silvia utterly rejected the suit of Proteus; and Julia, or the page Sebastian as she was called, entered into conversation with Silvia about

Proteus' first love, the forsaken Lady Julia. She putting in (as one may say) a good word for herself, said she knew Julia; as well she might, being herself the Julia of whom she spoke; telling how fondly Julia loved her master Proteus, and how his unkind neglect would grieve her: and then she with a pretty equivocation went on: 'Julia is about my height, and of my complexion, the colour of her eyes and hair the same as mine:' and indeed Julia looked a most beautiful youth in her boy's attire. Silvia was moved to pity this lovely lady, who was so sadly forsaken by the man she loved; and when Julia offered the ring which Proteus had sent, refused it, saying, 'The more shame for him that he sends me that ring; I will not take it; for I have often heard him say his Julia gave it to him. I love thee, gentle youth, for pitying her, poor lady! Here is a purse; I give it you for Julia's sake.' These comfortable words coming from her kind rival's tongue cheered the drooping heart of the disguised lady.

But to return to the banished Valentine; who scarce knew which way to bend his course, being unwilling to return home to his father a disgraced and banished man: as he was wandering over a lonely forest, not far distant from Milan, where he had left his heart's dear treasure, the Lady Silvia, he was set upon by robbers, who demanded his money.

Valentine told them that he was a man crossed by adversity, that he was going into banishment, and that he had no money, the clothes he had on being all his riches.

The robbers, hearing that he was a distressed man, and being struck with his noble air and manly behaviour, told him if he would live with them, and be their chief, or captain, they would put themselves under his command; but that if he refused to accept their offer, they would kill him.

Valentine, who cared little what became of himself, said he would consent to live with them and be their captain, provided they did no outrage on women or poor passengers.

Thus the noble Valentine became, like Robin Hood, of whom we read in ballads, a captain of robbers and outlawed banditti; and in this situation he was found by Silvia, and in this manner it came to pass.

Silvia, to avoid a marriage with Thurio, whom her father insisted upon her no longer refusing, came at last to the resolution of following Valentine to Mantua, at which place she had heard her lover had taken refuge; but in this account she was misinformed, for he still lived in the forest among the robbers, bearing the name of their captain, but taking no part in their depredations, and using the authority which they had imposed upon him in no other way than to compel them to show compassion to the travellers they robbed.

Silvia contrived to effect her escape from her father's palace in company with a worthy old gentleman, whose name was Eglamour, whom she took along with her for protection on the road. She had to pass through the forest where Valentine and the banditti dwelt; and one of these robbers seized on Silvia, and would also have taken Eglamour, but he escaped.

The robber who had taken Silvia, seeing the terror she was in, bid her not be alarmed, for that he was only going to carry her to a cave where his captain lived, and that she need not be afraid, for their captain had an honourable mind, and always showed humanity to women. Silvia found little comfort in hearing she was going to be carried as a prisoner before the captain of a lawless banditti. 'O Valentine,' she cried, 'this I endure for thee!'

But as the robber was conveying her to the cave of his captain, he was stopped by Proteus, who, still attended by Julia in the disguise of a page, having heard of the flight of Silvia, had traced her steps to this forest. Proteus now rescued her from the hands of the robber; but scarce had she time to thank him for the service he had done her, before he began to distress her afresh with his love suit; and while he was rudely pressing her to consent to marry him, and his page (the forlorn Julia) was standing beside him in great anxiety of mind, fearing lest the great service which Proteus had just done to Silvia should win her to show him some favour, they were all strangely surprised with the sudden appearance of Valentine, who, having heard his robbers had taken a lady prisoner, came to console and relieve her.

Proteus was courting Silvia, and he was so much ashamed of being caught by his friend, that he was all at once seized with penitence and remorse; and he expressed such a lively sorrow for the injuries he had done to Valentine, that Valentine, whose nature was noble and generous, even to a romantic degree, not only forgave and restored him to his former place in his friendship, but in a sudden flight of heroism he said,

'I freely do forgive you; and all the interest I have in Silvia, I give it up to you.' Julia, who was standing beside her master as a page, hearing this strange offer, and fearing Proteus would not be able with this new-found virtue to refuse Silvia, fainted, and they were all employed in recovering her: else would Silvia have been offended at being thus made over to Proteus, though she could scarcely think that Valentine would long persevere in this overstrained and too generous act of friendship. When Julia recovered from the fainting fit, she said, 'I had forgot, my master ordered me to deliver this ring to Silvia.' Proteus, looking upon the ring, saw that it was the one he gave to Julia, in return for that which he received from her, and which he had sent by the supposed page to Silvia. 'How is this?' said he, 'this is Julia's ring: how came you by it, boy?' Julia answered, 'Julia herself did give it me, and Julia herself hath brought it hither.'

Proteus, now looking earnestly upon her, plainly perceived that the page Sebastian was no other than the Lady Julia herself; and the proof she had given of her constancy and true love so wrought in him, that his love for her returned into his heart, and he took again his own dear lady, and joyfully resigned all pretensions to the Lady Silvia to Valentine, who had so well deserved her.

Proteus and Valentine were expressing their happiness in their reconciliation, and in the love of their faithful ladies when they were surprised with the sight of the Duke of Milan and Thurio, who came there in pursuit of Silvia.

Thurio first approached, and attempted to seize Silvia, saying, 'Silvia is mine.' Upon this Valentine said to him in a very spirited manner, 'Thurio, keep back: if once again you say that Silvia is yours, you shall embrace your death. Here she stands, take but possession of her with a touch! I dare you but to breathe upon my love.' Hearing this threat, Thurio, who was a great coward, drew back, and said he cared not for her, and that none but a fool would fight for a girl who loved him not.

The duke, who was a very brave man himself, said now in great anger, 'The more base and degenerate in you to take such means for her as you have done, and leave her on such slight conditions.' Then turning to Valentine, he said, 'I do applaud your spirit, Valentine, and think you worthy of an empress' love. You shall have Silvia, for you have well deserved her.' Valentine then with great humility kissed the duke's hand, and accepted the noble present which he had made him of his daughter with becoming thankfulness: taking occasion of this joyful minute to entreat the good-humoured duke to pardon the thieves with whom he had associated in the forest, assuring him, that when reformed and restored to society, there would be found among them many good, and fit for great employment; for the most of them had been banished, like Valentine, for state offences, rather than for any black crimes they had been guilty of. To this the ready duke consented: and now nothing remained but that Proteus, the false friend, was ordained, by way of penance for his love-prompted faults, to be present at the recital of the whole story of his loves and falsehoods before the duke; and the shame of the recital to his awakened conscience was judged sufficient punishment: which being done, the lovers, all four, returned back to Milan, and their nuptials were solemnised in the presence of the duke, with high triumphs and feasting.

THE MERRY WIVES OF WINDSOR

Upon a winter day in Windsor, early in the fifteenth century, a talkative group had gathered before the house of Master Page, a wealthy townsman. The most voluble man in the group, small, elderly, and wizened, with a straggling grey beard, was Robert Shallow, a justice of the peace from Gloucestershire. 'Sir Hugh,' he was crying to a little Welsh parson who sought to calm him, 'Sir Hugh, persuade me not. I will not be abused if he were twenty Sir John Falstaffs.' His complaints were seconded by his much younger cousin, a drawling, affected ninny, whose name was Abraham Slender.

It seemed that Sir John Falstaff, a knight as irresponsible as he was fat, had killed Shallow's deer, beaten his men, and broken into his lodge. It was the kind of exploit of which the rogue, with his followers, Bardolph, Pistol, and Nym, thought nothing. They lived on their sharp wits; and Falstaff was so genial a ruffian that he could often persuade tolerant folk to believe him and to accept him for the sake of his roaring good nature and the wit that brightened his speech. Here in Windsor he was staying at the Garter Inn, but on this cold morning when Shallow was calling for revenge upon him, he was being entertained in the house of Master Page. Slender, who had griefs of his own, was preoccupied about the possibility of his marriage to sweet Mistress Anne, Page's daughter, who had had a rich legacy from her grandfather.

'She has good gifts,' he said to Parson Hugh Evans; and the eager Welshman answered seriously, 'Seven hundred pounds, and possibilities, is indeed good gifts.'

While they were talking together excitedly, Falstaff appeared, red-faced, white-whiskered, and dominating, a great bulk of a man rolling along like a high-built galleon. 'Now, Master Shallow,' he said, 'do I hear you'll complain of me to the King?' And when Shallow advanced in a fury, wagging his stick, Falstaff observed with great calm, 'I have done all you say,' and passed the matter off with a laugh. Then he turned to Slender. 'I broke your head: what matter have you against me?' When Slender, in his high drawl, said that Bardolph, Nym, and Pistol, had borne him off to the tavern, made him drunk, and picked his pocket, the three retainers came forward threateningly with their denials: Bardolph a little man whose face seemed to be aflame, Nym a peevish fellow who used a string of repetitions, and Pistol a loud-mouthed swaggerer.

Nobody could get any further that morning. Once again Falstaff and his crew had triumphed by sheer effrontery. Mistress Page and her friend and neighbour Mistress Ford hurried out with Anne Page who was carrying a hospitable wine-tray; clearly, for the moment, it was well to break off dispute, and Page said in his bluff manner, 'Wife, bid these gentlemen welcome. We have a hot venison pasty for dinner; I hope we shall drink down all unkindness.' Shallow and Slender remained outside for a while, the old man striving to get the young one, who was foolishly diffident, to propose marriage to Anne. At last Anne came out to fetch them. After Shallow had entered, she said politely to Slender, 'Will it please your worship to come in, sir?' Slender simpered, 'No, I thank you forsooth, heartily. I am very well.'

Anne, who knew the kind of man he was, repeated, 'The dinner awaits you, sir.' 'I am not hungry, I thank you, forsooth,' minced Slender; but Anne stood there until the foolish fellow turned the conversation to barking dogs and to the presence of bears in the town. He rambled on while Anne watched quizzically, realising that before long her father would arrive in a cheerful flurry and pull Slender in to the table. Presently he did. The moment they had gone, Parson Hugh Evans darted out with Slender's servant, a youth called Simple, telling him to run to a friend of Anne Page, Mistress Quickly, who was the housekeeper of a French physician, Dr Caius. 'Give her this letter,' said Evans: it asked her to do what she could to recommend Slender to Anne. Satisfied that he had done his own share in helping, Evans went back rosily to the dinner, murmuring as he rubbed his hands, 'There's pippins and cheese to come.'

Falstaff was not finding life easy at this stage. To live, as he was living, in some luxury at the Garter Inn, meant that he could not keep his followers with him. The amiable landlord of the Garter agreed to employ Bardolph – probably on the strength of his complexion – as a tapster. But there were still heavy charges to meet, and on the day after his visit to Page's, Falstaff, ever ready with ideas, ordered his other men to take wooing letters to Mistresses Page and Ford. Each had a wealthy husband; each, he was sure, would be easy to win. 'They shall be my east and west Indies,' he declared, 'and I will trade to them both. Go, bear you this letter to Mistress Page, and you, Pistol, this to Mistress Ford: we shall thrive, lads, we shall thrive.' Unexpectedly, the two rascals, Pistol and Nym, protested that they would not do such work as this, and Falstaff, in wrath, gave the letters to his page Robin, crying, 'Sail like my pinnace to these golden shores!' He discharged the others with an angry, 'Hence, avaunt! Vanish like hailstones!' Left alone, they vowed their revenge. Nym would disclose the plan to Page, and Pistol to Ford. 'Troop on!' exclaimed the swaggerer with a flourish as they hastened out to the streets of Windsor.

Mistress Quickly, in the house of the French doctor, was still talking to herself about the letter Parson Hugh had sent to her. The brisk little woman did not merely converse. If anyone was with her she ran on so rapidly that it was hard to wedge a word into her chatter. 'I wash, wring, brew, bake, scour, dress meat and drink, make the beds, and do all . . .' No doubt when she was alone she found it difficult to listen to herself. Though she kept on saying that she knew Anne Page's mind, 'Never a woman in Windsor knows more of Anne's mind than I do,' she must have realised very well her own cheerful readiness, at a wink and a coin, to turn from one suitor to another, from Slender to her explosively French master or the young and handsome Master Fenton. On this particular morning her master bustled in, picked up the letter, discovered that Parson Hugh was supporting Slender's claim, and at once sat down to scribble a challenge. 'I will kill de Jack priest,' he muttered when he had sent it off. 'I will myself have Anne Page.' And out he went, raging.

By then Falstaff's Robin had brought the wooing messages to Mistress Page and Mistress Ford. The first read on in amazement: 'Let it suffice thee – at least if the love of a soldier can suffice – that I love thee. I will not say, pity me – 'tis not a soldier-like phrase; but I say, love me. By me,

Thine own true knight,
By day or night:
Or any kind of light,
With all his might,
For thee to fight. *John Falstaff.*'

'Heaven forgive me!' she cried. 'Why, I'll enter a bill in the Parliament for the putting down of men. How shall I be revenged on him?' Just as she said this, her friend Alice Ford hurried up to the house where Mistress Page stood by the door, and begged her urgently for advice. 'Here, read, read.' She thrust a paper into Mistress Page's hand and then saw to her astonishment that her friend was comparing it with another, line by line and word by word. 'With all his might for thee to fight . . .' Mistress Page turned with an incredulous laugh: 'Letter for letter, Alice, but that the names of Page and Ford differ. I warrant that he has a thousand of these already written, with blank spaces for different names.'

'What does he think of us?' said Mistress Ford in anger.

'I know not,' said Mistress Page. Then she paused. 'Let's be revenged on the man. Let's appoint a meeting, make him believe that he is winning us, and so lead him on.' In sudden merriment they slipped aside into the house as Ford walked down the street, talking moodily to Pistol, and Page with him, listening amiably to Nym. The rogues had disclosed Falstaff's scheme; but though the hasty and jealous Ford was quite ready to credit the story, the generous Page laughed at it as nonsense. Ford was still brooding when the wives, who had emerged to greet their husbands, noticed Quickly coming towards them with her usual cheerful bounce. Taking her aside hastily, they despatched her as their messenger to Falstaff.

Ford continued to wonder, to Page's impatience, whether there was any truth in Pistol's story; and he was not put off even by the appearance of the Host of the Garter with old Shallow to say that there was a duel to be fought that morning between the French doctor and the Welsh parson. Page readily went to see the fun; but Ford stayed by himself to consider a plan for calling in disguise upon Falstaff at the Garter Inn and probing the business for himself. By then Quickly was on her way to the Garter with a greeting from the wives. Mistress Ford, she explained after a long babble that reduced Falstaff to dumbness, would be at home at a certain hour when her husband was absent; and Mistress Page, though her own husband was seldom away from home, desired Falstaff to let her make use of little Robin so that the boy could go to and fro between them. Falstaff began to look worried. 'Wait,' he said, 'have Ford's wife and Page's wife told each other how they love me?' Quickly replied with a ready scorn, 'That were a jest indeed! They have not such little grace, I hope.'

She had hardly trotted off, leaving Falstaff excited and expectant, before news came that a Master Brook was below and desired to speak and to drink with the knight. Presently the visitor appeared, heavily cloaked and even more heavily moustached, a dramatic figure at any time but especially in a country town on a winter day. 'Sir,' he said, clutching a small bag that jingled, 'I am a gentleman that has spent much. My name is Brook.' 'I desire more acquaintance of you,' said Falstaff affably, asking himself why the curious man had called. It appeared that Brook – who was Ford in disguise – wanted Falstaff to help him to gain the love of Mistress Ford: 'There is money. Spend it, spend it, spend more. Spend all I have. And in exchange, Sir John, use your art of wooing, and win Ford's wife.'

The money delighted Falstaff, for the bag was heavier than he had thought. But he could not yet understand why Master Brook wanted somebody to woo for him. The visitor explained. Mistress Ford, being very honest, would not accept his love. Still, if once she consented to Falstaff's wooing – and the knight would succeed if anybody could – then all would be clear for Brook to say to her, 'You have fallen in love once. Why not again, and with me?' Falstaff, listening with amusement, said that he was bound for Mistress Ford's house early that afternoon, and if Brook returned to him at night he would describe what his fortune had been. 'Come to me at night,' he repeated as he wound his muffler about him and left the inn; and Ford, snatching off his disguise, said gleefully, 'Two o'clock the hour! I will prevent this, detect my wife, be revenged on Falstaff, and laugh at Page.'

A great deal was going on at Windsor that day. Caius and Parson Hugh were waiting for their duel, and the Host of the Garter and the others had carefully sent each of the men to a different place. When finally they did meet, in a field near Frogmore, they were persuaded to make their peace and to troop back to Windsor with the rest of the party, Shallow gripping his oaken staff, Slender crying 'Sweet Anne Page!' but doing nothing about it, Master Page striding on ahead, and the sport-loving Host singing to himself in his leathery voice. In Windsor they ran into Ford, walking fiercely towards his house. 'I have good cheer at home,' he told them, 'and I pray you all go with me.' Page, Caius, and Parson Hugh consented; but Shallow and Slender excused themselves on the plea that they had an appointment to dine with Mistress Anne Page. Her father said in amiable farewell, 'Master Slender, I stand wholly for you, but my wife, master doctor, is for you entirely.' The Host broke in, 'What say you to young Master Fenton? He capers, he dances, he has eyes of youth; he writes verses, he speaks holiday, he smells April and May. He will carry it, he will carry it.' Page received this coldly: 'Not by my consent.' Fenton, he said, had no fortune, and moreover had kept company with the notoriously wild Prince Hal.

Ford, who had been listening with some impatience, burst out now, 'It is past two o'clock. Go home with me to dinner. Besides your cheer, you shall have sport. I will show you a monster.' And crying, 'Have with you, to see this monster!' Page and Caius and Parson Hugh followed him down the cobbled street.

A little earlier, Mistresses Ford and Page had waited in Ford's house for the coming of Falstaff. All preparation was made. Servants had brought in a great laundry basket for soiled clothes and set it down conspicuously on the parlour rushes. Mistress Ford warned them to come quickly when they were called, and then, 'without any pause or staggering,' to lift up the basket upon their shoulders, to bear it with haste to Datchet Mead where clothes were set to dry and to be bleached, and at last to empty the contents of the basket into a muddy ditch beside the river Thames. These directions had hardly been given before Falstaff was announced at the back door; Mistress Page hid herself; Mistress Ford, dropping into a chair, pretended to sleep; and Falstaff plunging in, began fervently to woo her: 'I love you, no one else, and you deserve it.'

'Do not betray me, Sir John. I fear you love Mistress Page,' said Alice Ford.

Falstaff continued to protest that he loved her, and her alone. But Robin called anxiously from the door that Mistress Page had arrived, 'sweating, and blowing, and looking wildly'; Falstaff stumbled hastily behind a curtain; and Mistress Page rushed into the room as dramatically as she could and stared about her. 'O, Mistress Ford, dear Alice Ford, you are shamed, you're overthrown. Your husband is coming hither, with all the officers in Windsor, to search for a gentleman that he says is here now in this house.'

'What shall I do?' asked Mistress Ford, wringing her hands. 'There is certainly a gentleman here, one who is my dear friend. I had rather than a thousand pounds that he were out of the house.'

'O how you have deceived me,' responded Mistress Page, trying to hide her laughter. Then, in wide-eyed astonishment, 'Why, look, here is a basket. Now if your friend be of any reasonable stature, he may creep into it, and we'll throw fresh linen upon him, and send him by your two men to Datchet Mead.'

Mistress Ford shook her head. 'Alas, he's too big to go in there.' But Falstaff exploded from behind the curtain, puffing in anger and fear, 'Let me see it, let me see it, O let me see it. I'll in, I'll in. Follow your friend's counsel, Mistress Ford, I'll in.' And he looked helplessly from one to the other as they held up his letters and he tried vainly to get his legs over the rim of the basket. At length he managed it, falling in like a small mountain; with much trouble they pushed him down, crammed clothing in upon him, banged the lid, and summoned the servants to thrust two poles through the basket handles and to hoist the full load upon their shoulders. 'Don't loiter!' cried Mistress Ford. 'Carry this to the laundress in Datchet Mead. Quickly away!'

It was only just in time, for the whole band pushed in at the door, Ford and Page and Caius and the little parson. Ford, lifting his cudgel, looked in suspicion at the basket. 'Whither bear you this?' 'To the laundress, sir,' said one of the servants. 'Why, what have you to do with it?' asked Mistress Ford mildly as the men disappeared with the huge basket, staggering a little in spite of themselves, and Ford swung on his heel to survey the room. 'Gentlemen,' he said, ignoring his wife, 'here be my keys. Ascend my chambers, search, seek, find out. I warrant we'll unkennel the fox. But let me stop this way first.' And he locked the door, pocketing the key.

'Good master Ford, be contented,' pleaded Page. But Ford had made for the stairs; the others, shrugging their shoulders, tramped up after him, and Mistress Ford turned in barely controlled delight to Mistress Page: 'I know not which pleases me better, that my husband is deceived, or Sir John.' Upstairs there was a clatter of feet, a banging of overtossed furniture. 'We'll yet have more tricks with Falstaff,' whispered Mistress Page, and Alice Ford – after a wry glance at the ceiling – said eagerly, 'Shall we send Quickly to him again? She can sympathise with his ride in the basket and give him another hope – all that we may punish him further.'

'We will do it,' said Mistress Page. 'Let him be here to-morrow at nine o'clock.' As she spoke they heard a wild clamour on the stair. Ford and his followers were back. They had discovered nothing, and Alice Ford feigned to weep: 'You think you use me well, do you?' Page said roundly, 'Master Ford, are you not ashamed? What devil suggested this?' Ford drooped for a moment, dejected: 'Come, wife; come, Mistress Page. I pray you pardon me.' But though he spoke humbly, he had yet a suspicious glint in his eye. Master Brook must discover more.

Later that afternoon, at Page's house, the gallant Fenton told Anne that she meant more to him than all her father's wealth. Shallow and Slender interrupted their talk. Once more Slender began one of his fatuous conversations, and while he was at it Anne's mother and father entered. 'Ah, Master Slender,' said Page; 'Love him, daughter Anne. But Master Fenton, you do me wrong, sir, thus to haunt my house.' Mistress Page could give no hope to Fenton. She wished to marry Anne to the French doctor, and on hearing this the unhappy girl cried, 'I had rather be bowled to death with turnips.' At length Quickly, who had been standing by, was left to herself, murmuring, 'I would my master had Mistress Anne, or I would Master Slender had her; or, in sooth, I would Master Fenton had her . . . Time for that. I must remember my new errand to Sir John for my two mistresses.'

Falstaff, when she next discovered him at the Garter, was in a dreary state, heavy with a sneezing cold, and recalling miserably how he had been thrown into the Thames. He was as cold, he said, as if he had swallowed snowballs, and he was in no mood whatever for messages from Mistress Ford who had brought this damp humiliation. Even so, he cheered a little when told that she desired to make amends, and that between nine and ten next morning, while her husband was away, she would expect him back. In half an hour or so Master Brook was announced to hear what had happened to Falstaff, and how, after the fat knight had endured the heat of close confinement in the basket, he had been thrown into the river 'and cooled, glowing hot, in that surge like a horseshoe. Think of that: hissing hot. Think of that, Master Brook.'

Ford did think of it, and with less feeling for Falstaff than wrath at the way he himself had been tricked. There would soon be retribution, for Falstaff, he gathered, was going again to the Fords' at nine o'clock next morning. 'Come to me at your convenient leisure,' said the knight, 'and you shall know how I fared.' His face disappeared behind a tankard of sack, and Ford, clinging to a moustache that was in danger of slipping, walked glumly downstairs. 'Is this a vision, a dream?' he asked. So this it was to have linen and laundry baskets! But he would proclaim himself. Next time Falstaff would not escape; it was improbable that he could creep into a purse or a pepper-pot. But lest the devil should aid the knight – and doubtless they were in league – Ford vowed that he would search all possible and impossible places. Clapping on his hat, he strode from the Garter.

Next morning Falstaff, well wrapped, was at the house before the time appointed. 'Are you sure of your husband now?' he asked. And pat on his question came the agitated voice of Mistress Page outside. In peevish exasperation Falstaff hid himself again, only to hear as he sought vainly to keep the curtain from bulging, that Ford, hot with rage, was making for the house with his friends to conduct a second search. 'I am undone, the knight is here,' confessed Mistress Ford, her eyes downcast. 'What can we do? . . . The basket again?'

'No!' shouted Falstaff from behind the curtain. 'No, I'll not go in the basket.' He stumbled out. 'Can I not escape before he comes?'

Mistress Page sighed: 'Three of Master Ford's brothers watch the door with pistols, Sir John.'

'What shall I do? I'll creep up into the chimney.'

'Why,' said Mistress Ford, 'it is up the chimney that they discharge their guns. Press, coffer, trunk, walls, vault. My husband knows them all. There is no hiding you in the house, Sir John.'

The only hope was disguise, but there could be no woman's gown big enough for him, otherwise he might put on a hat, a kerchief, and a muffler, and so escape. 'Devise something!' groaned Falstaff in real fear; and Alice Ford trilled with laughter as if a plan had suddenly occurred to her. At that moment her maid's aunt, the fat woman of Brentford, who was as big as Falstaff, was sitting upstairs; he could use her gown, her muffler, and her fringed hat, and they would get some linen for his head. This imposture should serve. 'Hasten!' cried Mistress Page. 'Put on the gown.' Falstaff tottered out. He did not hear Alice Ford say, 'I would my husband could meet him in this shape. He cannot abide the old woman of Brentford. He swears that she's a witch, has forbidden her the house, and threatens to beat her.' 'Heaven guide him to your husband's cudgel!' said Mistress Page. After telling the servants to have the laundry-basket ready as before, so that it might deceive Ford, the wives ran up to dress Falstaff – no simple task – as the woman of Brentford. They were above when Ford, Page, Shallow, the parson, and the doctor streamed in, and Ford, on seeing the basket, gave a loud cry. So that was the place, was it? They were repeating the trick, were they? Very well. 'Put down the basket. Somebody call my wife! . . . What, wife, I say! Come forth and show me what honest clothes you send to bleaching.' As she descended he leapt at the basket and scattered its contents all over the floor until it was empty and the room was strewn with linen. Red with disappointment, he kicked the basket over and thrust his cudgel into it. 'Here's no man,' said Page. 'Then help to search my house,' cried Ford unappeased. 'Satisfy me once more; once more search with me.'

Mistress Ford raised her voice. 'What ho! Mistress Page! Come you and the old woman down; my husband will go up into the room.'

'Old woman?' snapped Ford. 'What old woman is that?'

'Why, it is my maid's aunt of Brentford who begged to stay last night with her niece.'

Ford's fury mounted. 'A witch! Have I not forbidden her my house? We are simple men, we do not know what's brought to pass under the profession of fortune-telling. Come on down, you witch, you hag – come down, I say!'

'Good gentlemen,' exclaimed Mistress Ford, appealing to the company. 'Let him not strike the old woman.' At the foot of the stair appeared Mistress Page, leading an enormous, shapeless figure huddled into a loose gown and with features almost invisible between muffler and hat and kerchief. Ford rushed at the figure, brandishing his cudgel. 'Out of my door, you witch, you baggage! Out, out! I'll conjure you, I'll fortune-tell you!' And, struggling to avoid the blows of the cudgel, the disguised Falstaff lurched from the house. 'A desperate witch!' said Ford. Parson Hugh Evans was murmuring to himself. 'By yea and no, I think the 'oman is a witch indeed. I like it not when a 'oman has a great beard; I spy a great beard under her muffler.'

Wearily, Ford appealed to his friends. 'Will you follow, gentlemen? I beseech you, follow!' And humouring him still, with meaning grimaces, they made the now familiar round and passed again into the street, leaving the parlour scattered with dirty linen and overturned furniture. The wives, hugging each other, sat down to laugh. 'May we pursue him with any further revenge?' asked the insatiable Alice Ford. 'Shall we tell our husbands how we have served him?' Mistress Page agreed. After all, they said, the man ought to be shamed publicly, and they moved off to devise a way.

Soon, when they were together with their husbands and Parson Hugh, they related the story in full. 'Pardon me, wife,' said Ford; 'Henceforth do what you will.' Peace had returned to the Ford household, but Falstaff had yet to be put to his public shame, and Mistress Page had the plan for this. There was, she reminded them, a tale that on winter nights the ghost of Herne the Hunter, who was once a keeper in Windsor Forest, would walk round an oak, shaking a chain and wearing great ragged horns. Because of this many people feared to stir at midnight by Herne's Oak: it was a part of the forest dreaded, lonely, and haunted. Then, said Mistress Page, why should not the wives arrange that Falstaff, disguised as Herne, should meet them at this place? Once he was there, Anne Page and some of the Windsor children, dressed like goblins and fairies, with wax tapers on their heads and rattles in their hands, would swoop on Falstaff, encircle him, and pinch him black and blue. In the midst of his humiliation the wives and their husbands would appear, publicly disclose the knight, and mock him home to Windsor. At once it was decided. Anne Page would be the queen of the fairies, dressed in a white robe; and her father said to himself, 'In that time shall Master Slender steal my Anne away and marry her at Eton.' His wife was also thinking to herself, 'I'll to the doctor. None but he shall have her.'

It was now almost the end of Falstaff's distresses. Ill-served though he had been, he was ready for one trial more when Quickly brought to him news of the assignation at Herne's Oak. Much would rest upon this midnight adventure. It was Fenton's chance to gain his Anne, and he told the Host of the Garter what he proposed to do. Anne's father had planned that, in white, she should slip away with Slender; her mother had decided that, wearing green, Anne must be seized by the doctor and borne off to marriage. But Anne intended to deceive them all and to marry Fenton; it was his part to ask the Host to find a clergyman, one ready and willing to await them both at church.

By the deep winter midnight everything had been arranged. Anne, Parson Hugh, and their procession of mock-fairies and goblins, waited in a pit by Herne's Oak, hiding the lights they carried. Twelve o'clock struck; and when the final notes of the Windsor bell throbbed away across the forest, Falstaff, rattling a chain and wearing the branching horns, stood by the great tree-trunk. 'The minute draws on,' he said with a shiver; 'Who comes here?' 'Sir John, are you there?' replied Alice Ford. As he sat uncomfortably on a tree root, and Mistress Ford balanced herself with equal discomfort on his knee, he saw to his dismay that Mistress Page had arrived as well. What did it matter? She could have his other knee. 'As I am a true spirit, welcome!'

At these words a strange singing rose from beneath their feet. Lights began to glimmer in the dark, and as Falstaff mumbled 'What should this be?', the wives, crying 'Away, away!' fled into the depths of the forest. Falstaff, left surrounded by sprites and goblins, sank in desperation upon the cold turf. Above him a voice was declaiming:

> 'About, about;
> Search Windsor Castle, elves, within, and out:
> The several chairs of order look you scour
> With juice of balm, and every precious flower:
> Each fair instalment, coat, and several crest,
> With royal blazon, evermore be blest!
> And nightly, meadow-fairies, look you sing,
> Like to the Garter's compass, in a ring . . .
> Away, disperse; but till 'tis one o'clock,
> Our dance of custom, round about the oak
> Of Herne the Hunter, let us not forget.'

Another voice, that of Parson Hugh who led the fairies, was heard to say, 'I smell a man of middle earth.' Falstaff moaned to himself, 'Heaven defend me from that Welsh fairy, lest he transform me to a piece of cheese.' At this members of the band closed tightly in upon him, dancing in a circle and burning him with fifty tapers as they sang:

> 'Pinch him, and burn him, and turn him about,
> Till candles, and starlight, and moonshine be out.'

While they bent over Falstaff, Doctor Caius stole from the shadows and beckoned to him a boy in green; from another side tiptoed Slender who took a boy in white; and the last to come was Fenton who hurried away with Anne Page. Somewhere a hunting-horn sounded; the fairies dispersed. After a moment's indecision Falstaff rose with painful stiffness and pulled off his headdress. Then he blinked in a flare of lantern-light; the wives of Windsor and their husbands were studying him happily. 'Nay,' said Page; 'Do not fly, Sir John. Will none but Herne the Hunter serve your turn?' Mistress Page echoed, 'How like you Windsor wives?' And Ford, dabbing on a moustache, said grimly, 'Master Brook, Falstaff's a knave.' For once in his tumultuous life Falstaff could find nothing to say but the feeble 'I do perceive that I am made an ass.'

As he stood dispirited while they mocked him, Page clapped him upon the shoulder: 'Yet be cheerful, Sir John. You shall eat tonight at my house where I shall desire you to laugh at my wife who is now laughing at you. Tell her Master Slender has married her daughter.' Mistress Page said to herself, 'If Anne Page be my daughter, she is by now the wife of Doctor Caius.'

Anne was married to neither of them, for Slender ran up, weeping petulantly, to say that the girl in white he had stolen away was no girl but 'a great lubberly boy,' and Caius, even angrier, reported that he had 'married un garçon, a boy; it is not Anne Page'. To end all doubts, Anne herself then sped up with Fenton, straight from their marriage. 'She and I,' said Fenton, 'are now so sure that nothing can dissolve us.'

So, in the small hours of the winter morning, all was pardoned. 'Fenton, heaven give you joy!' said Page; and his wife added, 'Heaven give you many, many merry days.' She glanced at Falstaff who had been leaning on the oak, chuckling, in spite of his misery, at the sudden twist of fortune. 'Good husband,' said Alice Ford, following her friend's glance, 'let us everyone go home, and laugh this sport over by a country fire . . . Sir John and all.'

'Let it be so,' put in Ford. Falstaff, no longer embarrassed, raised his head in the old bravado, and the little group walked off down the forest ride until the spark of the lanterns had vanished with the last note of laughter, and about Herne's Oak nothing stirred now in the thick darkness and the winter silence.

MEASURE FOR MEASURE

IN the city of Vienna there once reigned a duke of such a mild and gentle temper, that he suffered his subjects to neglect the laws with impunity; and there was in particular one law, the existence of which was almost forgotten, the duke never having put it in force during his whole reign. This was a law dooming any man to the punishment of death, who should live with a woman that was not his wife; and this law, through the lenity of the duke, being utterly disregarded, the holy institution of marriage became neglected, and complaints were every day made to the duke by the parents of the young ladies in Vienna, that their daughters had been seduced from their protection, and were living as the companions of single men.

The good duke perceived with sorrow this growing evil among his subjects; but he thought that a sudden change in himself from the indulgence he had hitherto shown, to the strict severity requisite to check this abuse, would make his people (who had hitherto loved him) consider him as a tyrant; therefore he determined to absent himself a while from his dukedom, and depute another to the full exercise of his power, that the law against these dishonourable lovers might be put in effect, without giving offence by an unusual severity in his own person.

Angelo, a man who bore the reputation of a saint in Vienna for his strict and rigid life, was chosen by the duke as a fit person to undertake this important charge; and when the duke imparted his design to Lord Escalus, his chief councillor, Escalus said, 'If any man in Vienna be of worth to undergo such ample grace and honour, it is Lord Angelo.' And now the duke departed from Vienna under pretence of making a journey into Poland, leaving Angelo to act as the lord deputy in his absence; but the duke's absence was only a feigned one, for he privately returned to

Vienna, habited like a friar, with the intent to watch unseen the conduct of the saintly-seeming Angelo.

It happened just about the time that Angelo was invested with his new dignity, that a gentleman, whose name was Claudio, had seduced a young lady from her parents; and for this offence, by command of the new lord deputy, Claudio was taken up and committed to prison, and by virtue of the old law which had been so long neglected, Angelo sentenced Claudio to be beheaded. Great interest was made for the pardon of young Claudio, and the good old Lord Escalus himself interceded for him. 'Alas,' said he, 'this gentleman whom I would save had an honourable father, for whose sake I pray you pardon the young man's transgression.' But Angelo replied, 'We must not make a scare-crow of the law, setting it up to frighten birds of prey, till custom, finding it harmless, makes it their perch, and not their terror. Sir, he must die.'

Lucio, the friend of Claudio, visited him in the prison, and Claudio said to him, 'I pray you, Lucio, do me this kind service. Go to my sister Isabel, who this day proposes to enter the convent of Saint Clare; acquaint her with the danger of my state; implore her that she make friends with the strict deputy; bid her go herself to Angelo. I have great hopes in that; for she can discourse with prosperous art, and well she can persuade; besides, there is a speechless dialect in youthful sorrow, such as moves men.'

Isabel, the sister of Claudio, had, as he said, that day entered upon her noviciate in the convent, and it was her intent, after passing through her probation as a novice, to take the veil, and she was inquiring of a nun concerning the rules of the convent, when they heard the voice of Lucio, who, as he entered that religious house, said, 'Peace be in this place!' – 'Who is it that speaks?' said Isabel. 'It is a man's voice,' replied the nun: 'Gentle Isabel, go to him, and learn his business; you may, I may not. When you have taken the veil, you must not speak with men but in the presence of the prioress; then if you speak you must not show your face, or if you show your face, you must not speak.' – 'And have you nuns no further privileges?' said Isabel. 'Are not these large enough?' replied the nun. 'Yes, truly,' said Isabel: 'I speak not as desiring more, but rather wishing a more strict restraint upon the sisterhood, the votarists of Saint Clare.' Again they heard the voice of Lucio and the nun said, 'He calls again. I pray you answer him.' Isabel then went out to Lucio, and in answer to his salutation, said, 'Peace and Prosperity! Who is it that calls?' Then Lucio, approaching her with reverence, said, 'Hail, virgin, if such you be, as the roses on your cheeks proclaim you are no less! can you bring me to the sight of Isabel, a novice of this place, and the fair sister to her unhappy brother Claudio?' – 'Why her unhappy brother?' said Isabel, 'let me ask! for I am that Isabel, and his sister.' – 'Fair and gentle lady,' he replied, 'your brother kindly greets you by me; he is in prison.' – 'Woe is me! for what?' said Isabel. Lucio then told her, Claudio was imprisoned for seducing a young maiden. 'Ah,' said she, 'I fear it is my cousin Juliet.' Juliet and Isabel were not related, but they called each other cousin in remembrance of their school days' friendship; and as Isabel knew that Juliet loved Claudio, she feared she had been led by her affection for him into this transgression. 'She it is,' replied Lucio. 'Why then, let my brother marry Juliet,' said Isabel. Lucio replied that Claudio would gladly marry Juliet, but that the lord deputy had sentenced him to die for his offence; 'Unless,' said he, 'you have the grace by your fair prayer to soften Angelo, and that is my business between you and your poor brother.' – 'Alas!' said Isabel, 'what poor ability is there in me to do him good? I doubt I have no power to move Angelo.' – 'Our doubts are traitors,' said Lucio, 'and make us lose the good we might often win, by fearing to attempt it. Go to Lord Angelo! When maidens sue, and kneel, and weep, men give like gods.' – 'I will see what I can do,' said Isabel: 'I will but stay to give the prioress notice of the affair, and then I will go to Angelo. Commend me to my brother: soon at night I will send word of my success.'

Isabel hastened to the palace, and threw herself on her knees before Angelo, saying, 'I am a woeful suitor to your honour, if it will please your honour to hear me.' – 'Well, what is your suit?' said Angelo. She then made her petition in the most moving terms for her brother's life. But Angelo said, 'Maiden, there is no remedy; your brother is sentenced, and he must die.' – 'O just, but severe law,' said Isabel: 'I had a brother then – Heaven keep your honour!' and she was about to depart. But Lucio, who had accompanied her, said, 'Give it not over so; return to him again, entreat him, kneel down before him, hang upon his gown. You are too cold; if you should need a pin, you could not with a more tame tongue desire it.' Then Isabel on her knees implored for mercy. 'He is sentenced,' said Angelo: 'it is too late.' – 'Too late!' said Isabel: 'Why, no: I that do speak a word may call it back again. Believe this, my lord, no ceremony that to great ones belongs, not the king's crown, nor the deputed sword, the marshal's truncheon, nor the judge's robe, becomes them with one half so good a grace as mercy does.' – 'Pray you begone,' said Angelo. But still Isabel entreated; and she said, 'If my brother had been as you, and you as he, you might have slipped like him, but he, like you, would not have been so stern. I would to heaven I had your power, and you were Isabel. Should it then be thus? No, I would tell you what it were to be a judge, and what a prisoner.' – 'Be content, fair maid!' said Angelo: 'it is the law, not I, condemns your brother. Were he my kinsman, my brother, or my son, it should be thus with him. He must die to-morrow.' – 'To-morrow?' said Isabel; 'Oh, that is sudden: spare him, spare him; he is not prepared for death. Even for our kitchens we kill the fowl in season; shall we serve Heaven with less respect than we minister to our gross selves? Good, good, my lord, bethink you, none have died for my brother's offence, though many have committed it. So you would be the first that gives this sentence, and he the first that suffers it. Go to your own bosom, my lord; knock there, and ask your heart what it does know that is like my brother's fault; if it confess a natural guiltiness such as his is, let it not sound a thought against my brother's life!' Her last words more moved Angelo than all she had before said, for the beauty of Isabel had raised a guilty passion in his heart, and he began to form thoughts of dishonourable love, such as Claudio's crime had been; and the conflict in his mind made him to turn away from Isabel; but she called him back, saying, 'Gentle my lord, turn back; hark, how I will bribe you. Good my lord, turn back!' – 'How, bribe me!' said Angelo, astonished that she should think of offering him a bribe. 'Ay,' said Isabel, 'with such gifts that Heaven itself shall share with you; not with golden treasures, or those glittering stones, whose price is either rich or poor as fancy values them, but with true prayers that shall be up to Heaven before sunrise, – prayers from preserved souls, from fasting maids whose minds are dedicated to nothing temporal.' – 'Well, come to me to-morrow,' said Angelo. And for this short respite of her brother's life, and for this permission that she might be heard again, she left him with the joyful hope that she should at last prevail over his stern nature: and as she went away she said, 'Heaven keep your honour safe! Heaven save your honour!' Which when Angelo heard, he said within his heart, 'Amen, I would be saved from thee and from thy virtues:' and then, affrighted at his own evil thoughts, he said, 'What is this? What is this? Do I love her, that I desire to hear her speak again, and feast upon her eyes? What is it I dream on? The cunning enemy of mankind, to catch a saint, with saints does bait the hook. Never could an immodest woman once stir my temper, but this virtuous woman subdues me quite. Ever till now, when men were fond, I smiled and wondered at them.'

In the guilty conflict in his mind Angelo suffered more that night than the prisoner he had so severely sentenced; for in the prison Claudio was visited by the good duke, who, in his friar's habit, taught the young man the way to heaven, preaching to him the words of penitence and peace. But Angelo felt all the pangs of irresolute guilt: now wishing to seduce Isabel from the paths of innocence and honour, and now suffering remorse and horror for a crime as yet but intentional. But in the end his evil thoughts prevailed; and he who had so lately started at the offer of a bribe, resolved to tempt this maiden with so high a bribe, as she might not be able to resist, even with the precious gift of her dear brother's life.

When Isabel came in the morning, Angelo desired she might be admitted alone to his presence: and being there, he said to her, if she would yield to him her virgin honour and transgress even as Juliet had done with Claudio, he would give her her brother's life; 'For,' said he, 'I love you, Isabel.' – 'My brother,' said Isabel, 'did so love Juliet, and yet you tell me he shall die for it.' – 'But,' said Angelo, 'Claudio shall not die, if you consent to visit me by stealth at night, even as Juliet left her father's house at night to come to Claudio.' Isabel, in amazement at his words, that he should tempt her to the same fault for which he passed sentence upon her brother, said, 'I would do as much for my poor brother as for myself; that is, were I under sentence of death, the impression of keen whips I would wear as rubies, and go to my death as to a bed that longing I had been sick for, ere I would yield myself up to this shame.' And then she told him, she hoped he only spoke these words to try her virtue. But he said, 'Believe me, on my honour, my words express my purpose.' Isabel, angered to the heart to hear him use the word Honour to express such dishonourable purposes, said, 'Ha! little honour to be much believed; and most pernicious purpose. I will proclaim thee, Angelo, look for it! Sign me a present pardon for my brother, or I will tell the world aloud what man thou art!' – 'Who will believe you, Isabel?' said Angelo; 'my unsoiled name, the austereness of my life, my word vouched against yours, will outweigh your accusation. Redeem your brother by yielding to my will, or he shall die to-morrow. As for you, say what you can, my false will overweigh your true story. Answer me to-morrow.'

'To whom should I complain? Did I tell this, who would believe me?' said Isabel, as she went towards the dreary prison where her brother was confined. When she arrived there, her brother was in pious conversation with the duke, who in his friar's habit had also visited Juliet, and brought both these guilty lovers to a proper sense of their fault; an unhappy Juliet with tears and a true remorse confessed that she was more to blame than Claudio, in that she willingly consented to his dishonourable solicitations.

As Isabel entered the room where Claudio was confined, she said, 'Peace be here, grace, and good company!' – 'Who is there?' said the disguised duke; 'come in; the wish deserves a welcome.' – 'My business is a word or two with Claudio,' said Isabel. Then the duke left them together, and desired the provost, who had the charge of the prisoners, to place him where he might overhear their conversation.

'Now, sister, what is the comfort?' said Claudio. Isabel told him he must prepare for death on the morrow. 'Is there no remedy?' said Claudio. – 'Yes, brother,' replied Isabel, 'there is; but such a one, as if you consented to it would strip your honour from you, and leave you naked.' – 'Let me know the point,' said Claudio. 'O, I do fear you, Claudio!' replied his sister; 'and I quake, lest you should wish to live, and more respect the trifling term of six or seven winters added to your life, than your perpetual honour! Do you dare to die? The sense of death is most in apprehension, and the poor beetle that we tread upon, feels a pang as great as when a giant dies.' 'Why do you give me this shame?' said Claudio. 'Think you I can fetch a resolution from flowery tenderness? If I must die, I will encounter darkness as a bride, and hug it in my arms.' – 'There spoke my brother,' said Isabel; 'there my father's grave did utter forth a voice. Yes, you must die; yet would you think it, Claudio! this outward sainted deputy, if I would yield to him my virgin honour, would grant your life. O, were it but my life, I would lay it down for your deliverance as frankly as a pin!' – 'Thanks, dear Isabel,' said Claudio. 'Be ready to die to-morrow,' said Isabel. 'Death is a fearful thing,' said Claudio. 'And shamed life a hateful,' replied his sister. But the thoughts of death now overcame the constancy of Claudio's temper, and terrors, such as the guilty only at their deaths do know, assailing him, he cried out, 'Sweet sister, let me live! The sin you do to save a brother's life, nature dispenses with the deed so far, that it becomes a virtue.' – 'O faithless coward! O dishonest wretch!' said Isabel; 'would you preserve your life by your sister's shame? O fie, fie, fie! I thought, my brother, you had in you such a mind of honour, that had you twenty heads to render up on twenty blocks, you would have yielded them up all, before your sister should stoop to such dishonour.' 'Nay, hear me, Isabel!' said Claudio. But what he would have said in defence of his weakness, in desiring to live by the dishonour of his virtuous sister, was interrupted by the entrance of the duke; who said, 'Claudio, I have overheard what has passed between you and your sister. Angelo had never the purpose to corrupt her; what he said, has only been to make trial of her virtue. She having the truth of honour in her, has given him the gracious denial which he is most glad to receive. There is no hope that he will pardon you; therefore pass your hours in prayer, and make ready for death.' Then Claudio repented of his weakness, and said, 'Let me ask my sister's pardon! I am so out of love with life, that I will sue to be rid of it.' And Claudio retired, overwhelmed with shame and sorrow for his fault.

The duke being now alone with Isabel, commended her virtuous resolution, saying, 'The hand that made you fair, has made you good.' – 'O,' said Isabel, 'how much is the good duke deceived in Angelo! if ever he return, and I can speak to him, I will discover his government.' Isabel knew not that she was even now making the discovery she threatened. The duke replied, 'That shall not be much amiss; yet as the matter now stands, Angelo will repel your accusation; therefore lend an attentive ear to my advisings. I believe that you may most righteously do a poor wronged lady a merited benefit, redeem your brother from the angry law, do no stain to your own most gracious person, and much please the absent duke, if peradventure he shall ever return to have notice of this business.' Isabel said, she had a spirit to do anything he desired, provided it was nothing wrong. 'Virtue is bold, and never fearful,' said the duke: and then he asked her, if she had ever heard of Mariana, the sister of Frederick, the great soldier who was drowned at sea. 'I have heard of the lady,' said Isabel, 'and good words went with her name.' – 'This lady,' said the duke, 'is the wife of Angelo; but her marriage dowry was on board the vessel in which her brother perished, and mark how heavily this befell to the poor gentlewoman! for, beside the loss of a most noble and renowned brother, who in his love towards her was ever most kind and natural, in the wreck of her fortune she lost the affections of her husband, the well-seeming Angelo; who pretending to discover some dishonour in this honourable lady (though the true cause was the loss of her dowry) left her in tears, and dried not one of them with his comfort. His unjust unkindness, that in all reason should have quenched her love, has, like an impediment in the current, made it more unruly, and Mariana loves her cruel husband with the full continuance of her first affection.' The duke then more plainly unfolded his plan. It was, that Isabel should go to Lord Angelo, and seemingly consent to come to him as he desired at midnight; that by this means she would obtain the promised pardon; and that Mariana should go in her stead to the appointment, and pass herself upon Angelo in the dark for Isabel. 'Nor, gentle daughter,' said the feigned friar, 'fear you to do this thing; Angelo is her husband, and to bring them thus together is no sin.' Isabel being pleased with this project, departed to do as he directed her; and he went to apprise Mariana of their intention. He had before this time visited this unhappy lady in his assumed character, giving her religious instruction and friendly consolation, at which times he had learned her sad story from her own lips; and now she, looking upon him as a holy man, readily consented to be directed by him in this undertaking.

When Isabel returned from her interview with Angelo, to the house of Mariana, where the duke had appointed her to meet him, he said, 'Well met, and in good time; what is the news from this good deputy?' Isabel related the manner in which she had settled the affair. 'Angelo,' said she, 'has a garden surrounded with a brick wall, on the western side of which is a vineyard, and to that vineyard is a gate.' And then she showed to the duke and Mariana two keys that Angelo had given her; and she said, 'This bigger key opens the vineyard gate; this other a little door which leads from the vineyard to the garden. There I have made my promise at the dead of the night to call upon him, and have got from him his word of assurance for my brother's life. I have taken a due and wary note of the place; and with whispering and most guilty diligence he showed me the way twice over.' – 'Are there no other tokens agreed upon between you, that Mariana must observe?' said the duke. 'No, none,' said Isabel, 'only to go when it is dark. I have told him my time can be but short; for I have made him think a servant comes along with me, and that this servant is persuaded I come about my brother.' The duke commended her discreet management, and she, turning to Mariana, said, 'Little have you to say to Angelo, when you depart from him, but soft and low, *Remember now my brother!*'

Mariana was that night conducted to the appointed place by Isabel, who rejoiced that she had, as she supposed, by this device preserved both her brother's life and her own honour. But that her brother's life was safe the duke was not well satisfied, and therefore at midnight he again repaired to the prison, and it was well for Claudio that he did so, else would Claudio have that night been beheaded; for soon after the duke entered the prison, an order came from the cruel deputy, commanding that Claudio should be beheaded, and his head sent to him by five o'clock in the morning. But the duke persuaded the provost to put off the execution of Claudio, and to deceive Angelo, by sending him the head of a man who died that morning in the prison. And to prevail upon the provost to agree to this, the duke, whom still the provost suspected not to be anything more or greater than he seemed, showed the provost a letter written with the duke's hand, and sealed with his seal, which when the provost saw, he concluded this friar must have some secret order from the absent duke, and therefore he consented to spare Claudio; and he cut off the dead man's head, and carried it to Angelo.

Then the duke in his own name, wrote to Angelo a letter, saying, that certain accidents had put a stop to his journey, and that he should be in Vienna by the following morning, requiring Angelo to meet him at the entrance of the city, there to deliver up his authority; and the duke also commanded it to be proclaimed, that if any of his subjects craved redress for injustice, they should exhibit their petitions in the street on his first entrance into the city.

Early in the morning Isabel came to the prison, and the duke, who there awaited her coming, for secret reasons thought it good to tell her that Claudio was beheaded; therefore when Isabel inquired if Angelo had sent the pardon for her brother, he said, 'Angelo has released Claudio from this world. His head is off, and sent to the deputy.' The much-grieved sister cried out, 'O unhappy Claudio, wretched Isabel, injurious world, most wicked Angelo!' The seeming friar bid her take comfort, and when she was become a little calm, he acquainted her with the near prospect of the duke's return, and told her in what manner she should proceed in preferring her complaint against Angelo; and he bade her not fear if the cause should seem to go against her for a while. Leaving Isabel sufficiently instructed, he next went to Mariana, and gave her counsel in what manner she also should act.

Then the duke laid aside his friar's habit, and in his own royal robes, amidst a joyful crowd of his faithful subjects, assembled to greet his arrival, entered the city of Vienna, where he was met by Angelo, who delivered up his authority in the proper form. And there came Isabel, in the manner of a petitioner for redress, and said, 'Justice, most royal duke! I am the sister of one Claudio, who, for the seducing a young maid, was condemned to lose his head. I made my suit to Lord Angelo for my brother's pardon. It were needless to tell your grace how I prayed and kneeled, how he repelled me, and how I replied; for this was of much length. The vile conclusion I now begin with grief and shame to utter. Angelo would not but by my yielding to his dishonourable love release my brother; and after much debate within myself, my sisterly remorse overcame my virtue, and I did yield to him. But the next morning betimes, Angelo, forfeiting his promise, sent a warrant for my poor brother's head!' The duke affected to disbelieve her story; and Angelo said that grief for her brother's death, who had suffered by the due course of the law, had disordered her senses. And now another suitor approached, which was Mariana; and Mariana said, 'Noble prince, as there comes light from heaven, and truth from breath, as there is sense in truth and truth in virtue, I am this man's wife, and, my good lord, the words of Isabel are false; for the night she says she was with Angelo, I passed that night with him in the garden-house. As this is true, let me in safety rise, or else for ever be fixed here a marble monument.' Then did Isabel appeal for the truth of what she had said to Friar Lodowick, that being the name the duke had assumed in his disguise. Isabel and Mariana had both obeyed his instructions in what they said, the duke intending that the innocence of Isabel should be plainly proved in that public manner before the whole city of Vienna; but Angelo little thought that it was from such a cause that they thus differed in their story, and he hoped from their contradictory evidence to be able to clear himself from the accusation of Isabel; and he said, assuming the look of offended innocence, 'I did but smile till now; but, good my lord, my patience here is touched, and I perceive these poor distracted women are but the instruments of some greater one, who sets them on. Let me have way, my lord, to find this practice out.' – 'Ay, with all my heart,' said the duke, 'and punish them to the height of your pleasure. You, Lord Escalus, sit with Lord Angelo, lend him your pains to discover this abuse; the friar is sent for that set them on, and when he comes, do with injuries as may seem best in any chastisement. I for a while will leave you, but stir not you, Lord Angelo, till you have well determined upon this slander.' The duke then went away, leaving Angelo well pleased to be deputed judge and umpire in his own cause. But the duke was absent only while he threw off his royal robes and put on his friar's habit; and in that disguise again he presented himself before Angelo and Escalus: and the good old Escalus, who thought Angelo had been falsely accused, said to the supposed friar, 'Come, sir, did you set these women on to slander Lord Angelo?' He replied, 'Where is the duke? It is he who should hear me speak.' Escalus said, 'The duke is in us, and we will hear you. Speak justly.' – 'Boldly at least,' retorted the friar; and then he blamed the duke for leaving the cause of Isabel in the hands of him she had accused, and spoke so freely of many corrupt practices he had observed, while, as he said, he had been a looker-on in Vienna, that Escalus threatened him with the torture for speaking words against the state, and for censuring the conduct of the duke, and ordered him to be taken away to prison. Then, to the amazement of all present, and to the utter confusion of Angelo, the supposed friar threw off his disguise, and they saw it was the duke himself.

The duke first addressed Isabel. He said to her, 'Come hither, Isabel. Your friar is now your prince, but with my habit I have not changed my heart. I am still devoted to your service.' 'O give me pardon,' said Isabel, 'that I, your vassal, have employed and troubled your unknown sovereignty.' He answered that he had most need of forgiveness from her, for not having prevented the death of her brother – for not yet would he tell her that Claudio was living; meaning first to make a further trial of her goodness. Angelo now knew the duke had been a secret witness of his bad deeds, and he said, 'O my dread lord, I should be guiltier than my guiltiness, to think I can be undiscernible, when I perceive your grace, like power divine, has looked upon my actions. Then, good prince, no longer prolong my shame, but let my trial be my own confession. Immediate sentence and death is all the grace I beg.' The duke replied, 'Angelo, thy faults are manifest. We do condemn thee to the very block where Claudio stooped to death; and with like haste away with him; and for his possessions, Mariana, we do instate and widow you withal, to buy a better husband.' – 'O my dear lord,' said Mariana, 'I crave no other, nor no better man:' and then on her knees, even as Isabel had begged the life of Claudio, did this kind wife of an ungrateful husband beg the life of Angelo; and she said, 'Gentle my liege, O good my lord! Sweet Isabel, take my part! Lend me your knees, and all my life to come I will lend you all my life, to do you service!' The duke said, 'Against all sense you importune her. Should Isabel kneel down to beg for mercy, her brother's ghost would break his paved bed, and take her hence in horror.' Still Mariana said, 'Isabel, sweet Isabel, do but kneel by me, hold up your hand, say nothing! I will speak all. They say, best men are moulded out of faults, and for the most part become much the better for being a little bad. So may my husband. Oh, Isabel, will you lend a knee?' The duke then said, 'He dies for Claudio.' But much pleased was the good duke, when his own Isabel, from whom he expected all gracious and honourable acts, kneeled down before him, and said, 'Most bounteous sir, look, if it please you, on this man condemned, as if my brother lived. I partly think a due sincerity governed his deeds, till he did look on me. Since it is so, let him not die! My brother had but justice, in that he did the thing for which he died.'

The duke, as the best reply he could make to this noble petitioner for her enemy's life, sending for Claudio from his prison-house, where he lay doubtful of his destiny, presented to her this lamented brother living; and he said to Isabel, 'Give me your hand, Isabel; for your lovely sake I pardon Claudio. Say you will be mine, and he shall be my brother too.' By this time Lord Angelo perceived he was safe; and the duke, observing his eye to brighten up a little, said, 'Well, Angelo, look that you love your wife; her worth has obtained your pardon: joy to you, Mariana! Love her, Angelo! I have confessed her, and know her virtue.' Angelo remembered, when dressed in a little brief authority, how hard his heart had been, and felt how sweet is mercy.

The duke commanded Claudio to marry Juliet, and offered himself again to the acceptance of Isabel, whose virtuous and noble conduct had won her prince's heart. Isabel, not having taken the veil, was free to marry; and the friendly offices, while hid under the disguise of a humble friar, which the noble duke had done for her, made her with grateful joy accept the honour he offered her; and when she became Duchess of Vienna, the excellent example of the virtuous Isabel worked such a complete reformation among the young ladies of that city, that from that time none ever fell into the transgression of Juliet, the repentant wife of the reformed Claudio. And the mercy-loving duke long reigned with his beloved Isabel, the happiest of husbands and of princes.

THE COMEDY OF ERRORS

THE states of Syracuse and Ephesus being at variance, there was a cruel law made at Ephesus, ordaining that if any merchant of Syracuse was seen in the city of Ephesus, he was to be put to death, unless he could pay a thousand marks for the ransom of his life. Aegeon, an old merchant of Syracuse, was discovered in the streets of Ephesus, and brought before the duke, either to pay this heavy fine, or to receive sentence of death.

Aegeon had no money to pay the fine, and the duke, before he pronounced the sentence of death upon him, desired him to relate the history of his life, and to tell for what cause he had ventured to come to the city of Ephesus, which it was death for any Syracusan merchant to enter.

Aegeon said, that he did not fear to die, for sorrow had made him weary of his life, but that a heavier task could not have been imposed upon him than to relate the events of his unfortunate life. He then began his own history, in the following words:

'I was born at Syracuse, and brought up to the profession of a merchant. I married a lady, with whom I lived very happily, but being obliged to go to Epidamnum, I was detained there by my business six months, and then, finding I should be obliged to stay some time longer, I sent for my wife, who, as soon as she arrived, was brought to bed of two sons, and what was very strange, they were both so exactly alike, that it was impossible to distinguish the one from the other. At the same time that my wife was brought to bed of these twin boys, a poor woman in the inn where my wife lodged was brought to bed of two sons, and these twins were as much like each other as my two sons were. The parents of these children being exceeding poor, I bought the two boys, and brought them up to attend upon my sons.

'My sons were very fine children, and my wife was not a little proud of two such boys: and she daily wishing to return home, I unwillingly agreed, and in an evil hour we got on shipboard; for we had not sailed above a league from Epidamnum before a dreadful storm arose, which continued with such violence, that the sailors seeing no chance of saving the ship, crowded into the boat to save their own lives, leaving us alone in the ship, which we every moment expected would be destroyed by the fury of the storm.

'The incessant weeping of my wife, and the piteous complaints of the pretty babes, who, not knowing what to fear, wept for fashion, because they saw their mother weep, filled me with terror for them, though I did not for myself fear death; and all my thoughts were bent to contrive means for their safety. I tied my youngest son to the end of a small spare mast, such as seafaring men provide against storms; at the other end I bound the youngest of the twin slaves, and at the same time I directed my wife how to fasten the other children in like manner to another mast. She thus having the care of the two eldest children, and I of the two younger, we bound ourselves separately to these masts with the children; and but for this contrivance we had all been lost, for the ship split on a mighty rock, and was dashed in pieces; and we, clinging to these slender masts, were supported above the water, where I, having the care of two children, was unable to assist my wife, who with the other children was soon separated from me; but while they were yet in my sight, they were taken up by a boat of fishermen, from Corinth (as I supposed), and seeing them in safety, I had no care but to struggle with the wild sea-waves, to preserve my dear son and the youngest slave. At length we, in our turn, were taken up by a ship, and the sailors, knowing me, gave us kind welcome and assistance, and landed us in safety at Syracuse; but from that sad hour I have never known what became of my wife and eldest child.

'My youngest son, and now my only care, when he was eighteen years of age, began to be inquisitive after his mother and his brother, and often importuned me that he might take his attendant, the young slave, who had also lost his brother, and go in search of them: at length I unwillingly gave consent, for though I anxiously desired to hear tidings of my wife and eldest son, yet in sending my younger one to find them, I hazarded the loss of him also. It is now seven years since my son left me; five years have I passed in travelling through the world in search of him: I have been in farthest Greece, and through the bounds of Asia, and coasting homewards, I landed here in Ephesus, being unwilling to leave any place unsought that harbours men; but this day must end the story of my life, and happy should I think myself in my death, if I were assured my wife and sons were living.'

Here the hapless Aegeon ended the account of his misfortunes; and the duke, pitying this unfortunate father, who had brought upon himself this great peril by his love for his lost son, said, if it were not against the laws, which his oath and dignity did not permit him to alter, he would freely pardon him; yet, instead of dooming him to instant death, as the strict letter of the law required, he would give him that day to try if he could beg or borrow the money to pay the fine.

This day of grace did seem no great favour to Aegeon, for not knowing any man in Ephesus, there seemed to him but little chance that any stranger would lend or give him a thousand marks to pay the fine; and helpless and hopeless of any relief, he retired from the presence of the duke in the custody of a jailor.

Aegeon supposed he knew no person in Ephesus; but at the very time he was in danger of losing his life through the careful search he was making after his youngest son, that son and his eldest son also were both in the city of Ephesus.

Aegeon's sons, besides being exactly alike in face and person, were both named alike, being both called Antipholus, and the two twin slaves were also both named Dromio. Aegeon's youngest son, Antipholus of Syracuse, he whom the old man had come to Ephesus to seek, happened to arrive at Ephesus with his slave Dromio that very same day that Aegeon did; and he being also a merchant of Syracuse, he would have been in the same danger that his father was, but by good fortune he met a friend who told him the peril an old merchant of Syracuse was in, and advised him to pass for a merchant of Epidamnum; this Antipholus agreed to do, and he was sorry to hear one of his own countrymen was in this danger, but he little thought this old merchant was his own father.

The eldest son of Aegeon (who must be called Antipholus of Ephesus, to distinguish him from his brother Antipholus of Syracuse) had lived at Ephesus twenty years, and, being a rich man, was well able to have paid the money for the ransom of his father's life; but Antipholus knew nothing of his father, being so young when he was taken out of the sea with his mother by the fishermen that he only remembered he had been so preserved, but he had no recollection of either his father or his mother; the fishermen who took up this Antipholus and his mother and the young slave Dromio, having carried the two children away from her (to the great grief of that unhappy lady), intending to sell them.

Antipholus and Dromio were sold by them to Duke Menaphon, a famous warrior, who was uncle to the Duke of Ephesus, and he carried the boys to Ephesus when he went to visit the duke his nephew.

The Duke of Ephesus taking a liking to young Antipholus, when he grew up, made him an officer in his army, in which he distinguished himself by his great bravery in the wars, where he saved the life of his patron the duke, who rewarded his merit by marrying him to Adriana, a rich lady of Ephesus; with whom he was living (his slave Dromio still attending him) at the time his father came there.

Antipholus of Syracuse, when he parted with his friend, who advised him to say he came from Epidamnum, gave his slave Dromio some money to carry to the inn where he intended to dine, and in the meantime he said he would walk about and view the city, and observe the manners of the people.

Dromio was a pleasant fellow, and when Antipholus was dull and melancholy he used to divert himself with the odd humours and merry jests of his slave, so that the freedoms of speech he allowed in Dromio were greater than is usual between masters and their servants.

When Antipholus of Syracuse had sent Dromio away, he stood awhile thinking over his solitary wanderings in search of his mother and his brother, of whom in no place where he landed could he hear the least tidings; and he said sorrowfully to himself, 'I am like a drop of water in the ocean, which seeking to find its fellow drop, loses itself in the wide sea. So I unhappily, to find a mother and a brother, do lose myself.'

While he was thus meditating on his weary travels, which had hitherto been so useless, Dromio (as he thought) returned. Antipholus wondering that he came back so soon, asked him where he had left the money. Now it was not his own Dromio, but the twin-brother that lived with Antipholus of Ephesus, that he spoke to. The two Dromios and the two Antipholuses were still as much alike as Aegeon had said they were in their infancy; therefore no wonder Antipholus thought it was his own slave returned, and asked him why he came back so soon. Dromio replied, 'My mistress sent me to bid you to come to dinner. The capon burns, and the pig falls from the spit, and the meat will be all cold if you do not come home.' 'These jests are out of season,' said Antipholus: 'where did you leave the money?' Dromio still answering, that his mistress had sent him to fetch Antipholus to dinner: 'What mistress?' said Antipholus. 'Why, your worship's wife, sir,' replied Dromio. Antipholus having no wife, he was very angry with Dromio, and said, 'Because I familiarly sometimes chat with you, you presume to jest with me in this free manner. I am not in a sportive humour now: where is the money? we being strangers here, how dare you trust so great a charge from your own custody?' Dromio hearing his master, as he thought him, talk of their being strangers, supposing Antipholus was jesting, replied merrily, 'I pray you, sir, jest as you sit at dinner. I had no charge but to fetch you home, to dine with my mistress and her sister.' Now Antipholus lost all patience, and beat Dromio, who ran home, and told his mistress that his master had refused to come to dinner, and said that he had no wife.

Adriana, the wife of Antipholus of Ephesus, was very angry when she heard that her husband said he had no wife; for she was of a jealous temper, and she said her husband meant that he loved another lady better than herself; and she began to fret, and say unkind words of jealousy and reproach of her husband; and her sister Luciana, who lived with her, tried in vain to persuade her out of her groundless suspicions.

Antipholus of Syracuse went to the inn, and found Dromio with the money in safety there, and seeing his own Dromio, he was going again to chide him for his free jests, when Adriana came up to him, and not doubting but it was her husband she saw, she began to reproach him for looking strange upon her (as well he might, never having seen this angry lady before); and then she told him how well he loved her before they were married, and that now he loved some other lady instead of her.

'How comes it now, my husband,' said she, 'O how comes it that I have lost your love?' – 'Plead you to me, fair dame?' said the astonished Antipholus. It was in vain he told her he was not her husband, and that he had been in Ephesus but two hours; she insisted on his going home with her, and Antipholus at last, being unable to get away, went with her to his brother's house, and dined with Adriana and her sister, the one calling him husband, and the other brother, he, all amazed, thinking he must have been married to her in his sleep, or that he was sleeping now. And Dromio, who followed them, was no less surprised, for the cook-maid, who was his brother's wife, also claimed him for her husband.

While Antipholus of Syracuse was dining with his brother's wife, his brother, the real husband, returned home to dinner with his slave Dromio; but the servants would not open the door, because their mistress had ordered them not to admit any company; and when they repeatedly knocked, and said they were Antipholus and Dromio, the maids laughed at them, and said that Antipholus was at dinner with their mistress, and Dromio was in the kitchen; and though they almost knocked the door down, they could not gain admittance, and at last Antipholus went away very angry, and strangely surprised at hearing a gentleman was dining with his wife.

When Antipholus of Syracuse had finished his dinner, he was so perplexed at the lady's still persisting in calling him husband, and at hearing that Dromio had also been claimed by the cook-maid, that he left the house, as soon as he could find any pretence to get away; for though he was very much pleased with Luciana, the sister, yet the jealous-tempered Adriana he disliked very much, nor was Dromio at all better satisfied with his fair wife in the kitchen: therefore both master and man were glad to get away from their new wives as fast as they could.

The moment Antipholus of Syracuse had left the house, he was met by a goldsmith, who mistaking him, as Adriana had done, for Antipholus of Ephesus, gave him a gold chain, calling him by his name; and when Antipholus would have refused the chain, saying it did not belong to him, the goldsmith replied he made it by his own orders; and went away, leaving the chain in the hands of Antipholus, who ordered his man Dromio to get his things on board a ship, not choosing to stay in a place any longer, where he met with such strange adventures that he surely thought himself bewitched.

The goldsmith who had given the chain to the wrong Antipholus, was arrested immediately after for a sum of money he owed; and Antipholus, the married brother, to whom the goldsmith thought he had given the chain, happened to come to the place where the officer was arresting the goldsmith, who, when he saw Antipholus, asked him to pay for the gold chain he had just delivered to him, the price amounting to nearly the same sum as that for which he had been arrested. Antipholus denying the having received the chain, and the goldsmith persisting to declare that he had but a few minutes before given it to him, they disputed this matter a long time, both thinking they were right: for Antipholus knew the goldsmith never gave him the chain, and so like were the two brothers, the goldsmith was as certain he had delivered the chain into his hands, till at last the officer took the goldsmith away to prison for the debt he owed, and at the same time the goldsmith made the officer arrest Antipholus for the price of the chain; so that at the conclusion of their dispute, Antipholus and the merchant were both taken away to prison together.

As Antipholus was going to prison, he met Dromio of Syracuse, his brother's slave, and mistaking him for his own, he ordered him to go to Adriana his wife, and tell her to send the money for which he was arrested. Dromio wondering that his master should send him back to the strange house where he dined, and from which he had just before been in such haste to depart, did not dare to reply, though he came to tell his master the ship was ready to sail: for he saw Antipholus was in no humour to be jested with. Therefore he went away, grumbling within himself, that he must return to Adriana's house, 'Where,' said he, 'Dowsabel claims me for a husband: but I must go, for servants must obey their masters' commands.'

Adriana gave him the money, and as Dromio was returning, he met Antipholus of Syracuse, who was still in amaze at the surprising adventures he met with; for his brother being well known in Ephesus, there was hardly a man he met in the streets but saluted him as an old acquaintance: some offered him money which they said was owing to him, some invited him to come and see them, and some gave him thanks for kindnesses they said he had done them, all mistaking him for his brother. A tailor showed him some silks he had bought for him, and insisted upon taking measure of him for some clothes.

Antipholus began to think he was among a nation of sorcerers and witches, and Dromio did not at all relieve his master from his bewildered thoughts, by asking him how he got free from the officer who was carrying him to prison, and giving him the purse of gold which Adriana had sent to pay the debt with. This talk of Dromio's of the arrest and of a prison, and of the money he had brought from Adriana, perfectly confounded Antipholus, and he said, 'This fellow Dromio is certainly distracted, and we wander here in illusions;' and quite terrified at his own confused thoughts, he cried out, 'Some blessed power deliver us from this strange place!'

And now another stranger came up to him, and she was a lady, and she too called him Antipholus, and told him he had dined with her that day, and asked him for a gold chain which she said he had promised to give her. Antipholus now lost all patience, and calling her a sorceress, he denied that he had ever promised her a chain, or dined with her, or had even seen her face before that moment. The lady persisted in affirming he had dined with her, and had promised her a chain, which Antipholus still denying, she further said, that she had given him a valuable ring, and if he would not give her the gold chain, she insisted upon having her own ring again. On this Antipholus became quite frantic, and again calling her sorceress and witch, and denying all knowledge of her or her ring, ran away from her, leaving her astonished at his words and his wild looks, for nothing to her appeared more certain than that he had dined with her, and that she had given him a ring, in consequence of his promising to make her a present of a gold chain. But this lady had fallen into the same mistake the others had done, for she had taken him for his brother: the married Antipholus had done all the things she taxed this Antipholus with.

When the married Antipholus was denied entrance into his own house (those within supposing him to be already there), he had gone away very angry, believing it to be one of his wife's jealous freaks, to which she was very subject, and remembering that she had often falsely accused him of visiting other ladies, he, to be revenged on her for shutting him out of his own house, determined to go and dine with this lady, and she receiving him with great civility, and his wife having so highly offended him, Antipholus promised to give her a gold chain, which he had intended as a present for his wife; it was the same chain which the goldsmith by mistake had given to his brother. The lady liked so well the thoughts of having a fine gold chain, that she gave the married Antipholus a ring; which when, as she supposed (taking his brother for him), he denied, and said he did not know her, and left her in such a wild passion, she began to think he was certainly out of his senses; and presently she resolved to go and tell Adriana that her husband was mad. And while she was telling it to Adriana, he came, attended by the jailor (who allowed him to come home to get the money to pay the debt), for the purse of money, which Adriana had sent by Dromio, and he had delivered to the other Antipholus.

Adriana believed the story the lady told her of her husband's madness must be true, when he reproached her for shutting him out of his own house; and remembering how he had protested all dinner-time that he was not her husband, and had never been in Ephesus till that day, she had no doubt that he was mad; she therefore paid the jailor the money, and having discharged him, she ordered her servants to bind her husband with ropes, and had him conveyed into a dark room, and sent for a doctor to come and cure him of his madness: Antipholus all the while hotly exclaiming against this false accusation, which the exact likeness he bore to his brother had brought upon him. But his rage only the more confirmed them in the belief that he was mad; and Dromio persisting in the same story, they bound him also, and took him away along with his master.

Soon after Adriana had put her husband into confinement, a servant came to tell her that Antipholus and Dromio must have broken loose from their keepers, for that they were both walking at liberty in the next street. On hearing this, Adriana ran out to fetch him home, taking some people with her to secure her husband again; and her sister went along with her. When they came to the gates of a convent in their neighbourhood, there they saw Antipholus and Dromio, as they thought, being again deceived by the likeness of the twin-brothers.

Antipholus of Syracuse was still beset with the perplexities this likeness had brought upon him. The chain which the goldsmith had given him was about his neck, and the goldsmith was reproaching him for denying that he had it, and refusing to pay for it, and Antipholus was protesting that the goldsmith freely gave him the chain in the morning, and that from that hour he had never seen the goldsmith again.

And now Adriana came up to him and claimed him as her lunatic husband, who had escaped from his keepers; and the men she brought with her were going to lay violent hands on Antipholus and Dromio; but they ran into the convent, and Antipholus begged the abbess to give him shelter in her house.

And now came out the lady abbess herself to inquire into the cause of this disturbance. She was a grave and venerable lady, and wise to judge of what she saw, and she would not too hastily give up the man who had sought protection in her house; so she strictly questioned the wife about the story she told of her husband's madness, and she said, 'What is the cause of this sudden distemper of your husband's? Has he lost his wealth at sea? Or is it the death of some dear friend that has disturbed his mind?' Adriana replied, that no such things as these had been the cause. 'Perhaps,' said the abbess, 'he has fixed his affections on some other lady than you his wife; and that has driven him to this state.' Adriana said she had long thought the love of some other lady was the cause of his frequent absences from home. Now it was not his love for another, but the teasing jealousy of his wife's temper, that often obliged Antipholus to leave his home; and (the abbess suspecting this from the vehemence of Adriana's manner) to learn the truth, she said, 'You should have reprehended him for this.' – 'Why, so I did,' replied Adriana. 'Ay,' said the abbess, 'but perhaps not enough.' Adriana, willing to convince the abbess that she had said enough to Antipholus on this subject, replied, 'It was the constant subject of our conversation: in bed I would not let him sleep for speaking of it. At the table I would not let him eat for speaking of it. When I was alone with him, I talked of nothing else; and in company I gave him frequent hints of it. Still all my talk was how vile and bad it was in him to love any lady better than me.'

The lady abbess, having drawn this full confession from the jealous

Adriana, now said, 'And therefore comes it that your husband is mad. The venomous clamour of a jealous woman is a more deadly poison than a mad dog's tooth. It seems his sleep was hindered by your railing; no wonder that his head is light: and his meat was sauced with your upbraidings; unquiet meals make ill digestions, and that has thrown him into this fever. You say his sports were disturbed by your brawls; being debarred from the enjoyment of society and recreation, what could ensue but dull melancholy and comfortless despair? The consequence is then, that your jealous fits have made your husband mad.'

Luciana would have excused her sister, saying, she always reprehended her husband mildly; and she said to her sister, 'Why do you hear these rebukes without answering them?' But the abbess had made her so plainly perceive her fault, that she could only answer, 'She has betrayed me to my own reproof.'

Adriana, though ashamed of her own conduct, still insisted on having her husband delivered up to her; but the abbess would suffer no person to enter her house, nor would she deliver up this unhappy man to the care of the jealous wife, determining herself to use gentle means for his recovery, and she retired into her house again, and ordered her gates to be shut against them.

During the course of this eventful day, in which so many errors had happened from the likeness the twin brothers bore to each other, old Aegeon's day of grace was passing away, it being now near sunset; and at sunset he was doomed to die, if he could not pay the money.

The place of his execution was near this convent, and here he arrived just as the abbess retired into the convent; the duke attending in person, that if any offered to pay the money, he might be present to pardon him.

Adriana stopped this melancholy procession, and cried out to the duke for justice, telling him that the abbess had refused to deliver up her lunatic husband to her care. While she was speaking, her real husband and his servant Dromio, who had got loose, came before the duke to demand justice, complaining that his wife had confined him on a false charge of lunacy; and telling in what manner he had broken his bands, and eluded the vigilance of his keepers. Adriana was strangely surprised to see her husband, when she thought he had been within the convent.

Aegeon, seeing his son, concluded this was the son who had left him to go in search of his mother and his brother; and he felt secure that this dear son would readily pay the money demanded for his ransom. He therefore spoke to Antipholus in words of fatherly affection, with joyful hope that he should now be released. But to the utter astonishment of Aegeon, his son denied all knowledge of him, as well he might, for this Antipholus had never seen his father since they were separated in the storm in his infancy; but while the poor old Aegeon was in vain endeavouring to make his son acknowledge him, thinking surely that either his griefs and the anxieties he had suffered had so strangely altered him that his son did not know him, or else that he was ashamed to acknowledge his father in his misery; in the midst of this perplexity, the lady abbess and the other Antipholus and Dromio came out, and wondering Adriana saw two husbands and two Dromios standing before her.

And now these riddling errors, which had so perplexed them all, were clearly made out. When the duke saw the two Antipholuses and the two Dromios both so exactly alike, he at once conjectured aright of these seeming mysteries, for he remembered the story Aegeon had told him in the morning; and he said, these men must be the two sons of Aegeon and their twin slaves.

But now an unlooked-for joy indeed completed the history of Aegeon; and the tale he had in the morning told in sorrow, and under sentence of death, before the setting sun went down was brought to a happy conclusion, for the venerable lady abbess made herself known to be the long-lost wife of Aegeon, and the fond mother of the two Antipholuses.

When the fishermen took the eldest Antipholus and Dromio away from her, she entered a nunnery, and by her wise and virtuous conduct, she was at length made lady abbess of this convent, and in discharging the rites of hospitality to an unhappy stranger she had unknowingly protected her own son.

Joyful congratulations and affectionate greetings between these long separated parents and their children made them for a while forget that Aegeon was yet under sentence of death; but when they were become a little calm, Antipholus of Ephesus offered the duke the ransom money for his father's life; but the duke freely pardoned Aegeon, and would not take the money. And the duke went with the abbess and her newly-found husband and children into the convent, to hear this happy family discourse at leisure of the blessed ending of their adverse fortunes. And the two Dromios' humble joy must not be forgotten; they had their congratulations and greetings too, and each Dromio pleasantly complimented his brother on his good looks, being well pleased to see his own person (as in a glass) show so handsome in his brother.

Adriana had so well profited by the good counsel of her mother-in-law, that she never after cherished unjust suspicions, or was jealous of her husband.

Antipholus of Syracuse married the fair Luciana, the sister of his brother's wife; and the good old Aegeon, with his wife and sons, lived at Ephesus many years. Nor did the unravelling of these perplexities so entirely remove every ground of mistake for the future, but that sometimes, to remind them of adventures past, comical blunders would happen, and the one Antipholus, and the one Dromio, be mistaken for the other, making altogether a pleasant and diverting Comedy of Errors.

MUCH ADO ABOUT NOTHING

THERE lived in the palace at Messina two ladies, whose names were Hero and Beatrice. Hero was the daughter, and Beatrice the niece, of Leonato, the governor of Messina.

Beatrice was of a lively temper, and loved to divert her cousin Hero, who was of a more serious disposition, with her sprightly sallies. Whatever was going forward was sure to make matter of mirth for the light-hearted Beatrice.

At the time the history of these ladies commences some young men of high rank in the army, as they were passing through Messina on their return from a war that was just ended, in which they had distinguished themselves by their great bravery, came to visit Leonato. Among these were Don Pedro, the Prince of Arragon; and his friend Claudio, who was a lord of Florence; and with them came the wild and witty Benedick, and he was a lord of Padua.

These strangers had been at Messina before, and the hospitable governor introduced them to his daughter and his niece as their old friends and acquaintance.

Benedick, the moment he entered the room, began a lively conversation with Leonato and the prince. Beatrice, who liked not to be left out of any discourse, interrupted Benedick with saying, 'I wonder that you will still be talking, Signior Benedick: nobody marks you.' Benedick was just such another rattle-brain as Beatrice, yet he was not pleased at this free salutation; he thought it did not become a well-bred lady to be so flippant with her tongue; and he remembered, when he was last at Messina, that Beatrice used to select him to make her merry jests upon. And as there is no one who so little likes to be made a jest of as those who are apt to take the same liberty themselves, so it was with Benedick and Beatrice; these two sharp wits never met in former times but a perfect war of raillery was kept up between them, and they always parted mutually displeased with each other. Therefore when Beatrice stopped him in the middle of his discourse with telling him nobody marked what he was saying, Benedick, affecting not to have observed before that she was present, said, 'What, my dear Lady Disdain, are you yet living?' And now war broke out afresh between them, and a long jangling argument ensued, during which Beatrice, although she knew he had so well approved his valour in the late war, said that she would eat all he had killed there: and observing the prince take delight in Benedick's conversation she called him 'the prince's jester'. This sarcasm sunk deeper into the mind of Benedick than all Beatrice had said before. The hint she gave him that he was a coward, by saying she would eat all he had killed, he did not regard, knowing himself to be a brave man; but there is nothing that great wits so much dread as the imputation of buffoonery, because the charge comes sometimes a little too near the truth: therefore Benedick perfectly hated Beatrice when she called him 'the prince's jester'.

The modest lady Hero was silent before the noble guests; and while Claudio was attentively observing the improvement which time had made in her beauty, and was contemplating the exquisite graces of her fine figure (for she was an admirable young lady), the prince was highly amused with listening to the humorous dialogue between Benedick and Beatrice; and he said in a whisper to Leonato, 'This is a pleasant-spirited young lady. She were an excellent wife for Benedick.' Leonato replied to this suggestion, 'O, my lord, if they were but a week married, they would talk themselves mad.' But though Leonato thought they would make a discordant pair, the prince did not give up the idea of matching these two keen wits together.

When the prince returned with Claudio from the palace, he found that the marriage he had devised between Benedick and Beatrice was not the only one projected in that good company, for Claudio spoke in such terms of Hero, as made the prince guess at what was passing in his heart; and he liked it well, and he said to Claudio, 'Do you affect Hero?' To this question Claudio replied, 'O my lord, when I was last at Messina, I looked upon her with a soldier's eye, that liked, but had no leisure for loving; but now, in this happy time of peace, thoughts of war have left their places vacant in my mind, and in their room come thronging soft and delicate thoughts, all prompting me how fair young Hero is, reminding me that I liked her before I went to the wars.' Claudio's confession of his love for Hero so wrought upon the prince, that he lost no time in soliciting the consent of Leonato to accept of Claudio for a son-in-law. Leonato agreed to this proposal, and the prince found no great difficulty in persuading the gentle Hero herself to listen to the suit of the noble Claudio, who was a lord of rare endowments, and highly accomplished, and Claudio, assisted by his kind prince, soon prevailed upon Leonato to fix an early day for the celebration of his marriage with Hero.

Claudio was to wait but a few days before he was to be married to his fair lady; yet he complained of the interval being tedious, as indeed most young men are impatient when they are waiting for the accomplishment of any event they have set their hearts upon: the prince, therefore, to make the time seem short to him, proposed as a kind of merry pastime that they should invent some artful scheme to make Benedick and Beatrice fall in love with each other. Claudio entered with great satisfaction into this whim of the prince, and Leonato promised them his assistance, and even Hero said she would do any modest office to help her cousin to a good husband.

The device the prince invented was, that the gentlemen should make Benedick believe that Beatrice was in love with him, and that Hero should make Beatrice believe that Benedick was in love with her.

The prince, Leonato, and Claudio began their operations first: and watching upon an opportunity when Benedick was quietly seated reading in an arbour, the prince and his assistants took their station among the trees behind the arbour, so near that Benedick could not choose but hear all they said; and after some careless talk the prince said, 'Come hither, Leonato. What was it you told me the other day – that your niece Beatrice was in love with signior Benedick? I did never think that lady would have loved any man.' 'No, nor I neither, my lord,' answered Leonato. 'It is most wonderful that she should so dote on Benedick, whom she in all outward behaviour seemed ever to dislike.' Claudio confirmed all this with saying that Hero had told him Beatrice was so in love with Benedick, that she would certainly die of grief, if he could not be brought to love her; which Leonato and Claudio seemed to agree was impossible, he having always been such a railer against all fair ladies, and in particular against Beatrice.

The prince affected to hearken to all this with great compassion for Beatrice, and he said, 'It were good that Benedick were told of this.' 'To what end?' said Claudio; 'he would but make sport of it, and torment the poor lady worse.' 'And if he should,' said the prince, 'it were a good deed to hang him; for Beatrice is an excellent sweet lady, and exceeding wise in everything but in loving Benedick.' Then the prince motioned to his companions that they should walk on, and leave Benedick to meditate upon what he had overheard.

Benedick had been listening with great eagerness to this conversation; and he said to himself when he heard Beatrice loved him, 'Is it possible? Sits the wind in that corner?' And when they were gone, he began to reason in this manner with himself: 'This can be no trick! they were very serious, and they have the truth from Hero, and seem to pity the lady. Love me! Why, it must be requited! I did never think to marry. But when I said I should die a bachelor, I did not think I should live to be married. They say the lady is virtuous and fair. She is so. And wise in everything but loving me. Why, that is no great argument of her folly. But here comes Beatrice. By this day, she is a fair lady. I do spy some marks of love in her.' Beatrice now approached him, and said with her usual tartness, 'Against my will I am sent to bid you come in to dinner.' Benedick, who never felt himself disposed to speak so politely to her before, replied, 'Fair Beatrice, I thank you for your pains:' and when Beatrice, after two or three more rude speeches, left him, Benedick thought he observed a concealed meaning of kindness under the uncivil words she uttered, and he said aloud, 'If I do not take pity on her, I am a villain. If I do not love her, I am a Jew. I will go get her picture.'

The gentleman being thus caught in the net they had spread for him, it was now Hero's turn to play her part with Beatrice; and for this purpose she sent for Ursula and Margaret, two gentlewomen who attended upon her, and she said to Margaret, 'Good Margaret, run to the parlour; there you will find my cousin Beatrice talking with the prince and Claudio. Whisper in her ear, that I and Ursula are walking in the orchard, and that our discourse is all of her. Bid her steal into that pleasant arbour, where honeysuckles, ripened by the sun, like ungrateful minions, forbid the sun to enter.' This arbour, into which Hero desired Margaret to entice Beatrice, was the very same pleasant arbour where Benedick had so lately been an attentive listener.

'I will make her come, I warrant, presently,' said Margaret.

Hero, then taking Ursula with her into the orchard, said to her, 'Now, Ursula, when Beatrice comes, we will walk up and down this alley, and our talk must be only of Benedick, and when I name him, let it be your part to praise him more than ever man did merit. My talk to you must be how Benedick is in love with Beatrice. Now begin; for look where Beatrice like a lapwing runs close by the ground, to hear our conference.' They then began; Hero saying, as if in answer to something which Ursula had said, 'No, truly, Ursula. She is too disdainful; her spirits are as coy as wild birds of the rock.' 'But are you sure,' said Ursula, 'that Benedick loves Beatrice so entirely?' Hero replied, 'So says the prince, and my lord Claudio, and they entreated me to acquaint her with it; but I persuaded them, if they loved Benedick, never to let Beatrice know of it.' 'Certainly,' replied Ursula, 'it were not good she knew his love, lest she make sport of it.' 'Why, to say truth,' said Hero, 'I never yet saw a man, how wise soever, or noble, young, or rarely featured, but she would dispraise him.' 'Sure sure, such carping is not commendable,' said Ursula. 'No,' replied Hero, 'but who dare tell her so? If I should speak, she would mock me into air.' 'O! you wrong your cousin,' said Ursula: 'she cannot be so much without true judgment, as to refuse so rare a gentleman as signior Benedick.' 'He hath an excellent good name,' said Hero: 'indeed, he is the first man in Italy, always excepting my dear Claudio.' And now, Hero giving her attendant a hint that it was time to change the discourse, Ursula said, 'And when are you to be married, madam?' Hero then told her, that she was to be married to Claudio the next day, and desired she would go in with her, and look at some new attire, as she wished to consult with her on what she would wear on the morrow. Beatrice, who had been listening with breathless eagerness to this dialogue, when they went away, exclaimed, 'What fire is in mine ears? Can this be true? Farewell, contempt and scorn, and maiden pride, adieu! Benedick, love on! I will requite you, taming my wild heart to your loving hand.'

It must have been a pleasant sight to see these old enemies converted into new and loving friends, and to behold their first meeting after being cheated into mutual liking by the merry artifice of the good-humoured prince. But a sad reverse in the fortunes of Hero must now be thought of. The morrow, which was to have been her wedding-day, brought sorrow on the heart of Hero and her good father Leonato.

The prince had a half-brother, who came from the wars along with him to Messina. This brother (his name was Don John) was a melancholy, discontented man, whose spirits seemed to labour in the contriving of villainies. He hated the prince his brother, and he hated Claudio because he was the prince's friend, and determined to prevent Claudio's marriage with Hero, only for the malicious pleasure of making Claudio and the prince unhappy; for he knew the prince had set his heart upon this marriage, almost as much as Claudio himself; and to effect this wicked purpose, he employed one Borachio, a man as bad as himself, whom he encouraged with the offer of a great reward. This Borachio paid his court to Margaret, Hero's attendant; and Don John, knowing this, prevailed upon him to make Margaret promise to talk with him from her lady's chamber window that night, after Hero was asleep, and also to dress herself in Hero's clothes, the better to deceive Claudio into the belief that it was Hero; for that was the end he meant to compass by this wicked plot.

Don John then went to the prince and Claudio, and told them that Hero was an imprudent lady, and that she talked with men from her chamber window at midnight. Now this was the evening before the wedding, and he offered to take them that night, where they should themselves hear Hero discoursing with a man from her window; and they consented to go along with him, and Claudio said, 'If I see anything to-night why I should not marry her, to-morrow in the congregation, where I intended to wed her, there will I shame her.' The prince also said, 'And as I assisted you to obtain her, I will join with you to disgrace her.'

When Don John brought them near Hero's chamber that night, they saw Borachio standing under the window, and they saw Margaret looking out of Hero's window, and heard her talking with Borachio: and Margaret being dressed in the same clothes they had seen Hero wear, the prince and Claudio believed it was the lady Hero herself.

Nothing could equal the anger of Claudio, when he had made (as he thought) this discovery. All his love for the innocent Hero was at once converted into hatred, and he resolved to expose her in the church, as he had said he would, the next day; and the prince agreed to this, thinking no punishment could be too severe for the naughty lady, who talked with a man from her window the very night before she was going to be married to the noble Claudio.

The next day, when they were all met to celebrate the marriage, and Claudio and Hero were standing before the priest, and the priest, or friar, as he was called, was proceeding to pronounce the marriage ceremony, Claudio, in the most passionate language, proclaimed the guilt of the blameless Hero, who, amazed at the strange words he uttered, said meekly, 'Is my lord well, that he does speak so wide?'

Leonato, in the utmost horror, said to the prince, 'My lord, why speak not you?' 'What should I speak?' said the prince; 'I stand dishonoured, that have gone about to link my dear friend to an unworthy woman. Leonato, upon my honour, myself, my brother, and this grieved Claudio, did see and hear her last night at midnight talk with a man at her chamber window.'

Benedick, in astonishment at what he heard, said, 'This looks not like a nuptial.'

'True, O God!' replied the heart-struck Hero; and then this hapless lady sunk down in a fainting fit, to all appearance dead. The prince and Claudio left the church, without staying to see if Hero would recover, or at all regarding the distress into which they had thrown Leonato. So hard-hearted had their anger made them.

Benedick remained, and assisted Beatrice to recover Hero from her swoon, saying, 'How does the lady?' 'Dead, I think,' replied Beatrice in great agony, for she loved her cousin; and knowing her virtuous principles, she believed nothing of what she had heard spoken against her. Not so the poor old father; he believed the story of his child's shame, and it was piteous to hear him lamenting over her, as she lay like one dead before him, wishing she might never more open her eyes.

But the ancient friar was a wise man, and full of observation on human nature, and he had attentively marked the lady's countenance when she heard herself accused, and noted a thousand blushing shames to start into her face, and then he saw an angel-like whiteness bear away those blushes, and in her eye he saw a fire that did belie the error that the prince did speak against her maiden truth, and he said to the sorrowing father, 'Call me a fool; trust not my reading, nor my observation; trust not my age, my reverence, nor my calling, if this sweet lady lie not guiltless here under some biting error.'

When Hero had recovered from the swoon into which she had fallen, the friar said to her, 'Lady, what man is he you are accused of?' Hero replied, 'They know that do accuse me; I know of none:' then turning to Leonato, she said, 'O my father, if you can prove that any man has ever conversed with me at hours unmeet, or that I yesternight changed words with any creature, refuse me, hate me, torture me to death.'

'There is,' said the friar, 'some strange misunderstanding in the prince and Claudio;' and then he counselled Leonato, that he should report that Hero was dead; and he said that the death-like swoon in which they had left Hero would make this easy of belief; and he also advised him that he should put on mourning, and erect a monument for her, and do all rites that appertain to a burial. 'What shall become of this?' said Leonato; 'What will this do?' The friar replied, 'This report of her death shall change slander into pity: that is some good; but that is not all the good I hope for. When Claudio shall hear she died upon hearing his words, the idea of her life shall sweetly creep into his imagination. Then shall he mourn, if ever love had interest in his heart, and wish that he had not so accused her; yea, though he thought his accusation true.'

Benedick now said, 'Leonato, let the friar advise you; and though you know how well I love the prince and Claudio, yet on my honour I will not reveal this secret to them.'

Leonato, thus persuaded, yielded; and he said sorrowfully, 'I am so grieved, that the smallest twine may lead me.' The kind friar then led Leonato and Hero away to comfort and console them, and Beatrice and Benedick remained alone; and this was the meeting from which their friends, who contrived the merry plot against them, expected so much diversion; those friends who were now overwhelmed with affliction; and from whose minds all thoughts of merriment seemed for ever banished.

Benedick was the first who spoke, and he said, 'Lady Beatrice, have you wept all this while?' 'Yea, and I will weep a while longer,' said Beatrice. 'Surely,' said Benedick, 'I do believe your fair cousin is wronged.' 'Ah!' said Beatrice, 'how much might that man deserve of me who would right her!' Benedick then said, 'Is there any way to show such friendship? I do love nothing in the world so well as you: is not that strange?' 'It were as possible,' said Beatrice, 'for me to say I loved nothing in the world so well as you; but believe me not, and yet I lie not. I confess nothing, nor I deny nothing. I am sorry for my cousin.' 'By my sword,' said Benedick, 'you love me, and I protest I love you. Come, bid me do anything for you.' 'Kill Claudio,' said Beatrice. 'Ha! not for the wide world,' said Benedick; for he loved his friend Claudio, and he believed he had been imposed upon. 'Is not Claudio a villain, that has slandered, scorned, and dishonoured my cousin?' said Beatrice: 'O that I were a man!' 'Hear me, Beatrice!' said Benedick. But Beatrice would hear nothing in Claudio's defence; and she continued to urge on Benedick to revenge her cousin's wrongs: and she said, 'Talk with a man out of the window; a proper saying! Sweet Hero! she is wronged; she is slandered; she is undone. O that I were a man for Claudio's sake! or that I had any friend, who would be a man for my sake! but valour is melted into courtesies and compliments. I cannot be a man with wishing, therefore I will die a woman with grieving.' 'Tarry, good Beatrice,' said Benedick: 'by this hand I love you.' 'Use it for my love some other way than swearing by it,' said Beatrice. 'Think you on your soul that Claudio has wronged Hero?' asked Benedick. 'Yea,' answered Beatrice; 'as sure as I have a thought, or a soul.' 'Enough,' said Benedick; 'I am engaged; I will challenge him. I will kiss your hand, and so leave you. By this hand, Claudio shall render me a dear account! As you hear from me, so think of me. Go, comfort your cousin.'

While Beatrice was thus powerfully pleading with Benedick, and working his gallant temper by the spirit of her angry words, to engage in the cause of Hero, and fight even with his dear friend Claudio, Leonato was challenging the prince and Claudio to answer with their swords the injury they had done his child, who, he affirmed, had died for grief. But they respected his age and his sorrow, and they said, 'Nay, do not quarrel with us, good old man.' And now came Benedick, and he also challenged Claudio to answer with his sword the injury he had done to Hero; and Claudio and the prince said to each other, 'Beatrice has set him on to do this.' Claudio nevertheless must have accepted this challenge of Benedick, had not the justice of Heaven at the moment brought to pass a better proof of the innocence of Hero than the uncertain fortune of a duel.

While the prince and Claudio were yet talking of the challenge of Benedick, a magistrate brought Borachio as a prisoner before the prince. Borachio had been overheard talking with one of his companions of the mischief he had been employed by Don John to do.

Borachio made a full confession to the prince in Claudio's hearing, that it was Margaret dressed in her lady's clothes that he had talked with from the window, whom they had mistaken for the lady Hero herself; and no doubt continued on the minds of Claudio and the prince of the innocence of Hero. If a suspicion had remained it must have been removed by the flight of Don John, who, finding his villanies were detected, fled from Messina to avoid the just anger of his brother.

The heart of Claudio was sorely grieved when he found he had falsely accused Hero, who, he thought, died upon hearing his cruel words; and the memory of his beloved Hero's image came over him, in the rare semblance that he loved it first; and the prince asking him if what he heard did not run like iron through his soul, he answered, that he felt as if he had taken poison while Borachio was speaking.

And the repentant Claudio implored forgiveness of the old man Leonato for the injury he had done his child; and promised, that whatever penance Leonato would lay upon him for his fault in believing the false accusation against his betrothed wife, for her dear sake he would endure it.

The penance Leonato enjoined him was, to marry the next morning a cousin of Hero's, who, he said, was now his heir, and in person very like Hero. Claudio, regarding the solemn promise he made to Leonato, said, he would marry this unknown lady, even though she were an Ethiop: but his heart was very sorrowful, and he passed that night in tears, and in remorseful grief, at the tomb which Leonato had erected for Hero.

When the morning came, the prince accompanied Claudio to the church, where the good friar, and Leonato and his niece, were already assembled, to celebrate a second nuptial; and Leonato presented to Claudio his promised bride; and she wore a mask, that Claudio might not discover her face. And Claudio said to the lady in the mask, 'Give me your hand, before this holy friar; I am your husband, if you will marry me.' 'And when I lived I was your other wife,' said this unknown lady; and, taking off her mask, she proved to be no niece (as was pretended), but Leonato's very daughter, the Lady Hero herself. We may be sure that this proved a most agreeable surprise to Claudio, who thought her dead, so that he could scarcely for joy believe his eyes; and the prince, who was equally amazed at what he saw, exclaimed, 'Is not this Hero, Hero that was dead?' Leonato replied, 'She died, my lord, but while her slander lived.' The friar promised them an explanation of this seeming miracle, after the ceremony was ended; and was proceeding to marry them, when he was interrupted by Benedick, who desired to be married at the same time to Beatrice. Beatrice making some demur to this match, and Benedick challenging her with her love for him, which he had learned from Hero, a pleasant explanation took place; and they found they had both been tricked into belief of love, which had never existed, and had become lovers in truth by the power of a false jest: but the affection, which a merry invention had cheated them into, was grown too powerful to be shaken by a serious explanation; and since Benedick proposed to marry, he was resolved to think nothing to the purpose that the world could say against it; and he merrily kept up the jest, and swore to Beatrice, that he took her but for pity, and because he heard she was dying of love for him; and Beatrice protested, that she yielded but upon great persuasion, and partly to save his life, for she heard he was in a consumption. So these two mad wits were reconciled, and made a match of it, after Claudio and Hero were married; and to complete the history, Don John, the contriver of the villany, was taken in his flight, and brought back to Messina; and a brave punishment it was to this gloomy, discontented man, to see the joy and feastings which, by the disappointment of his plots, took place in the palace in Messina.

LOVE'S LABOUR'S LOST

FERDINAND, the young King of Navarre, was addressing his courtiers and friends, Berowne, Longaville, and Dumaine, in the park before his palace on a serene morning in June during the sixteenth century. It seemed strange that young men so gallant in appearance should be carrying large books; they were unnaturally serious as they stood together in the sunlight. Ferdinand spoke from behind a small table on which he had laid a parchment. As they knew, he said, he had resolved that his court should become famous as a school of studies. For that reason all four of them had sworn to live together for three years and to observe the oaths set out in a portentous schedule.

'Now sign your names,' said Ferdinand, 'and keep the statutes that are recorded here.'

First, he signed his own name and contemplated with pleasure his elaborate script. Lord Longaville followed; after him, the even more boyish Dumaine. Their gay comrade, Lord Berowne, dropped his volume of philosophy upon the turf and hesitated before he picked up the pen. 'My dear liege,' he said, 'I have already sworn to live and study with you for three years. But there are other vows here I shall find hard to keep: not to see a woman in that time, to touch no food on one day in every week, on any day to have only one meal, and in any night to sleep for but three hours. O, these are barren tasks!'

'You have passed an oath,' said the King. But Berowne shook his head. 'No, my liege, I swore only to study with you and to stay here in your court.'

'You swore to that, Berowne – and to the rest,' put in Longaville.

Berowne looked round the group. Clearly there was no hope of escape; still he made a final attempt. 'I was jesting then . . .' he began. He got no further, for the King frowned and interrupted him, 'Well, sit you out, Berowne. Go home. Adieu!'

The parchment was being rolled up. Berowne took it with a shrug. 'Very well, my lord. Give me that paper, and when I have read it I will abide by its strictest decrees.' He sighed. 'Let me look. "That no woman shall come within a mile of my court" . . . Has this been proclaimed?'

'Four days ago,' said Longaville, opening his book resolutely and considering it with some distaste. Berowne went on reading. '"If any man be seen to talk with a woman within the term of three years, he shall endure such public shame as the rest of the court can devise." But, my liege, this is impossible. You must break it yourself. Have you forgotten that the daughter of the French King is coming here on an embassy? If you try to keep the law, her task will have been in vain.'

Ferdinand looked uneasy. 'This was quite forgotten. We must dispense with the decree.' Berowne, smiling, signed his name with a flourish. 'Necessity will make us all forsworn. There, my liege, I have signed, and I believe I shall be the last of us to break his oath . . . Now, can we leave this for a time? Is there no news, nothing for our recreation?' He looked about at the park drowsing in the heat.

The King handed the parchment to an officer and stood for a moment in thought. 'What has happened,' he asked, 'to that amusing traveller, the Spaniard Armado? There is a man to talk with – full of new fashions, strange phrases, and fantastic boasts.' 'A man of fire-new words,' confirmed Berowne; and Longaville said cheerfully, 'We can have sport with him and the peasant Costard: no two are less alike.'

He had just uttered the words when a loutish constable named Antony Dull approached the group, leading Costard, a youth with an open smile and a crest of red hair. Dull handed to the King a letter. 'From Signor Armado,' he announced in his stolid way. 'We have villainy abroad, your grace. This letter will tell you more.' It was a long letter, written in affected phrases; and solemnly Ferdinand read it out. 'That low-spirited swain, that base minnow of thy mirth . . . which, as I remember, hight Costard . . . sorted and consorted, contrary to thy established proclaimed edict . . . with a child of our Grandmother Eve, a female.' Therefore Armado had sent Costard with Dull to receive the royal punishment.

'Sirrah,' said the King, 'You heard the proclamation: a year's imprisonment for anyone found in company with a woman . . . But I shall be lenient with you: you shall fast for a week on bran and water.'

'I had rather pray a month with mutton and porridge,' replied Costard hopefully.

'And Don Adriano de Armado shall be your keeper,' the King went on unheeding. 'My lord Berowne, see him delivered. And you, Dumaine and Longaville, let us go in now, remembering our oaths.' Self-consciously, they picked up their books.

Berowne watched them go. 'I'll lay my head to any man's hat that these oaths and bonds will be scorned. Well, sirrah, come with me.' Restoring Costard to Dull's charge, he ordered the constable to deliver the fellow to Armado. Presently, on their progress through the park, Dull (who had collected the girl Jaquenetta on the way) met the lean and melancholy Spaniard, Armado, his long fingers poised about the black cane that pointed his dignity and his face saddened by the thinly-falling crescents of moustache that curled from his upper lip. With him was his young page Moth. Costard, used now to being passed from hand to hand, stood meekly behind Armado, while Dull kept a firm grip on Jaquenetta whom he was taking down to the lodge to help the dairy-woman.

Armado viewed her lovingly. 'I do betray myself with blushing . . . Maid!'

'Man!' said Jaquenetta rudely.

'I will visit thee at the lodge and I will tell thee wonders.'

'With that face?' said Jaquenetta.

'I love thee.'

'So I heard you say,' she replied with a grimace as Dull dragged her off. Sternly, Armado instructed Moth to take Costard and to shut him up. Musing upon his love for the young woman, he stalked away across the turf, contemplating a sonnet to Jaquenetta.

Meanwhile the Princess of France was on her way to visit the King. A few days later, with her maids of honour, Rosaline, Maria, and

Katharine, and the elderly lord Boyet, who acted as her master of ceremonies, she rode into the royal park. 'Boyet,' she said imperiously, 'we hear Navarre has made a vow that for three years no woman shall approach his court. Because our entrance is forbidden, we must know his pleasure with us, and immediately. Go then and tell him that the daughter of the King of France seeks to confer with him, and that her business brooks no delay.' Bowing, Boyet entered the tall iron gates beyond which a fountain plashed softly. The Princess turned to her ladies: 'What do you know of Navarre's courtiers?'

'Madam,' said Maria, 'I remember Lord Longaville: I saw him last at a marriage feast in Normandy. He is a man well fitted in the arts and glorious in arms. His fault, if indeed he has one, is a too mocking wit.'

'Short-lived wits wither as they grow,' replied the Princess. 'Who are the rest?'

'The young Dumaine is a well-accomplished youth,' Katharine ventured. 'I saw him at the Duke Alençon's once.'

Next the black-eyed beauty Rosaline spoke with unexpected fervour. 'Another of these students was at Alençon's, madam. He is called Berowne, and I never yet found a merrier man or one able to speak in more apt and gracious words.'

Startled, the Princess looked from one to the other. 'God bless my ladies, are they all in love?' She did not speak further, for Boyet had returned to say that the King of Navarre and his courtiers were coming even then through the gates, and that they did not mean to let the Princess enter the palace.

Ferdinand, at his most dignified and solemn, approached with his three friends, who brightened when they saw the ladies. It was a courtly welcome but an uncomfortable one, for the King was resolved not to break his oath and the Princess was resolved to laugh at it. 'Vouchsafe,' she exclaimed at length, 'to read the purpose of my coming. Boyet, the letter.' Ferdinand gazed at the document with its affairs of state between Navarre and France. Certain papers had not come, but Boyet promised that they would be there on the next day; and Ferdinand, with as much grace as he could summon – for he knew he was being laughed at – said farewell until the morrow, adding a little lamely, 'Fair princess, you may not come within my gates, but here you shall be looked after so well that you may believe yourself within my house.' The Princess said gravely that she would try to believe it.

The King and his courtiers re-entered the palace gates. Presently, one by one, and unknown to the others, they slipped back round the fountain to speak to Boyet. 'What lady is that?' asked Dumaine. 'She is Katharine,' Boyet said, 'the heiress of Alençon.' 'What is she in the white?' whispered Longaville. 'An heiress of Falconbridge,' said Boyet. Lastly, 'What's her name – in the cap?' asked Berowne, and Boyet told him, 'Rosaline.' The ladies watched with discreet amusement. 'That last,' said Maria, 'must be young Berowne, the merry madcap lord. Every word with him, they say, is a jest.' She glanced at Rosaline who had moved to the gates and seemed to be trying to peer through the fountain and an inner wall.

The ladies settled in their pavilion, one raised swiftly and furnished sumptuously by a score of Navarre's men. The short summer night passed. On the next morning, early, with dew still heavy on the great lawns, Armado handed a letter to Costard, telling him he could have his liberty if he would convey a message to the dairymaid Jaquenetta. While Costard was looking perplexed at the three farthings Armado had lavished on him for the service, Berowne strolled up through the park. 'Costard,' he said, 'the Princess will come to hunt this afternoon. Give this letter to the hand of the lady Rosaline, and here is a shilling for your reward.' Costard hurried off, and Berowne lingered, musing wryly. He of all men, one that had laughed at love, was now himself in love:

'It is a plague
That Cupid will impose for my neglect
Of his almighty, dreadful little might.'

That afternoon, when the Princess and her ladies were hunting the deer, Costard, having spent the morning with his friends, ran up eagerly with 'a letter from Monsieur Berowne to one Lady Rosaline'. But in his muddled state the letter he brought was Armado's to Jaquenetta, and the Princess ordered Boyet to read it aloud in all its affectation:

'Shall I command thy love? I may. Shall I enforce thy love? I could. Shall I entreat thy love? I will. What shalt thou exchange for rags? – robes. For tittles? – titles. For thyself? – me! Thus expecting thy reply, I profane my lips on thy foot, my eyes on thy picture, and my heart on thy every part.'

'What plume of feathers is he that wrote this letter?' asked the Princess, and Boyet told her, with the appropriate airs, that it was Don Adriano de Armado, the fantastic who made sport for the King and his three friends.

Shortly afterwards, Costard delivered to Jaquenetta Berowne's letter to Rosaline. Unable to read it, she gave it to the milky mouse, the curate Nathaniel, who had been in a learned discussion with Holofernes, the schoolmaster, Dull standing by. Jaquenetta said, 'Be so good as to read me this letter. It was sent me from Don Armado.' The letter contained a love sonnet; and Holofernes, taking it from Nathaniel, read the direction, 'To the snow-white hand of the most beauteous Lady Rosaline,' and the signature, 'Your ladyship's in all desired employment, Berowne.' This, said Holofernes, might concern much, and he ordered Jaquenetta at once to take the letter to the King.

Ferdinand was supposed to be hunting. But when Berowne, who had gone to walk by himself in the glades, roughing out a sonnet, heard footsteps and climbed up into an oak-tree, he realised that the wanderer was the King himself, holding a scribbled paper. 'Ay me,' groaned Ferdinand; and Berowne recognised the sign. 'Shot, by heaven!' he murmured. 'Proceed, sweet Cupid!' Unaware that he could be heard, Ferdinand began to read out his newly written sonnet, rapturous love lines to the Princess that ended with the couplet:

'O Queen of Queens, how far dost thou excel
No thought can think, nor tongue of mortal tell.'

'How shall she know my griefs?' exclaimed Ferdinand. 'I'll drop the paper . . . But who is he comes here?' He stepped behind a flowering bush, and Longaville strolled into the glade, also reading to himself. His was a sonnet to Maria:

'A woman I forswore, but I will prove
Thou being a goddess, I forswore not thee . . .'

'By whom shall I send this?' he pondered. More steps cut him short. He whisked into the shelter of a tree just as Dumaine approached with a paper, inevitably verses to Katharine, and Berowne, above, said to himself in delight:

> 'Like a demigod here sit I in the sky,
> And wretched fools' secrets heedfully o'ereye.
> More sacks to the mill! O heaven, I have my wish -
> Dumaine transformed, four woodcocks in a dish!'

Dumaine, too, was ready to try his lines:

> 'On a day, alack the day!
> Love, whose month is ever May,
> Spied a blossom passing fair
> Playing in the wanton air . . .'

When he had finished, he sighed despairingly, 'O would the King, Berowne, and Longaville were lovers too!' Then he started in alarm. Longaville had stolen up behind him with a firm reproof, 'I should blush, I know, to be overheard and taken napping like this.' Hardly were the words uttered than the King, thrusting apart the bushes, was at his side. 'Come, Longaville, do I see you blush? You chide at him and offend twice as much yourself. Ah, both of you, what will Berowne say to this? How will he scorn you? For all the world's wealth, I would not have him find me in your plight.'

From above them drifted a smothered laugh, a laugh they recognised. They heard a rustle and creak among the branches, and of a sudden Berowne had leapt down beside them. 'Now step I forth to whip hypocrisy!' He spared them nothing. 'My liege, why do you reprove these men for loving when you are so much in love yourself? Are you not ashamed, all three of you? Have you not betrayed me, I that am honest and hold it sin to break my vow? When do you see me writing rhymes, or groaning for a woman, or praising a hand or a foot or a face or an eye? . . .'

He had not observed, in his delight, that Costard and Jaquenetta had sought them over the park and in the forest, and that the girl was now addressing the King. 'I beseech your grace, let this letter be read.' Ferdinand waved it off impatiently, 'Read it, Berowne.' Then, suddenly curious, 'How now, Berowne, why do you tear it up?'

'A mere toy, my liege,' said Berowne, elaborately offhand. 'Your grace need not trouble yourself.'

Longaville inspected him with growing doubt. 'It moved him to passion, Dumaine. Let's hear it.' Dumaine collected the scattered pieces and fitted them together while Berowne strove to snatch them. 'Why, it is Berowne's own writing. See if he has not signed it.' Costard and Jaquenetta, embracing each other, were looking on peacefully, and Berowne turned on Costard in helpless anger, 'Ah you loggerhead!' But he knew that he had been caught, and he threw his hands up. 'Guilty, my lord, guilty, I confess, I confess.'

'The number is even,' said Dumaine. Berowne, blushing as they all were, capped him, 'True, true, we are four.'

Petulantly, the King ordered Costard and Jaquenetta to leave them. Then the four young men studied the ruin of their hopes, the futile plan to shut out love from their lives. They knew that nothing, neither edicts nor oaths, could check their passion, and now only one thing remained. Berowne, who could find an answer to any problem, must persuade them somehow that their loving was lawful and that they had not broken their faith. He, if anyone, would know how to prove it, to find (as Dumaine said) some cure for perjury. Berowne reflected for a while; at last, standing on a grassy mound underneath the oak, his arms outspread, he launched into a defence of love. How could any of them have studied aright without the influence of a woman's face? It was love that doubled every human power:

> 'It adds a precious seeing to the eye;
> A lover's eye will gaze an eagle blind;
> A lover's ear will hear the lowest sound.'

And again:

> 'For valour is not love a Hercules,
> Still climbing trees in the Hesperides?
> Subtle as Sphinx, as sweet and musical
> As bright Apollo's lute, strung with his hair;
> And when love speaks, the voice of all the gods
> Makes heaven drowsy with the harmony . . .'

So Berowne went on as love's advocate, proving to their satisfaction that to find themselves fully they must forswear their oaths. It was needed eloquence. As it ended the King cried, 'Saint Cupid then! and soldiers to the field!' and Longaville exclaimed, 'Now to plain dealing. Shall we resolve to woo these girls of France?'

'And win them too!' said Ferdinand, all vows forgotten in a day. 'Let us think of entertainment for them in their tents.' Heads together, the gallants marched off.

In the late afternoon schoolmaster and curate were at their everlasting talk, Holofernes bristling and pedantic, Nathaniel like a rabbit nibbling jelly. Don Adriano de Armado strutted up to them with news. The King, he explained, had asked him to present before the Princess some 'delightful ostentation, or show, or pageant, or antic, or firework.' Could they help him to devise something? Holofernes, as usual, had the answer at once. It should be the pageant of the Nine Worthies, and he would play three of them himself, a suggestion that caused Nathaniel to look at him with round-eyed admiration. In earnest discussion schoolmaster, curate, and Spaniard moved off to the house of Holofernes.

Before their pavilion, in front of the palace gates, the Princess and her ladies were looking at gifts newly sent to them from the King and his lords: diamonds, a pair of gloves, pearls, love-rhymes. As they laughed at this sudden change of temperature, Boyet stalked up, nearly incoherent with his own laughter. Ferdinand and the rest, he said, were on the way, disguised as Russians, 'to parley, court, and dance,' once the page Moth had recited a speech to introduce them.

Immediately the Princess ordered Rosaline, Katharine, and Maria to mask themselves and to exchange the presents that had been sent to them. 'Take my fan, Rosaline, so that the King will court you, and give me yours so that Berowne will come at once towards me. Do not dance, ladies, when they invite you, and turn away your faces when the page speaks his lines. They mean to have sport with us, but nothing is better than sport by sport overthrown.'

Trumpets sounded; the ladies put on their masks; and the King and the lords entered, also masked heavily and in cumbrous Russian disguises, with Moth – looking nervous and muttering his words to himself – as their spokesman. He began well enough, 'All hail, the richest beauties on the earth—.' But when the richest beauties turned their backs on him, he started to halt and to stammer, and finally he stopped altogether. Fiercely, Berowne ordered him to be gone. Rosaline, wearing the favours of the Princess, turned proudly to Boyet: 'What would these strangers? Boyet, know their minds.'

'Say to her,' responded the King, 'that we have measured many a mile to tread a measure with her on this grass.' Rosaline took up the words mockingly. The courtiers were fumbling and self-conscious. The ladies would not dance. All they consented to do was to talk a little behind their masks, and the mock-Russians, unaware, found themselves promising love to the wrong beauties and getting only the faintest encouragement. Suddenly Rosaline cried, 'Not one more word, my maids, break off, break off!' and the ladies slipped by their partners and ran within the pavilion, leaving the men nothing to do but clump away in their furs. As soon as they had gone, the ladies peeped out and returned.

'But will you hear?' laughed Rosaline. 'The King is my love sworn.'

'Quick Berowne,' said the Princess, 'has plighted love to me.'

'Longaville,' said Katharine, 'was for my service born'; and Maria completed the chime, 'Dumaine is mine, as sure as bark on tree.'

They saw that the King and the lords were marching back through the palace gates, the Russian disguise removed. 'Swiftly,' said Rosaline, 'let's mock them still, complain what fools were here disguised as Muscovites, and wonder why they made this silly show.' The ladies hastened to the pavilion; and when they emerged from it again, demurely, to curtsey to the lords, they wore their own favours and the masks were off. Ferdinand endeavoured at once to gloss over the last half-hour with an adroit excuse, 'You have lived in desolation, unseen and unvisited. We are ashamed of it.'

'Not so, my lord,' rejoined the Princess briskly. 'We have had pleasant games here. A mess of Russians has just left us.'

'A mess of – Russians?' said the King inquiringly, with a sharp side-glance at Berowne.

'Yes,' Rosaline added. 'We four, my lord, were confronted with four men in Russian habits. They stayed talking for an hour, and did not say one happy word.'

It was apparent that the lords were defeated. 'They'll mock us downright,' whispered the King. 'Shall we confess and turn it to a joke?' asked Dumaine. As they spoke under their breaths, the Princess said innocently, 'Why looks your highness sad?' And Rosaline followed, 'Yes, why look you pale? . . . Sea-sick, I think, coming from Muscovy.'

The jest was over, and Berowne had to admit it: 'Can any face of brass hold longer out?' He would never again use these masks and affectations, but speak honestly and plainly. The King, too, confessed. Within a few minutes all was made clear, the lovers' plot, the change of favours, the muddled wooing (the ladies accused the lords of breaking both their vows to study and their vows of love). While Ferdinand and Berowne, Longaville and Dumaine studied the grass shamefacedly, Costard puffed up to ask whether the Worthies should begin their show on a neighbouring lawn beside the lake. When all had taken their places, Armado presented a paper to the King, and the royal party settled to watch. It was not very successful. Costard, as Pompey the Great, tripped over his sword and had to face the company's flying wit. The curate, as Alexander, could not struggle beyond his first three lines, and Costard had to apologise for him, which he did with great tact, 'A marvellous good neighbour, i'faith, and a very good bowler; but for Alisander, alas you see how 'tis – a little overparted.' Moth appeared as the child Hercules strangling the snakes. Holofernes, as Judas Maccabaeus, was put out of countenance by continual interruption ('Alas,' said the Princess, 'how he has been baited!'), and finally Armado, as Hector of Troy, and Costard, as Pompey, were set to begin a ludicrous and unprepared duel. While the spectators rocked with mirth, they heard first a distant rattle, and then a quick thud-thud, of galloping as a rider left the roadway for the grass of the park. The noise ceased, and a figure in deepest black appeared bowing before the Princess.

In an absolute hush the newcomer said, 'I am sorry, madam, that the news I bring is heavy on my tongue. The King your father—.' The Princess had paled. 'Dead, by my life.' 'Even so,' said the messenger. 'My tale is told.' Berowne waved away the players, and the King advanced to the Princess: 'How fares your majesty?' 'Boyet,' she ordered, 'I will away tonight.' She turned to the King with sad and gracious thanks; and though Ferdinand could not find fitting words to express his thought, Berowne spoke for him, declaring their love and regretting that their well-meant humours had seemed absurd.

The King put it plainly at last. 'Now at the latest minute of the hour, grant us your loves.' And the Princess replied that she would give him hers if, after twelve months in a hermitage, remote from all the pleasures of the world, he still could make his offer. Katharine and Maria joined their mistress. To Longaville and Dumaine they said, 'Come when the King does to our lady come.' Last of all, Rosaline challenged Berowne to spend the year in guarding the beds of the speechless sick, and, with the fierce endeavour of his wit, forcing the weary invalids to smile. Berowne, after an involuntary protest, yielded to her:

'A twelvemonth? well, befall what will befall,
I'll jest a twelvemonth in a hospital.'

Now, in the growing summer darkness, Don Adriano de Armado returned to them. 'Was not that Hector?' said the Princess; and Armado answered, 'I am a votary. I have vowed to Jaquenetta to follow the plough for her sweet love three years.' He had come back to ask if the royal party would hear what should have been the end of the entertainment, a dialogue between the owl and the cuckoo. When the King assented, there walked from one side a group that represented winter, and from the other a group that represented spring. 'This side,' said Armado, 'is Hiems, winter; this Ver, the spring. The one is governed by the Owl, as the other by the Cuckoo.' First, the Cuckoo sang:

When daisies pied, and violets blue,
  And lady-smocks all silver-white:
And cuckoo-buds of yellow hue,
  Do paint the meadows with delight:
The cuckoo then, on every tree,
Mocks married men; for thus sings he,
    Cuckoo;
Cuckoo, cuckoo: O word of fear,
Unpleasing to a married ear!

When shepherds pipe on oaten straws,
  And merry larks are ploughmen's clocks,

When turtles tread, and rooks, and daws,
And maidens bleach their summer smocks,
The cuckoo then, on every tree
Mocks married men: for thus sings he,
Cuckoo;
Cuckoo, cuckoo: O word of fear,
Unpleasing to a married ear!

Then the Owl sang in his turn:

When icicles hang by the wall,
And Dick the shepherd blows his nail,
And Tom bears logs into the hall,
And milk comes frozen home in pail,
When blood is nipp'd, and ways be foul,
Then nightly sings the staring owl,
Tu-whit, tu-who,
A merry note,
While greasy Joan doth keel the pot.

When all aloud the wind doth blow,
And coughing drowns the parson's saw,
And birds sit brooding in the snow,
And Marian's nose looks red and raw,
When roasted crabs hiss in the bowl,
Then nightly sings the staring owl,
Tu-whit, tu-who,
A merry note,
While greasy Joan doth keel the pot.

The song ceased. It was quite dark now, and the groups of Spring and Winter – Nathaniel in one, Holofernes in the other – stood against a rosy flare of torchlight reflected back from the lilied water. Armado, tall, sombre, wistful, approached the King and Princess. 'The words of Mercury,' he said, bowing, 'are harsh after the songs of Apollo. You that way; we this way.' Within a few moments the lawn lay deserted, and the torchbearers were guiding the Princess and her ladies towards their pavilion and the night's weary road.

A MIDSUMMER NIGHT'S DREAM

THERE was a law in the city of Athens which gave to its citizens the power of compelling their daughters to marry whomsoever they pleased; for upon a daughter's refusing to marry the man her father had chosen to be her husband, the father was empowered by this law to cause her to be put to death; but as fathers do not often desire the death of their own daughters, even though they do happen to prove a little refractory, this law was seldom or never put into execution, though perhaps the young ladies of that city were not unfrequently threatened by their parents with the terrors of it.

There was one instance, however, of an old man, whose name was Egeus, who actually did come before Theseus (at that time the reigning Duke of Athens), to complain that his daughter Hermia, whom he had commanded to marry Demetrius, a young man of a noble Athenian family, refused to obey him, because she loved another young Athenian, named Lysander. Egeus demanded justice of Theseus, and desired that this cruel law might be put in force against his daughter.

Hermia pleaded in excuse for her disobedience, that Demetrius had formerly professed love for her dear friend Helena, and that Helena loved Demetrius to distraction; but this honourable reason, which Hermia gave for not obeying her father's command, moved not the stern Egeus.

Theseus, though a great and merciful prince, had no power to alter the laws of his country; therefore he could only give Hermia four days to consider of it: and at the end of that time, if she still refused to marry Demetrius, she was to be put to death.

When Hermia was dismissed from the presence of the duke, she went to her lover Lysander, and told him the peril she was in, and that she must either give him up and marry Demetrius, or lose her life in four days.

Lysander was in great affliction at hearing these evil tidings; but recollecting that he had an aunt who lived at some distance from Athens, and that at the place where she lived the cruel law could not be put in force against Hermia (this law not extending beyond the boundaries of the city), he proposed to Hermia that she should steal out of her father's house that night, and go with him to his aunt's house, where he would marry her. 'I will meet you,' said Lysander, 'in the wood a few miles without the city; in that delightful wood where we have so often walked with Helena in the pleasant month of May.'

To this proposal Hermia joyfully agreed; and she told no one of her intended flight but her friend Helena. Helena (as maidens will do foolish things for love) very ungenerously resolved to go and tell this to Demetrius, though she could hope no benefit from betraying her friend's secret, but the poor pleasure of following her faithless lover to the wood; for she well knew that Demetrius would go thither in pursuit of Hermia.

The wood in which Lysander and Hermia proposed to meet was the favourite haunt of those little beings known by the name of *Fairies*.

Oberon the king, and Titania the queen of the Fairies, with all their tiny train of followers, in this wood held their midnight revels.

Between this little king and queen of sprites there happened, at this time, a sad disagreement; they never met by moonlight in the shady walks of this pleasant wood, but they were quarrelling, till all their fairy elves would creep into acorn-cups and hide themselves for fear.

The cause of this unhappy disagreement was Titania's refusing to give Oberon a little changeling boy, whose mother had been Titania's friend; and upon her death the fairy queen stole the child from its nurse, and brought him up in the woods.

The night on which the lovers were to meet in this wood, as Titania was walking with some of her maids of honour, she met Oberon attended by his train of fairy courtiers.

'Ill met by moonlight, proud Titania,' said the fairy king. The queen replied, 'What, jealous Oberon, is it you? Fairies, skip hence; I have forsworn his company.' 'Tarry, rash fairy,' said Oberon; 'am not I thy lord? Why does Titania cross her Oberon? Give me your little changeling boy to be my page.'

'Set your heart at rest,' answered the queen; 'your whole fairy kingdom buys not the boy of me.' She then left her lord in great anger. 'Well, go your way,' said Oberon: 'before the morning dawns I will torment you for this injury.'

Oberon then sent for Puck, his chief favourite and privy counsellor.

Puck (or as he was sometimes called, Robin Goodfellow) was a shrewd and knavish sprite, that used to play comical pranks in the neighbouring villages; sometimes getting into the dairies and skimming the milk, sometimes plunging his light and airy form into the butter-churn, and while he was dancing his fantastic shape in the churn, in vain the dairy-maid would labour to change her cream into butter: nor had the village swains any better success; whenever Puck chose to play his freaks in the brewing copper, the ale was sure to be spoiled. When a few good neighbours were met to drink some comfortable ale together, Puck would jump into the bowl of ale in the likeness of a roasted crab, and when some old goody was going to drink he would bob against her lips, and spill the ale over her withered chin; and presently after, when the same old dame was gravely seating herself to tell her neighbours a sad and melancholy story, Puck would slip her three-legged stool from under her, and down toppled the poor old woman, and then the old gossips would hold their sides and laugh at her, and swear they never wasted a merrier hour.

'Come hither, Puck,' said Oberon to this little merry wanderer of the night; 'fetch me the flower which maids call *Love in Idleness;* the juice of that little purple flower laid in the eyelids of those who sleep, will make them, when they awake, dote on the first thing they see. Some of the juice of that flower I will drop on the eyelids of my Titania when she is asleep; and the first thing she looks upon when she opens her eyes she will fall in love with, even though it be a lion or a bear, a meddling monkey, or a busy ape; and before I will take this charm from off her sight, which I can do with another charm I know of, I will make her give me that boy to be my page.'

Puck, who loved mischief to his heart, was highly diverted with this intended frolic of his master, and ran to seek the flower; and while Oberon was waiting the return of Puck, he observed Demetrius and Helena enter the wood: he overheard Demetrius reproaching Helena for following him, and after many unkind words on his part, and gentle expostulations from Helena, reminding him of his former love and professions of true faith to her, he left her (as he said) to the mercy of the wild beasts, and she ran after him as swiftly as she could.

The fairy king, who was always friendly to true lovers, felt great compassion for Helena; and perhaps, as Lysander said they used to walk by moonlight in this pleasant wood, Oberon might have seen Helena in those happy times when she was beloved by Demetrius. However that might be, when Puck returned with the little purple flower, Oberon said to his favourite, 'Take a part of this flower; there has been a sweet Athenian lady here, who is in love with a disdainful youth; if you find him sleeping, drop some of the love-juice in his eyes, but contrive to do it when she is near him, that the first thing he sees when he awakes may be this despised lady. You will know the man by the Athenian garments which he wears.' Puck promised to manage this matter very dexterously: and then Oberon went, unperceived by Titania, to her bower, where she was preparing to go to rest. Her fairy bower was a bank, where grew wild thyme, cowslips, and sweet violets, under a canopy of wood-bine, musk-roses, and eglantine. There Titania always slept some part of the night; her coverlet the enamelled skin of a snake, which, though a small mantle, was wide enough to wrap a fairy in.

He found Titania giving orders to her fairies, how they were to employ themselves while she slept. 'Some of you,' said her majesty, 'must kill cankers in the musk-rose buds, and some wage war with the bats for their leathern wings, to make my small elves coats; and some of you keep watch that the clamorous owl, that nightly hoots, come not near me: but first sing me to sleep.' Then they began to sing this song:

'You spotted snakes with double tongue,
Thorny hedgehogs, be not seen;
Newts and blind-worms do no wrong;
Come not near our Fairy Queen.
Philomel, with melody,
Sing in our sweet lullaby,
Lulla, lulla, lullaby; lulla, lulla, lullaby;

Never harm, nor spell, nor charm,
Come our lovely lady nigh;
So good night with lullaby.'

When the fairies had sung their queen asleep with this pretty lullaby, they left her to perform the important services she had enjoined them. Oberon then softly drew near his Titania, and dropped some of the love juice on her eyelids, saying,

'What thou seest when thou dost wake,
Do it for thy true-love take.'

But to return to Hermia, who made her escape out of her father's house that night, to avoid the death she was doomed to for refusing to marry Demetrius. When she entered the wood, she found her dear Lysander waiting for her, to conduct her to his aunt's house; but before they had passed half through the wood, Hermia was so much fatigued, that Lysander, who was very careful of this dear lady, who had proved her affection for him even by hazarding her life for his sake, persuaded her to rest till morning on a bank of soft moss, and lying down himself on the ground at some little distance, they soon fell fast asleep. Here they were found by Puck, who, seeing a handsome young man asleep, and perceiving that his clothes were made in the Athenian fashion, and that a pretty lady was sleeping near him, concluded that this must be the Athenian maid and her disdainful lover whom Oberon had sent him to seek; and he naturally enough conjectured that, as they were alone together, she must be the first thing he would see when he awoke; so, without more ado, he proceeded to pour some of the juice of the little purple flower into his eyes. But it so fell out, that Helena came that way, and, instead of Hermia, was the first object Lysander beheld when he opened his eyes; and strange to relate, so powerful was the love-charm, all his love for Hermia vanished away, and Lysander fell in love with Helena.

Had he first seen Hermia when he awoke, the blunder Puck committed would have been of no consequence, for he could not love that faithful lady too well; but for poor Lysander to be forced by a fairy love-charm to forget his own true Hermia, and to run after another lady, and leave Hermia asleep quite alone in a wood at midnight, was a sad chance indeed.

Thus this misfortune happened. Helena, as has been before related, endeavoured to keep pace with Demetrius when he ran away so rudely from her; but she could not continue this unequal race long, men being always better runners in a long race than ladies. Helena soon lost sight of Demetrius; and as she was wandering about, dejected and forlorn, she arrived at the place where Lysander was sleeping. 'Ah!' said she, 'this is Lysander lying on the ground: is he dead or asleep?' Then gently touching him, she said, 'Good sir, if you are alive, awake.' Upon this Lysander opened his eyes, and (the love-charm beginning to work) immediately addressed her in terms of extravagant love and admiration; telling her she as much excelled Hermia in beauty as a dove does a raven, and that he would run through fire for her sweet sake; and many more such lover-like speeches. Helena, knowing Lysander was her friend Hermia's lover, and that he was solemnly engaged to marry her, was in the utmost rage when she heard herself addressed in this manner; for she thought (as well she might) that Lysander was making a jest of her. 'Oh!' said she, 'why was I born to be mocked and scorned by every one? Is it not enough, is it not enough, young man, that I can never get a sweet look or a kind word from Demetrius; but you, sir, must pretend in this disdainful manner to court me? I thought, Lysander, you were a lord of more true gentleness.' Saying these words in great anger, she ran away; and Lysander followed her, quite forgetful of his own Hermia, who was still asleep.

When Hermia awoke, she was in a sad fright at finding herself alone. She wandered about the wood, not knowing what was become of Lysander, or which way to go to seek for him. In the meantime Demetrius not being able to find Hermia and his rival Lysander, and fatigued with his fruitless search, was observed by Oberon fast asleep. Oberon had learnt by some questions he had asked of Puck, that he had applied the love-charm to the wrong person's eyes; and now having found the person first intended, he touched the eyelids of the sleeping Demetrius with the love-juice, and he instantly awoke; and the first thing he saw being Helena, he, as Lysander had done before, began to address love-speeches to her; and just at that moment Lysander, followed by Hermia (for through Puck's unlucky mistake it was now become Hermia's turn to run after her lover) made his appearance; and then Lysander and Demetrius, both speaking together, made love to Helena, they being each one under the influence of the same potent charm.

The astonished Helena thought that Demetrius, Lysander, and her once dear friend Hermia, were all in a plot together to make a jest of her.

Hermia was as much surprised as Helena: she knew not why Lysander and Demetrius, who both before loved her, were now become the lovers of Helena; and to Hermia the matter seemed to be no jest.

The ladies, who before had always been the dearest of friends, now fell to high words together.

'Unkind Hermia,' said Helena, 'it is you have set Lysander on to vex me with mock praises; and your other lover Demetrius, who used almost to spurn me with his foot, have you not bid him call me Goddess, Nymph, rare, precious, and celestial? He would not speak thus to me, whom he hates, if you did not set him on to make a jest of me. Unkind Hermia, to join with men in scorning your poor friend. Have you forgot our school-day friendship? How often, Hermia, have we two, sitting on one cushion, both singing one song, with our needles working the same flower, both on the same sampler wrought; growing up together in fashion of a double cherry, scarcely seeming parted! Hermia, it is not friendly in you, it is not maidenly to join with men in scorning your poor friend.'

'I am amazed at your passionate words,' said Hermia: 'I scorn you not; it seems you scorn me.' 'Ay, do,' returned Helena, 'persevere, counterfeit serious looks, and make mouths at me when I turn my back; then wink at each other, and hold the sweet jest up. If you had any pity, grace, or manners, you would not use me thus.'

While Helena and Hermia were speaking these angry words to each other, Demetrius and Lysander left them, to fight together in the wood for the love of Helena.

When they found the gentlemen had left them, they departed, and once more wandered weary in the wood in search of their lovers.

As soon as they were gone, the fairy king, who with little Puck had been listening to their quarrels, said to him, 'This is your negligence, Puck; or did you do this wilfully?' 'Believe me, king of shadows,' answered Puck, 'it was a mistake; did not you tell me I should know the man by his Athenian garments? However, I am not sorry this has happened, for I think their jangling makes excellent sport.' 'You heard,' said Oberon, 'that Demetrius and Lysander are gone to seek a convenient place to fight in. I command you to overhang the night with a thick fog, and lead these quarrelsome lovers so astray in the dark, that they shall not be able to find each other. Counterfeit each of their voices to the other, and with bitter taunts provoke them to follow you, while they think it is their rival's tongue they hear. See you do this, till they are so weary they can go no farther; and when you find they are asleep, drop the juice of this other flower into Lysander's eyes, and when he awakes he will forget his new love for Helena, and return to his old passion for Hermia; and then the two fair ladies may each one be happy with the man she loves, and they will think all that has passed a vexatious dream. About this quickly, Puck, and I will go and see what sweet love my Titania has found.'

Titania was still sleeping, and Oberon seeing a clown near her, who had lost his way in the wood, and was likewise asleep: 'This fellow,' said he, 'shall be my Titania's true love;' and clapping an ass's head over the clown's, it seemed to fit him as well as if it had grown upon his own shoulders. Though Oberon fixed the ass's head on very gently, it awakened him, and rising up, unconscious of what Oberon had done to him, he went towards the bower where the fairy queen slept.

'Ah! what angel is that I see?' said Titania, opening her eyes, and the juice of the little purple flower beginning to take effect: 'are you as wise as you are beautiful?'

'Why, mistress,' said the foolish clown, 'if I have wit enough to find the way out of this wood, I have enough to serve my turn.'

'Out of the wood do not desire to go,' said the enamoured queen. 'I am a spirit of no common rate. I love you. Go with me, and I will give you fairies to attend upon you.'

She then called four of her fairies: their names were, Pease-blossom, Cobweb, Moth, and Mustard-seed.

'Attend,' said the queen, 'upon this sweet gentleman; hop in his walks, and gambol in his sight; feed him with grapes and apricots, and steal for him the honey-bags from the bees. Come, sit with me,' said she to the clown, 'and let me play with your amiable hairy cheeks, my beautiful ass! and kiss your large ears, my gentle joy!'

'Where is Pease-blossom?' said the ass-headed clown, not much regarding the fairy queen's courtship, but very proud of his new attendants.

'Here, sir,' said little Pease-blossom.

'Scratch my head,' said the clown. 'Where is Cobweb?'

'Here, sir,' said Cobweb.

'Good Mr Cobweb,' said the foolish clown, 'kill me the red humble bee on the top of that thistle yonder; and, good Mr Cobweb, bring me the honey-bag. Do not fret yourself too much in the action, Mr Cobweb, and take care the honey-bag break not; I should be sorry to have you overflown with a honey-bag. Where is Mustard-seed?'

'Here, sir,' said Mustard-seed: 'what is your will?'

'Nothing,' said the clown, 'good Mr Mustard-seed, but to help Mr Pease-blossom to scratch; I must go to a barber's, Mr Mustard-seed, for methinks I am marvellous hairy about the face.'

'My sweet love,' said the queen, 'what will you have to eat? I have a venturous fairy shall seek the squirrel's hoard, and fetch you some new nuts.'

'I had rather have a handful of dried pease,' said the clown, who with his ass's head had got an ass's appetite. 'But, I pray, let none of your people disturb me, for I have a mind to sleep.'

'Sleep, then,' said the queen, 'and I will wind you in my arms. O how I love you! how I dote upon you!'

When the fairy king saw the clown sleeping in the arms of his queen, he advanced within her sight, and reproached her with having lavished her favours upon an ass.

This she could not deny, as the clown was then sleeping within her arms, with his ass's head crowned by her with flowers.

When Oberon had teased her for some time, he again demanded the changeling boy; which she, ashamed of being discovered by her lord with her new favourite, did not dare to refuse him.

Oberon, having thus obtained the little boy he had so long wished for to be his page, took pity on the disgraceful situation into which, by his merry contrivance, he had brought his Titania, and threw some of the juice of the other flower into her eyes; and the fairy queen immediately recovered her senses, and wondered at her late dotage, saying how she now loathed the sight of the strange monster.

Oberon likewise took the ass's head off the clown, and left him to finish his nap with his own fool's head upon his shoulders.

Oberon and his Titania being now perfectly reconciled, he related to her the history of the lovers, and their midnight quarrels; and she agreed to go with him and see the end of their adventures.

The fairy king and queen found the lovers and their fair ladies, at no great distance from each other, sleeping on a grass-plot; for Puck, to make amends for his former mistake, had contrived with the utmost diligence to bring them all to the same spot, unknown to each other; and he had carefully removed the charm from off the eyes of Lysander with the antidote the fairy king gave to him.

Hermia first awoke, and finding her lost Lysander asleep so near her, was looking at him and wondering at his strange inconstancy. Lysander presently opening his eyes, and seeing his dear Hermia, recovered his reason which the fairy charm had before clouded, and with his reason, his love for Hermia; and they began to talk over the adventures of the night, doubting if these things had really happened, or if they had both been dreaming the same bewildering dream.

Helena and Demetrius were by this time awake; and a sweet sleep having quieted Helena's disturbed and angry spirits, she listened with delight to the professions of love which Demetrius still made to her, and which, to her surprise as well as pleasure, she began to perceive were sincere.

These fair night-wandering ladies, now no longer rivals, became once more true friends; all the unkind words which had passed were forgiven, and they calmly consulted together what was best to be done in their present situation. It was soon agreed that, as Demetrius had given up his pretensions to Hermia, he should endeavour to prevail upon her father to revoke the cruel sentence of death which had been passed against her. Demetrius was preparing to return to Athens for this friendly purpose, when they were surprised with the sight of Egeus, Hermia's father, who came to the wood in pursuit of his runaway daughter.

When Egeus understood that Demetrius would not now marry his daughter, he no longer opposed her marriage with Lysander, but gave his consent that they should be wedded on the fourth day from that time, being the same day on which Hermia had been condemned to lose her life; and on that same day Helena joyfully agreed to marry her beloved and now faithful Demetrius.

The fairy king and queen, who were invisible spectators of this reconciliation, and now saw the happy ending of the lovers' history, brought about through the good offices of Oberon, received so much pleasure, that these kind spirits resolved to celebrate the approaching nuptials with sports and revels throughout their fairy kingdom.

And now, if any are offended with this story of fairies and their pranks, as judging it incredible and strange, they have only to think that they have been asleep and dreaming, and that all these adventures were visions which they saw in their sleep: and I hope none of my readers will be so unreasonable as to be offended with a pretty harmless Midsummer Night's Dream.

THE MERCHANT OF VENICE

SHYLOCK, the Jew, lived at Venice: he was an usurer, who had amassed an immense fortune by lending money at great interest to Christian merchants. Shylock, being a hard-hearted man, exacted the payment of the money he lent with such severity that he was much disliked by all good men, and particularly by Antonio, a young merchant of Venice; and Shylock as much hated Antonio, because he used to lend money to people in distress, and would never take any interest for the money he lent; therefore there was great enmity between this covetous Jew and the generous merchant Antonio. Whenever Antonio met Shylock on the Rialto (or Exchange), he used to reproach him with his usuries and hard dealings, which the Jew would bear with seeming patience, while he secretly meditated revenge.

Antonio was the kindest man that lived, the best conditioned, and had the most unwearied spirit in doing courtesies; indeed, he was one in whom the ancient Roman honour more appeared than in any that drew breath in Italy. He was greatly beloved by all his fellow-citizens; but the friend who was nearest and dearest to his heart was Bassanio, a noble Venetian, who, having but a small patrimony, had nearly exhausted his little fortune by living in too expensive a manner for his slender means, as young men of high rank with small fortunes are too apt to do. Whenever Bassanio wanted money, Antonio assisted him; and it seemed as if they had but one heart and one pulse between them.

One day Bassanio came to Antonio, and told him that he wished to repair his fortune by a wealthy marriage with a lady whom he dearly loved, whose father, that was lately dead, had left her sole heiress to a large estate; and that in her father's lifetime he used to visit at her house, when he thought he had observed this lady had sometimes from her eyes sent speechless messages, that seemed to say he would be no unwelcome suitor; but not having money to furnish himself with an appearance befitting the lover of so rich an heiress, he besought Antonio to add to the many favours he had shown him, by lending him three thousand ducats.

Antonio had no money by him at that time to lend his friend; but expecting soon to have some ships come home laden with merchandise, he said he would go to Shylock, the rich money-lender, and borrow the money upon the credit of those ships.

Antonio and Bassanio went together to Shylock, and Antonio asked the Jew to lend him three thousand ducats upon any interest he should require, to be paid out of the merchandise contained in his ships at sea. On this, Shylock thought within himself, 'If I can once catch him on the hip, I will feed fat the ancient grudge I bear him; he hates our Jewish nation; he lends out money gratis, and among the merchants he rails at me and my well-earned bargains, which he calls interest. Cursed be my tribe if I forgive him!' Antonio finding he was musing within himself and did not answer, and being impatient for the money said, 'Shylock, do you hear? will you lend the money?' To this question the Jew replied, 'Signior Antonio, on the Rialto many a time and often you have railed at me about my monies and my usuries, and I have borne it with a patient shrug, for sufferance is the badge of all our tribe; and then you have called me unbeliever, cut-throat dog, and spit upon my Jewish garments, and spurned at me with your foot, as if I was a cur. Well then, it appears you need my help; and you come to me, and say, *Shylock, lend me monies*. Has a dog money? Is it possible a cur should lend three thousand ducats? Shall I bend low and say, Fair sir, you spit upon me on Wednesday last, another time you called me dog, for these courtesies I am to lend you monies.' Antonio replied, 'I am as like to call you so again, to spit on you again, and spurn you too. If you will lend me this money, lend it not to me as to a friend, but rather lend it to me as to an enemy, that, if I break, you may with better face exact the penalty.' – 'Why, look you,' said Shylock, 'how you storm! I would be friends with you, and have your love. I will forget the shames you have put upon me. I will supply your wants, and take no interest for my money.' This seemingly kind offer greatly surprised Antonio; and then Shylock, still pretending kindness, and that all he did was to gain Antonio's love, again said he would lend him the three thousand ducats, and take no interest for his money; only Antonio should go with him to a lawyer, and there sign in merry sport a bond, that if he did not repay the money by a certain day, he would forfeit a pound of flesh, to be cut off from any part of his body that Shylock pleased.

'Content,' said Antonio: 'I will sign to this bond, and say there is much kindness in the Jew.'

Bassanio said Antonio should not sign to such a bond for him; but still Antonio insisted that he would sign it, for that before the day of payment came, his ships would return laden with many times the value of the money.

Shylock, hearing this debate, exclaimed, 'O, father Abraham, what suspicious people these Christians are! Their own hard dealings teach them to suspect the thoughts of others. I pray you tell me this, Bassanio: if he should break his day, what should I gain by the exaction of the forfeiture? A pound of man's flesh, taken from a man, is not so estimable, nor profitable neither, as the flesh of mutton or beef. I say, to buy his favour I offer this friendship: if he will take it, so; if not, adieu.'

At last, against the advice of Bassanio, who, notwithstanding all the Jew had said of his kind intentions, did not like his friend should run the hazard of this shocking penalty for his sake, Antonio signed the bond, thinking it really was (as the Jew said) merely in sport.

The rich heiress that Bassanio wished to marry lived near Venice, at a place called Belmont: her name was Portia, and in the graces of her person and her mind she was nothing inferior to that Portia, of whom we read, who was Cato's daughter, and the wife of Brutus.

Bassanio being so kindly supplied with money by his friend Antonio, at the hazard of his life, set out for Belmont with a splendid train, and attended by a gentleman of the name of Gratiano.

Bassanio proving successful in his suit, Portia in a short time consented to accept of him for a husband.

Bassanio confessed to Portia that he had no fortune, and that his high birth and noble ancestry was all that he could boast of; she, who loved him for his worthy qualities, and had riches enough not to regard wealth in a husband, answered with a graceful modesty, that she would wish herself a thousand times more fair, and ten thousand times more rich, to be more worthy of him; and then the accomplished Portia prettily dispraised herself, and said she was an unlessoned girl, unschooled, unpractised, yet not so old but that she could learn, and that she would commit her gentle spirit to be directed and governed by him in all things; and she said, 'Myself and what is mine, to you and yours is now converted. But yesterday, Bassanio, I was the lady of this fair mansion, queen of myself, and mistress over these servants; and now this house, these servants, and myself, are yours, my lord; I give them with this ring;' presenting a ring to Bassanio.

Bassanio was so overpowered with gratitude and wonder at the gracious manner in which the rich and noble Portia accepted of a man of his humble fortunes, that he could not express his joy and reverence to the dear lady who so honoured him, by anything but broken words of love and thankfulness; and taking the ring, he vowed never to part with it.

Gratiano and Nerissa, Portia's waiting-maid, were in attendance upon their lord and lady, when Portia so gracefully promised to become the obedient wife of Bassanio; and Gratiano, wishing Bassanio and the generous lady joy, desired permission to be married at the same time.

'With all my heart, Gratiano,' said Bassanio, 'if you can get a wife.'

Gratiano then said that he loved the Lady Portia's fair waiting gentlewoman Nerissa, and that she had promised to be his wife, if her lady married Bassanio. Portia asked Nerissa if this was true. Nerissa replied, 'Madam, it is so, if you approve of it.' Portia willingly consenting, Bassanio pleasantly said, 'Then our wedding-feast shall be much honoured by your marriage, Gratiano.'

The happiness of these lovers was sadly crossed at this moment by the entrance of a messenger, who brought a letter from Antonio containing fearful tidings. When Bassanio read Antonio's letter, Portia feared it was to tell him of the death of some dear friend, he looked so pale; and inquiring what was the news which had so distressed him, he said, 'O sweet Portia, here are a few of the unpleasantest words that ever blotted paper; gentle lady, when I first imparted my love to you, I freely told you all the wealth I had ran in my veins; but I should have told you that I had less than nothing, being in debt.' Bassanio then told Portia what has been here related, of his borrowing the money of Antonio, and of Antonio's procuring it of Shylock the Jew, and of the bond by which Antonio had engaged to forfeit a pound of flesh, if it was not repaid by a certain day: and then Bassanio read Antonio's letter; the words of which were, '*Sweet Bassanio, my ships are all lost, my bond to the Jew is forfeited, and since in paying it is impossible I should live, I could wish to see you at my death; notwithstanding, use your pleasure; if your love for me do not persuade you to come, let not my letter.*' 'O, my dear love,' said Portia, 'despatch all business, and begone; you shall have gold to pay the money twenty times over, before this kind friend shall lose a hair by my Bassanio's fault; and as you are so dearly bought, I will dearly love you.' Portia then said she would be married to Bassanio before he set out, to give a legal right to her money; and that same day they were married, and Gratiano was also married to Nerissa; and Bassanio and Gratiano, the instant they were married, set out in great haste for Venice, where Bassanio found Antonio in prison.

The day of payment being past, the cruel Jew would not accept of the money which Bassanio offered him, but insisted upon having a pound of Antonio's flesh. A day was appointed to try this shocking cause before the Duke of Venice, and Bassanio awaited in dreadful suspense the event of the trial.

When Portia parted with her husband, she spoke cheeringly to him, and bade him bring his dear friend along with him when he returned; yet she feared it would go hard with Antonio, and when she was left alone, she began to think and consider within herself, if she could by any means be instrumental in saving the life of her dear Bassanio's friend; and notwithstanding when she wished to honour her Bassanio, she had said to him with such a meek and wife-like grace, that she would submit in all things to be governed by his superior wisdom, yet being now called forth into action by the peril of her honoured husband's friend, she did nothing doubt her own powers, and by the sole guidance of her own true and perfect judgment, at once resolved to go herself to Venice, and speak in Antonio's defence.

Portia had a relation who was a counsellor in the law; to this gentleman, whose name was Bellario, she wrote, and stating the case to him, desired his opinion, and that with his advice he would also send her the dress worn by a counsellor. When the messenger returned, he brought letters from Bellario of advice how to proceed, and also everything necessary for her equipment.

Portia dressed herself and her maid Nerissa in men's apparel, and putting on the robes of a counsellor, she took Nerissa along with her as her clerk; and setting out immediately, they arrived at Venice on the very day of the trial. The cause was just going to be heard before the duke and senators of Venice in the senate-house, when Portia entered this high court of justice, and presented a letter from Bellario, in which that learned counsellor wrote to the duke, saying, he would have come himself to plead for Antonio, but that he was prevented by sickness, and he requested that the learned young doctor Balthasar (so he called Portia) might be permitted to plead in his stead. This the duke granted, much wondering at the youthful appearance of the stranger, who was prettily disguised by her counsellor's robes and her large wig.

And now began this important trial. Portia looked around her, and she saw the merciless Jew; and she saw Bassanio, but he knew her not in her disguise. He was standing beside Antonio, in an agony of distress and fear for his friend.

The importance of the arduous task Portia had engaged in gave this tender lady courage, and she boldly proceeded in the duty she had undertaken to perform: and first of all she addressed herself to Shylock; and allowing that he had a right by the Venetian law to have the forfeit expressed in the bond, she spoke so sweetly of the noble quality of *mercy*, as would have softened any heart but the unfeeling Shylock's; saying, that it dropped as gentle rain from heaven upon the place beneath; and how mercy was a double blessing, it blessed him that gave, and him that received it; and how it became monarchs better than their crowns, being an attribute of God himself; and that earthly power came nearest to God's, in proportion as mercy tempered justice; and she bid Shylock remember that as we all pray for mercy, that same prayer should teach us to show mercy. Shylock only answered her by desiring to have the penalty forfeited in the bond. 'Is he not able to pay the money?' asked Portia. Bassanio then offered the Jew the payment of the three thousand ducats as many times over as he should desire; which Shylock refusing, and still insisting upon having a pound of Antonio's flesh, Bassanio begged the learned young counsellor would endeavour to wrest the law a little, to save Antonio's life. But Portia gravely answered, that laws once established must never be altered. Shylock hearing Portia say that the law might not be altered, it seemed to him that she was pleading in his favour, and he said, 'A Daniel is come to judgment! O wise young judge, how I do honour you! How much elder are you than your looks!'

Portia now desired Shylock to let her look at the bond; and when she had read it, she said, 'This bond is forfeited, and by this the Jew may lawfully claim a pound of flesh, to be by him cut off nearest Antonio's heart.' Then she said to Shylock, 'Be merciful: take the money, and bid me tear the bond.' But no mercy would the cruel Shylock show; and he said, 'By my soul I swear, there is no power in the tongue of man to alter me.' – 'Why then, Antonio,' said Portia, 'you must prepare your bosom for the knife:' and while Shylock was sharpening the long knife with great eagerness to cut off the pound of flesh, Portia said to Antonio, 'Have you anything to say?' Antonio with a calm resignation replied, that he had but little to say, for that he had prepared his mind for death. Then he said to Bassanio, 'Give me your hand, Bassanio! Fare you well! Grieve not that I am fallen into this misfortune for you. Commend me to your honourable wife, and tell her how I have loved you!' Bassanio in the deepest affliction replied, 'Antonio, I am married to a wife, who is as dear to me as life itself; but life itself, my wife, and all the world, are not esteemed with me above your life: I would lose all, I would sacrifice all to this devil here, to deliver you.'

Portia hearing this, though the kind-hearted lady was not at all offended with her husband for expressing the love he owed to so true a friend as Antonio in these strong terms, yet could not help answering, 'Your wife would give you little thanks, if she were present, to hear you make this offer.' And then Gratiano, who loved to copy what his lord did, thought he must make a speech like Bassanio's, and he said, in Nerissa's hearing, who was writing in her clerk's dress by the side of

Portia, 'I have a wife, whom I protest I love; I wish she were in heaven, if she could but entreat some power there to change the cruel temper of this currish Jew.' 'It is well you wish this behind her back, else you would have but an unquiet house,' said Nerissa.

Shylock now cried out impatiently, 'We trifle time; I pray pronounce the sentence.' And now all was awful expectation in the court, and every heart was full of grief for Antonio.

Portia asked if the scales were ready to weigh the flesh; and she said to the Jew, 'Shylock, you must have some surgeon by, lest he bleed to death.' Shylock, whose whole intent was that Antonio should bleed to death, said, 'It is not so named in the bond.' Portia replied, 'It is not so named in the bond, but what of that? It were good you did so much for charity.' To this all the answer Shylock would make was, 'I cannot find it; it is not in the bond.' 'Then,' said Portia, 'a pound of Antonio's flesh is thine. The law allows it, and the court awards it. And you may cut this flesh from off his breast. The law allows it and the court awards it.' Again Shylock exclaimed, 'O wise and upright judge! A Daniel is come to judgment!' And then he sharpened his long knife again, and looking eagerly on Antonio, he said, 'Come, prepare!'

'Tarry a little, Jew,' said Portia; 'there is something else. This bond here gives you no drop of blood; the words expressly are, "a pound of flesh." If in the cutting off the pound of flesh you shed one drop of Christian blood, your lands and goods are by the law to be confiscated to the state of Venice.' Now as it was utterly impossible for Shylock to cut off the pound of flesh without shedding some of Antonio's blood, this wise discovery of Portia's, that it was flesh and not blood that was named in the bond, saved the life of Antonio; and all admiring the wonderful sagacity of the young counsellor, who had so happily thought of this expedient, plaudits resounded from every part of the senate-house; and Gratiano exclaimed, in the words which Shylock had used, 'O wise and upright judge! mark, Jew, a Daniel is come to judgment!'

Shylock, finding himself defeated in his cruel intent, said with a disappointed look, that he would take the money; and Bassanio, rejoiced beyond measure at Antonio's unexpected deliverance, cried out, 'Here is the money!' But Portia stopped him, saying, 'Softly; there is no haste; the Jew shall have nothing but the penalty: therefore prepare, Shylock, to cut off the flesh; but mind you shed no blood: nor do not cut off more nor less than just a pound; be it more or less by one poor scruple, nay if the scale turn but by the weight of a single hair, you are condemned by the laws of Venice to die, and all your wealth is forfeited to the senate.' 'Give me my money, and let me go,' said Shylock. 'I have it ready,' said Bassanio: 'here it is.'

Shylock was going to take the money, when Portia again stopped him, saying, 'Tarry, Jew; I have yet another hold upon you. By the laws of Venice, your wealth is forfeited to the state, for having conspired against the life of one of its citizens, and your life lies at the mercy of the duke; therefore, down on your knees, and ask him to pardon you.'

The duke then said to Shylock, 'That you may see the difference of our Christian spirit, I pardon you your life before you ask it; half your wealth belongs to Antonio, the other half comes to the state.'

The generous Antonio then said that he would give up his share of Shylock's wealth, if Shylock would sign a deed to make it over at his death to his daughter and her husband; for Antonio knew that the Jew had an only daughter who had lately married against his consent to a young Christian, named Lorenzo, a friend of Antonio's, which had so offended Shylock, that he had disinherited her.

The Jew agreed to this: and being thus disappointed in his revenge, despoiled of his riches, he said, 'I am ill. Let me go home; send the deed after me, and I will sign over half my riches to my daughter.' – 'Get thee gone, then,' said the duke, 'and sign it; and if you repent your cruelty and turn Christian, the state will forgive you the fine of the other half of your riches.'

The duke now released Antonio, and dismissed the court. He then highly praised the wisdom and ingenuity of the young counsellor, and invited him home to dinner. Portia, who meant to return to Belmont before her husband, replied, 'I humbly thank your grace, but I must away directly.' The duke said he was sorry he had not leisure to stay and dine with him; and turning to Antonio, he added, 'Reward this gentleman; for in my mind you are much indebted to him.'

The duke and his senators left the court; and then Bassanio said to

Portia, 'Most worthy gentleman, I and my friend Antonio have by your wisdom been this day acquitted of grievous penalties, and I beg you will accept of the three thousand ducats due unto the Jew.' 'And we shall stand indebted to you over and above,' said Antonio, 'in love and service evermore.'

Portia could not be prevailed upon to accept the money; but upon Bassanio still pressing her to accept of some reward, she said, 'Give me your gloves; I will wear them for your sake;' and then Bassanio taking off his gloves, she espied the ring which she had given him upon his finger: now it was the ring the wily lady wanted to get from him to make a merry jest when she saw her Bassanio again, that made her ask him for his gloves; and she said, when she saw the ring, 'and for your love I will take this ring from you.' Bassanio was sadly distressed that the counsellor should ask him for the only thing he could not part with, and he replied in great confusion, that he could not give him that ring, because it was his wife's gift, and he had vowed never to part with it; but that he would give him the most valuable ring in Venice, and find it out by proclamation. On this Portia affected to be affronted, and left the court, saying, 'You teach me, sir, how a beggar should be answered.'

'Dear Bassanio,' said Antonio, 'let him have the ring; let my love and the great service he has done for me be valued against your wife's displeasure.' Bassanio, ashamed to appear so ungrateful, yielded, and sent Gratiano after Portia with the ring; and then the *clerk* Nerissa, who had also given Gratiano a ring, she begged his ring, and Gratiano (not choosing to be outdone in generosity by his lord) gave it to her. And there was laughing among these ladies to think, when they got home, how they would tax their husbands with giving away their rings, and swear that they had given them as a present to some woman.

Portia, when she returned, was in that happy temper of mind which never fails to attend the consciousness of having performed a good action; her cheerful spirits enjoyed everything she saw: the moon never seemed to shine so bright before; and when that pleasant moon was hid behind a cloud, then a light which she saw from her house at Belmont as well pleased her charmed fancy, and she said to Nerissa, 'That light we see is burning in my hall; how far that little candle throws its beams, so shines a good deed in a naughty world;' and hearing the sound of music from her house, she said, 'Methinks that music sounds much sweeter than by day.'

And now Portia and Nerissa entered the house, and dressing themselves in their own apparel, they awaited the arrival of their husbands, who soon followed them with Antonio; and Bassanio presenting his dear friend to the Lady Portia, the congratulations and welcomings of that lady were hardly over, when they perceived Nerissa and her husband quarrelling in a corner of the room. 'A quarrel already?' said Portia. 'What is the matter?' Gratiano replied, 'Lady, it is about a paltry gilt ring that Nerissa gave me, with words upon it like the poetry on a cutler's knife; *Love me, and leave me not.*'

'What does the poetry or the value of the ring signify?' said Nerissa. 'You swore to me when I gave it to you, that you would keep it till the hour of death; and now you say you gave it to the lawyer's clerk. I know you gave it to a woman.' – 'By this hand,' replied Gratiano, 'I gave it to a youth, a kind of boy, a little scrubbed boy, no higher than yourself; he was clerk to the young counsellor that by his wise pleading saved Antonio's life: this prating boy begged it for a fee, and I could not for my life deny him.' Portia said, 'You were to blame, Gratiano, to part with your wife's first gift. I gave my lord Bassanio a ring, and I am sure he would not part with it for all the world.' Gratiano, in excuse for his fault, now said, 'My lord Bassanio gave his ring away to the counsellor, and then the boy, his clerk, that took some pains in writing, he begged my ring.'

Portia, hearing this, seemed very angry, and reproached Bassanio for giving away her ring; and she said, Nerissa had taught her what to believe, and that she knew some woman had the ring. Bassanio was very unhappy to have offended his dear lady, and he said with great earnestness, 'No, by my honour, no woman had it, but a civil doctor, who refused three thousand ducats of me, and begged the ring, which when I denied him, he went displeased away. What could I do, sweet Portia? I was so beset with shame for my seeming ingratitude, that I was forced to send the ring after him. Pardon me, good lady; had you been there, I think you would have begged the ring of me to give the worthy doctor.'

'Ah!' said Antonio, 'I am the unhappy cause of these quarrels.'

Portia bid Antonio not to grieve at that, for that he was welcome notwithstanding; and then Antonio said, 'I once did lend my body for Bassanio's sake; and but for him to whom your husband gave the ring, I should have now been dead. I dare be bound again, my soul upon the forfeit, your lord will never more break his faith with you.' – 'Then you shall be his surety,' said Portia; 'give him this ring, and bid him keep it better than the other.'

When Bassanio looked at this ring, he was strangely surprised to find it was the same he gave away; and then Portia told him how she was the young counsellor, and Nerissa was her clerk; and Bassanio found, to his unspeakable wonder and delight, that it was by the noble courage and wisdom of his wife that Antonio's life was saved.

And Portia again welcomed Antonio, and gave him letters which by some chance had fallen into her hands, which contained an account of Antonio's ships, that were supposed lost, being safely arrived in the harbour. So these tragical beginnings of this rich merchant's story were all forgotten in the unexpected good fortune which ensued; and there was leisure to laugh at the comical adventure of the rings, and the husbands that did not know their own wives: Gratiano merrily swearing, in a sort of rhyming speech, that

> ————while he lived, he'd fear no other thing
> So sore, as keeping safe Nerissa's ring.

AS YOU LIKE IT

DURING the time that France was divided into provinces (or dukedoms as they were called) there reigned in one of these provinces an usurper, who had deposed and banished his elder brother, the lawful duke.

The duke, who was thus driven from his dominions, retired with a few faithful followers to the forest of Arden; and here the good duke lived with his loving friends, who had put themselves into a voluntary exile for his sake, while their land and revenues enriched the false usurper; and custom soon made the life of careless ease they led here more sweet to them than the pomp and uneasy splendour of a courtier's life. Here they lived like the old Robin Hood of England, and to this forest many noble youths daily resorted from the court, and did fleet the time carelessly, as they did who lived in the golden age. In the summer they lay along under the fine shade of the large forest trees, marking the playful sports of the wild deer; and so fond were they of these poor dappled fools, who seemed to be the native inhabitants of the forest, that it grieved them to be forced to kill them to supply themselves with venison for their food. When the cold winds of winter made the duke feel the change of his adverse fortune, he would endure it patiently, and say, 'These chilling winds which blow upon my body are true counsellors; they do not flatter, but represent truly to me my condition; and though they bite sharply, their tooth is nothing like so keen as that of unkindness and ingratitude. I find that howsoever men speak against adversity, yet some sweet uses are to be extracted from it;

like the jewel, precious for medicine, which is taken from the head of the venomous and despised toad.' In this manner did the patient duke draw a useful moral from everything that he saw; and by the help of this moralising turn, in that life of his, remote from public haunts, he could find tongues in trees, books in the running brooks, sermons in stones, and good in everything.

The banished duke had an only daughter, named Rosalind, whom the usurper, Duke Frederick, when he banished her father, still retained in his court as a companion for his own daughter Celia. A strict friendship subsisted between these ladies, which the disagreement between their fathers did not in the least interrupt, Celia striving by every kindness in her power to make amends to Rosalind for the injustice of her own father in deposing the father of Rosalind; and whenever the thoughts of her father's banishment, and her own dependence on the false usurper, made Rosalind melancholy, Celia's whole care was to comfort and console her.

One day, when Celia was talking in her usual kind manner to Rosalind, saying, 'I pray you, Rosalind, my sweet cousin, be merry,' a messenger entered from the duke, to tell them that if they wished to see a wrestling match, which was just going to begin, they must come instantly to the court before the palace; and Celia, thinking it would amuse Rosalind, agreed to go and see it.

In those times wrestling, which is only practised now by country clowns, was a favourite sport even in the courts of princes, and before fair ladies and princesses. To this wrestling match, therefore, Celia and Rosalind went. They found that it was likely to prove a very tragical sight; for a large and powerful man, who had been long practised in the art of wrestling, and had slain many men in contests of this kind, was just going to wrestle with a very young man, who, from his extreme youth and inexperience in the art, the beholders all thought would certainly be killed.

When the duke saw Celia and Rosalind, he said, 'How now, daughter and niece, are you crept hither to see the wrestling? You will take little delight in it, there is such odds in the men: in pity to this young man, I would wish to persuade him from wrestling. Speak to him, ladies, and see if you can move him.'

The ladies were well pleased to perform this humane office, and first Celia entreated the young stranger that he would desist from the attempt; and then Rosalind spoke so kindly to him, and with such feeling consideration for the danger he was about to undergo, that instead of being persuaded by her gentle words to forgo his purpose, all his thoughts were bent to distinguish himself by his courage in this lovely lady's eyes. He refused the request of Celia and Rosalind in such graceful and modest words, that they felt still more concern for him; he concluded his refusal with saying, 'I am sorry to deny such fair and excellent ladies anything. But let your fair eyes and gentle wishes go with me to my trial, wherein if I be conquered there is one shamed that was never gracious; if I am killed, there is one dead that is willing to die; I shall do my friends no wrong, for I have none to lament me; the world no injury, for in it I have nothing; for I only fill up a place in the world which may be better supplied when I have made it empty.'

And now the wrestling match began. Celia wished the young stranger might not be hurt; but Rosalind felt most for him. The friendless state which he said he was in, and that he wished to die, made Rosalind think that he was like herself, unfortunate; and she pitied him so much, and so deep an interest she took in his danger while he was wrestling, that she might almost be said at that moment to have fallen in love with him.

The kindness shown this unknown youth by these fair and noble ladies gave him courage and strength, so that he performed wonders; and in the end completely conquered his antagonist, who was so much hurt, that for a while he was unable to speak or move.

The Duke Frederick was much pleased with the courage and skill shown by this young stranger; and desired to know his name and parentage, meaning to take him under his protection.

The stranger said his name was Orlando, and that he was the youngest son of Sir Rowland de Boys.

Sir Rowland de Boys, the father of Orlando, had been dead some years; but when he was living, he had been a true subject and dear friend of the banished duke: therefore, when Frederick heard Orlando was the son of his banished brother's friend, all his liking for this brave young man was changed into displeasure, and he left the place in very ill humour. Hating to hear the very name of any of his brother's friends, and yet still admiring the valour of the youth, he said, as he went out, that he wished Orlando had been the son of any other man.

Rosalind was delighted to hear that her new favourite was the son of her father's old friend; and she said to Celia, 'My father loved Sir Rowland de Boys, and if I had known this young man was his son, I would have added tears to my entreaties before he should have ventured.'

The ladies then went up to him; and seeing him abashed by the sudden displeasure shown by the duke, they spoke kind and encouraging words to him; and Rosalind, when they were going away, turned back to speak some more civil things to the brave young son of her father's old friend; and taking a chain from off her neck, she said, 'Gentleman, wear this for me. I am out of suits with fortune, or I would give you a more valuable present.'

When the ladies were alone, Rosalind's talk being still of Orlando, Celia began to perceive her cousin had fallen in love with the handsome young wrestler, and she said to Rosalind, 'Is it possible you should fall in love so suddenly?' Rosalind replied, 'The duke, my father, loved his father dearly.' 'But,' said Celia, 'does it therefore follow that you should love his son dearly? for then I ought to hate him, for my father hated his father; yet I do not hate Orlando.'

Frederick being enraged at the sight of Sir Rowland de Boys' son, which reminded him of the many friends the banished duke had among the nobility, and having been for some time displeased with his niece, because the people praised her for her virtues, and pitied her for her good father's sake, his malice suddenly broke out against her; and while Celia and Rosalind were talking of Orlando, Frederick entered the room, and with looks full of anger ordered Rosalind instantly to leave the palace, and follow her father into banishment; telling Celia, who in vain pleaded for her, that he had only suffered Rosalind to stay upon her account. 'I did not then,' said Celia, 'entreat you to let her stay, for I was too young at the time to value her; but now that I know her worth, and that we so long have slept together, rose at the same instant, learned, played, and eat together, I cannot live out of her company.' Frederick replied, 'She is too subtle for you; her smoothness, her very silence, and her patience speak to the people, and they pity her. You are a fool to plead for her, for you will seem more bright and virtuous when she is gone; therefore open not your lips in her favour, for the doom which I have passed upon her is irrevocable.'

When Celia found she could not prevail upon her father to let Rosalind remain with her, she generously resolved to accompany her; and leaving her father's palace that night, she went along with her friend to seek Rosalind's father, the banished duke, in the forest of Arden.

Before they set out, Celia considered that it would be unsafe for two young ladies to travel in the rich clothes they then wore; she therefore proposed that they should disguise their rank by dressing themselves like country maids. Rosalind said it would be a still greater protection if one of them was to be dressed like a man; and so it was quickly agreed on between them, that as Rosalind was the tallest, she should wear the dress of a young countryman, and Celia should be habited like a country lass, and that they should say they were brother and sister, and Rosalind said she would be called Ganymede, and Celia chose the name of Aliena.

In this disguise, and taking their money and jewels to defray their expenses, these fair princesses set out on their long travel; for the forest of Arden was a long way off, beyond the boundaries of the duke's dominions.

The Lady Rosalind (or Ganymede as she must now be called) with her manly garb seemed to have put on a manly courage. The faithful friendship Celia had shown in accompanying Rosalind so many weary miles, made the new brother, in recompense for this true love, exert a cheerful spirit, as if he were indeed Ganymede, the rustic and stout-hearted brother of the gentle village maiden, Aliena.

When at last they came to the forest of Arden, they no longer found the convenient inns and good accommodations they had met with on the road; and being in want of food and rest, Ganymede, who had so merrily cheered his sister with pleasant speeches and happy remarks all the way, now owned to Aliena that he was so weary, he could find in his heart to disgrace his man's apparel, and cry like a woman; and Aliena declared she could go no farther; and then again Ganymede tried to recollect that it was a man's duty to comfort and console a woman, as the weaker vessel; and to seem courageous to his new sister, he said, 'Come, have a good heart, my sister Aliena; we are now at the end of our travel, in the forest of Arden.' But feigned manliness and forced courage would no longer support them; for though they were in the forest of Arden, they knew not where to find the duke: and here the travel of these weary ladies might have come to a sad conclusion, for they might have lost themselves, and perished for want of food; but providentially, as they were sitting on the grass, almost dying with fatigue and hopeless of any relief, a countryman chanced to pass that way, and Ganymede once more tried to speak with a manly boldness, saying, 'Shepherd, if love or gold can in this desert place procure us entertainment, I pray you bring us where we may rest ourselves; for this young maid, my sister, is much fatigued with travelling, and faints for want of food.'

The man replied that he was only a servant to a shepherd, and that his master's house was just going to be sold, and therefore they would find but poor entertainment; but that if they would go with him, they should be welcome to what there was. They followed the man, the near prospect of relief giving them fresh strength; and bought the house and sheep of the shepherd, and took the man who conducted them to the shepherd's house to wait on them; and being by this means so fortunately provided with a neat cottage, and well supplied with provisions, they agreed to stay here till they could learn in what part of the forest the duke dwelt.

When they were rested after the fatigue of their journey, they began to like their new way of life, and almost fancied themselves the shepherd and shepherdess they feigned to be; yet sometimes Ganymede remembered he had once been the same Lady Rosalind who had so dearly loved the brave Orlando, because he was the son of old Sir Rowland, her father's friend; and though Ganymede thought that Orlando was many miles distant, even so many weary miles as they had travelled, yet it soon appeared that Orlando was also in the forest of Arden: and in this manner this strange event came to pass.

Orlando was the youngest son of Sir Rowland de Boys, who, when he died, left him (Orlando being then very young) to the care of his eldest brother Oliver, charging Oliver on his blessing to give his brother a good education, and provide for him as became the dignity of their ancient house. Oliver proved an unworthy brother; and disregarding the commands of his dying father, he never put his brother to school, but kept him at home untaught and entirely neglected. But in his nature and in the noble qualities of his mind Orlando so much resembled his excellent father, that without any advantages of education he seemed like a youth who had been bred with the utmost care; and Oliver so envied the fine person and dignified manners of his untutored brother, that at last he wished to destroy him; and to effect this he set on people to persuade him to wrestle with the famous wrestler, who, as has been before related, had killed so many men. Now, it was this cruel brother's neglect of him which made Orlando say he wished to die, being so friendless.

When, contrary to the wicked hopes he had formed, his brother proved victorious, his envy and malice knew no bounds, and he swore he would burn the chamber where Orlando slept. He was overheard making this vow by one that had been an old and faithful servant to their father, and that loved Orlando because he resembled Sir Rowland. This old man went out to meet him when he returned from the duke's palace, and when he saw Orlando, the peril his dear young master was in made him break out into these passionate exclamations: 'O my gentle master, my sweet master, O you memory of old Sir Rowland! why are you virtuous? why are you gentle, strong, and valiant? and why would you be so fond to overcome the famous wrestler? Your praise is come too swiftly home before you.' Orlando, wondering what all this meant, asked him what was the matter. And then the old man told him how his wicked brother, envying the love all people bore him, and now hearing the fame he had gained by his victory in the duke's palace, intended to destroy him, by setting fire to his chamber that night; and in conclusion, advised him to escape the danger he was in by instant flight; and knowing Orlando had no money, Adam (for that was the good old man's name) had brought out with him his own little hoard, and he said, 'I have five hundred crowns, the thrifty hire I saved under your father, and laid by to be provision for me when my old limbs should become unfit for service; take that, and he that doth the ravens feed be comfort to my age! Here is the gold; all this I give to you: let me be your servant; though I look old I will do the service of a younger man in all your business and necessities.' 'O good old man!' said Orlando, 'how well appears in you the constant service of the old world! You are not for the fashion of these times. We will go along together, and before your youthful wages are spent, I shall light upon means for both our maintenance.'

Together then this faithful servant and his loved master set out; and Orlando and Adam travelled on, uncertain what course to pursue, till they came to the forest of Arden, and there they found themselves in the same distress for want of food that Ganymede and Aliena had been. They wandered on, seeking some human habitation, till they were almost spent with hunger and fatigue. Adam at last said, 'O my dear master, I die for want of food, I can go no farther!' He then laid himself down, thinking to make that place his grave, and bade his dear master farewell. Orlando, seeing him in this weak state, took his old servant up in his arms, and carried him under the shelter of some pleasant trees; and he said to him, 'Cheerly, old Adam, rest your weary limbs here awhile, and do not talk of dying!'

Orlando then searched about to find some food, and he happened to arrive at that part of the forest where the duke was; and he and his friends were just going to eat their dinner, this royal duke being seated on the grass, under no other canopy than the shady covert of some large trees.

Orlando, whom hunger had made desperate, drew his sword, intending to take their meat by force, and said, 'Forbear and eat no more; I must have your food!' The duke asked him, if distress had made him bold, or if he were a rude despiser of good manners? On this Orlando said, he was dying with hunger; and then the duke told him he was welcome to sit down and eat with them. Orlando hearing him speak so gently, put up his sword, and blushed with shame at the rude manner in which he had demanded their food. 'Pardon me, I pray you,' said he: 'I thought that all things had been savage here, and therefore I put on the countenance of stern command; but whatever men you are, that in this desert, under the shade of melancholy boughs, lose and neglect the creeping hours of time; if ever you have looked on better days; if ever you have been where bells have knolled to church; if you have ever sat at any good man's feast; if ever from your eyelids you have wiped a tear, and know what it is to pity or be pitied, may gentle speeches now move you to do me human courtesy!' The duke replied, 'True it is that we are men (as you say) who have seen better days, and though we have now our habitation in this wild forest, we have lived in towns and cities, and have with holy bell been knolled to church, have sat at good men's feasts, and from our eyes have wiped the drops which sacred pity has engendered; therefore sit you down, and take of our refreshment as much as will minister to your wants.' 'There is an old poor man,' answered Orlando, 'who has limped after me many a weary step in pure love, oppressed at once with two sad infirmities, age and hunger; till he be satisfied, I must not touch a bit.' 'Go, find him out, and bring him hither,' said the duke; 'we will forbear to eat till you return.' Then Orlando went like a doe to find its fawn and give it food; and presently returned bringing Adam in his arms; and the duke said, 'Set down your venerable burthen; you are both welcome:' and they fed the old man, and cheered his heart, and he revived, and recovered his health and strength again.

The duke inquired who Orlando was; and when he found that he was the son of his old friend, Sir Rowland de Boys, he took him under his protection, and Orlando and his old servant lived with the duke in the forest.

Orlando arrived in the forest not many days after Ganymede and Aliena came there, and (as has been before related) bought the shepherd's cottage.

Ganymede and Aliena were strangely surprised to find the name of Rosalind carved on the trees, and love-sonnets, fastened to them, all addressed to Rosalind; and while they were wondering how this could be, they met Orlando, and they perceived the chain which Rosalind had given him about his neck.

Orlando little thought that Ganymede was the fair Princess Rosalind, who, by her noble condescension and favour, had so won his heart that he passed his whole time in carving her name upon the trees, and writing sonnets in praise of her beauty: but being much pleased with the graceful air of this pretty shepherd-youth, he entered into conversation with him, and he thought he saw a likeness in Ganymede to his beloved Rosalind, but that he had none of the dignified deportment of that noble lady; for Ganymede assumed the forward manners often seen in youths when they are between boys and men, and with much archness and humour talked to Orlando of a certain lover, 'who,' said he, 'haunts our forest, and spoils our young trees with carving Rosalind upon their barks; and he hangs odes upon hawthorns, and elegies on brambles, all praising this same Rosalind. If I could find this lover, I would give him some good counsel that would soon cure him of his love.'

Orlando confessed that he was the fond lover of whom he spoke, and asked Ganymede to give him the good counsel he talked of. The remedy Ganymede proposed, and the counsel he gave him, was that Orlando should come every day to the cottage where he and his sister Aliena dwelt: 'And then,' said Ganymede, 'I will feign myself to be Rosalind, and you shall feign to court me in the same manner as you would do if I was Rosalind, and then I will imitate the fantastic ways of whimsical ladies to their lovers, till I make you ashamed of your love; and this is the way I propose to cure you.' Orlando had no great faith in the remedy, yet he agreed to come every day to Ganymede's cottage, and feign a playful courtship; and every day Orlando visited Ganymede and Aliena, and Orlando called the shepherd Ganymede his Rosalind, and every day talked over all the fine words and flattering compliments which young men delight to use when they court their mistresses. It does not appear, however, that Ganymede made any progress in curing Orlando of his love for Rosalind.

Though Orlando thought all this was but a sportive play (not dreaming that Ganymede was his very Rosalind), yet the opportunity it gave him of saying all the fond things he had in his heart, pleased his fancy almost as well as it did Ganymede's, who enjoyed the secret jest in knowing these fine love-speeches were all addressed to the right person.

In this manner many days passed pleasantly on with these young people; and the good-natured Aliena, seeing it made Ganymede happy, let him have his own way, and was diverted at the mock-courtship, and did not care to remind Ganymede that the Lady Rosalind had not yet made herself known to the duke her father, whose place of resort in the forest they had learnt from Orlando. Ganymede met the duke one day, and had some talk with him, and the duke asked of what parentage he came. Ganymede answered that he came of as good parentage as he did, which made the duke smile, for he did not suspect the pretty shepherd-boy came of royal lineage. Then seeing the duke look well and happy, Ganymede was content to put off all further explanation for a few days longer.

One morning, as Orlando was going to visit Ganymede, he saw a man lying asleep on the ground, and a large green snake had twisted itself about his neck. The snake, seeing Orlando approach, glided away among the bushes. Orlando went nearer, and then he discovered a lioness lie crouching, with her head on the ground, with a cat-like watch, waiting until the sleeping man awaked (for it is said that lions will prey on nothing that is dead or sleeping). It seemed as if Orlando was sent by Providence to free the man from the danger of the snake and lioness; but when Orlando looked in the man's face, he perceived that the sleeper who was exposed to this double peril, was his own brother Oliver, who had so cruelly used him, and had threatened to destroy him by fire; and he was almost tempted to leave him a prey to the hungry lioness; but brotherly affection and the gentleness of his nature soon overcame his first anger against his brother; and he drew his sword, and attacked the lioness, and slew her, and thus preserved his brother's life both from the venomous snake and from the furious lioness; but before Orlando could conquer the lioness, she had torn one of his arms with her sharp claws.

While Orlando was engaged with the lioness, Oliver awaked, and perceiving that his brother Orlando, whom he had so cruelly treated, was saving him from the fury of a wild beast at the risk of his own life, shame and remorse at once seized him, and he repented of his unworthy conduct, and besought with many tears his brother's pardon for the injuries he had done him. Orlando rejoiced to see him so penitent, and readily forgave him: they embraced each other; and from that hour Oliver loved Orlando with a true brotherly affection, though he had come to the forest bent on his destruction.

The wound in Orlando's arm having bled very much, he found himself too weak to go to visit Ganymede, and therefore he desired his brother to go and tell Ganymede, 'whom,' said Orlando, 'I in sport do call my Rosalind,' the accident which had befallen him.

Thither then Oliver went, and told to Ganymede and Aliena how Orlando had saved his life: and when he had finished the story of Orlando's bravery, and his own providential escape, he owned to them that he was Orlando's brother, who had so cruelly used him; and then he told them of their reconciliation.

The sincere sorrow that Oliver expressed for his offences made such a lively impression on the kind heart of Aliena, that she instantly fell in love with him; and Oliver observing how much she pitied the distress he told her he felt for his fault, he as suddenly fell in love with her. But while love was thus stealing into the hearts of Aliena and Oliver, he was no less busy with Ganymede, who hearing of the danger Orlando had been in, and that he was wounded by the lioness, fainted; and when he recovered, he pretended that he had counterfeited the swoon in the imaginary character of Rosalind, and Ganymede said to Oliver, 'Tell your brother Orlando how well I counterfeited a swoon.' But Oliver saw by the paleness of his complexion that he did really faint, and much wondering at the weakness of the young man, he said, 'Well, if you did counterfeit, take a good heart, and counterfeit to be a man.' 'So I do,' replied Ganymede, truly, 'but I should have been a woman by right.'

Oliver made this visit a very long one, and when at last he returned back to his brother, he had much news to tell him; for besides the account of Ganymede's fainting at the hearing that Orlando was wounded, Oliver told him how he had fallen in love with the fair shepherdess Aliena, and that she had lent a favourable ear to his suit, even in this their first interview; and he talked to his brother, as of a thing almost settled, that he should marry Aliena, saying, that he so well loved her, that he would live here as a shepherd, and settle his estate and house at home upon Orlando.

'You have my consent,' said Orlando. 'Let your wedding be to-morrow, and I will invite the duke and his friends. Go and persuade your shepherdess to agree to this: she is now alone; for look, here comes her brother.' Oliver went to Aliena; and Ganymede, whom Orlando had perceived approaching, came to inquire after the health of his wounded friend.

When Orlando and Ganymede began to talk over the sudden love which had taken place between Oliver and Aliena, Orlando said he had advised his brother to persuade his fair shepherdess to be married on the morrow, and then he added how much he could wish to be married on the same day to his Rosalind.

Ganymede, who well approved of this arrangement, said that if Orlando really loved Rosalind as well as he professed to do, he should have his wish; for on the morrow he would engage to make Rosalind appear in her own person, and also that Rosalind should be willing to marry Orlando.

This seemingly wonderful event, which, as Ganymede was the Lady Rosalind, he could so easily perform, he pretended he would bring to pass by the aid of magic, which he said he had learnt of an uncle who was a famous magician.

The fond lover Orlando, half believing and half doubting what he heard, asked Ganymede if he spoke in sober meaning. 'By my life I do,' said Ganymede; 'therefore put on your best clothes, and bid the duke and your friends to your wedding; for if you desire to be married to-morrow to Rosalind, she shall be here.'

The next morning, Oliver having obtained the consent of Aliena, they came into the presence of the duke, and with them also came Orlando.

They being all assembled to celebrate this double marriage, and as yet only one of the brides appearing, there was much of wondering and conjecture, but they mostly thought that Ganymede was making a jest of Orlando.

The duke, hearing that it was his own daughter that was to be brought in this strange way, asked Orlando if he believed the shepherd-boy could really do what he had promised; and while Orlando was answering that he knew not what to think Ganymede entered, and asked the duke, if he brought his daughter, whether he would consent to her marriage with Orlando. 'That I would,' said the duke, 'if I had kingdoms to give with her.' Ganymede then said to Orlando, 'And you say you will marry her if I bring her here.' 'That I would,' said Orlando, 'if I were king of many kingdoms.'

Ganymede and Aliena then went out together, and Ganymede throwing off his male attire, and being once more dressed in woman's apparel, quickly became Rosalind without the power of magic; and Aliena changing her country garb for her own rich clothes, was with as little trouble transformed into the Lady Celia.

While they were gone, the duke said to Orlando, that he thought the shepherd Ganymede very like his daughter Rosalind; and Orlando said, he also had observed the resemblance.

They had no time to wonder how all this would end, for Rosalind and Celia in their own clothes entered; and no longer pretending that it was by the power of magic that she came there, Rosalind threw herself on her knees before her father, and begged his blessing. It seemed so wonderful to all present that she should so suddenly appear, that it might well have passed for magic; but Rosalind would no longer trifle with her father, and told him the story of her banishment, and of her dwelling in the forest as a shepherd-boy, her cousin Celia passing as her sister.

The duke ratified the consent he had already given to the marriage; and Orlando and Rosalind, Oliver and Celia, were married at the same time. And though their wedding could not be celebrated in this wild forest with any of the parade or splendour usual on such occasions, yet a happier wedding-day was never passed: and while they were eating their venison under the cool shade of the pleasant trees, as if nothing should be wanting to complete the felicity of this good duke and the true lovers, an unexpected messenger arrived to tell the duke the joyful news, that his dukedom was restored to him.

The usurper, enraged at the flight of his daughter Celia, and hearing that every day men of great worth resorted to the forest of Arden to join the lawful duke in his exile, much envying that his brother should be so highly respected in his adversity, put himself at the head of a large force, and advanced towards the forest, intending to seize his brother, and put him with all his faithful followers to the sword; but, by a wonderful interposition of Providence, this bad brother was converted from his evil intention; for just as he entered the skirts of the wild forest, he was met by an old religious man, a hermit, with whom he had much talk, and who in the end completely turned his heart from his wicked design. Thenceforward he became a true penitent, and resolved, relinquishing his unjust dominion, to spend the remainder of his days in a religious house. The first act of his newly-conceived penitence was to send a messenger to his brother (as has been related) to offer to restore to him his dukedom, which he had usurped so long, and with it the lands and revenues of his friends, the faithful followers of his adversity.

This joyful news, as unexpected as it was welcome, came opportunely to heighten the festivity and rejoicings at the wedding of the princesses. Celia complimented her cousin on this good fortune which had happened to the duke, Rosalind's father, and wished her joy very sincerely, though she herself was no longer heir to the dukedom, but by this restoration which her father had made, Rosalind was now the heir: so completely was the love of these two cousins unmixed with anything of jealousy or of envy.

The duke had now an opportunity of rewarding those true friends who had stayed with him in his banishment; and these worthy followers, though they had patiently shared his adverse fortune, were very well pleased to return in peace and prosperity to the palace of their lawful duke.

THE TAMING OF THE SHREW

KATHARINE, the Shrew, was the eldest daughter of Baptista, a rich gentleman of Padua. She was a lady of such an ungovernable spirit and fiery temper, such a loud-tongued scold, that she was known in Padua by no other name than Katharine the Shrew. It seemed very unlikely, indeed impossible, that any gentleman would ever be found who would venture to marry this lady, and therefore Baptista was much blamed for deferring his consent to many excellent offers that were made to her gentle sister Bianca, putting off all Bianca's suitors with this excuse, that when the eldest sister was fairly off his hands, they should have free leave to address young Bianca.

It happened, however, that a gentleman, named Petruchio, came to Padua, purposely to look out for a wife, who, nothing discouraged by these reports of Katharine's temper, and hearing she was rich and handsome, resolved upon marrying this famous termagant, and taming her into a meek and manageable wife. And truly none was so fit to set about this herculean labour as Petruchio, whose spirit was as high as Katharine's, and he was a witty and most happy-tempered humorist, and withal so wise, and of such a true judgment, that he well knew how to feign a passionate and furious deportment, when his spirits were so calm that himself could have laughed merrily at his own angry feigning, for his natural temper was careless and easy; the boisterous airs he assumed when he became the husband of Katharine being but in sport, or more properly speaking, affected by his excellent discernment, as the only means to overcome, in her own way, the passionate ways of the furious Katharine.

A-courting then Petruchio went to Katharine the Shrew; and first of all he applied to Baptista her father, for leave to woo his *gentle daughter*

Katharine, as Petruchio called her, saying archly, that having heard of her bashful modesty and mild behaviour, he had come from Verona to solicit her love. Her father, though he wished her married, was forced to confess Katharine would ill answer this character, it being soon apparent of what manner of gentleness she was composed, for her music-master rushed into the room to complain that the gentle Katharine, his pupil, had broken his head with her lute, for presuming to find fault with her performance; which, when Petruchio heard, he said, 'It is a brave wench; I love her more than ever, and long to have some chat with her;' and hurrying the old gentleman for a positive answer, he said, 'My business is in haste, Signior Baptista, I cannot come every day to woo. You knew my father: he is dead, and has left me heir to all his lands and goods. Then tell me, if I get your daughter's love, what dowry you will give with her.' Baptista thought his manner was somewhat blunt for a lover; but being glad to get Katharine married, he answered that he would give her twenty thousand crowns for her dowry, and half his estate at his death: so this odd match was quickly agreed on, and Baptista went to apprise his shrewish daughter of her lover's addresses, and sent her in to Petruchio to listen to his suit.

In the meantime Petruchio was settling with himself the mode of courtship he should pursue; and he said, 'I will woo her with some spirit when she comes. If she rails at me, why then I will tell her she sings as sweetly as a nightingale; and if she frowns, I will say she looks as clear as roses newly washed with dew. If she will not speak a word, I will praise the eloquence of her language; and if she bids me leave her, I will give her thanks as if she bid me stay with her a week.' Now the stately Katharine entered, and Petruchio first addressed her with 'Good morrow, Kate, for that is your name, I hear.' Katharine, not liking this plain salutation, said disdainfully, 'They call me Katharine who do speak to me.' 'You lie,' replied the lover; 'for you are called plain Kate, and bonny Kate, and sometimes Kate the Shrew: but, Kate, you are the prettiest Kate in Christendom, and therefore, Kate, hearing your mildness praised in every town, I am come to woo you for my wife.'

A strange courtship they made of it. She in loud and angry terms showing him how justly she had gained the name of Shrew, while he still praised her sweet and courteous words, till at length, hearing her father coming, he said (intending to make as quick a wooing as possible), 'Sweet Katharine, let us set this idle chat aside, for your father has consented that you shall be my wife, your dowry is agreed on, and whether you will or no, I will marry you.'

And now Baptista entering, Petruchio told him his daughter had received him kindly, and that she had promised to be married the next Sunday. This Katharine denied, saying she would rather see him hanged on Sunday, and reproached her father for wishing to wed her to such a mad-cap ruffian as Petruchio. Petruchio desired her father not to regard her angry words, for they had agreed she should seem reluctant before him, but that when they were alone he had found her very fond and loving; and he said to her, 'Give me your hand, Kate; I will go to Venice to buy you fine apparel against our wedding day. Provide the feast, father, and bid the wedding guests. I will be sure to bring rings, fine array, and rich clothes, that my Katharine may be fine; and kiss me, Kate, for we will be married on Sunday.'

On the Sunday all the wedding guests were assembled, but they waited long before Petruchio came, and Katharine wept for vexation to think that Petruchio had only been making a jest of her. At last, however, he appeared; but he brought none of the bridal finery he had promised Katharine, nor was he dressed himself like a bridegroom, but in strange disordered attire, as if he meant to make a sport of the serious business he came about; and his servant and the very horses on which they rode were in like manner in mean and fantastic fashion habited.

Petruchio could not be persuaded to change his dress; he said Katharine was to be married to him, and not to his clothes; and finding it was in vain to argue with him, to the church they went, he still behaving in the same mad way, for when the priest asked Petruchio if Katharine should be his wife, he swore so loud that she should, that, all amazed, the priest let fall his book, and as he stooped to take it up, this mad-brained bridegroom gave him such a cuff, that down fell the priest and his book again. And all the while they were being married he stamped and swore so, that the high-spirited Katharine trembled and shook with fear. After the ceremony was over, while they were yet in the church, he called for wine, and drank a loud health to the company, threw a sop which was at the bottom of the glass full in the sexton's face, giving no other reason for this strange act, than that the sexton's beard grew thin and hungerly, and seemed to ask the sop as he was drinking. Never sure was there such a mad marriage; but Petruchio did but put this wildness on, the better to succeed in the plot he had formed to tame his shrewish wife.

Baptista had provided a sumptuous marriage feast, but when they returned from church, Petruchio, taking hold of Katharine, declared his intention of carrying his wife home instantly: and no remonstrance of his father-in-law, or angry words of the enraged Katharine, could make him change his purpose. He claimed a husband's right to dispose of his wife as he pleased, and away he hurried Katharine off: he seeming so daring and resolute that no one dared attempt to stop him.

Petruchio mounted his wife upon a miserable horse, lean and lank, which he had picked out for the purpose, and himself and his servant no better mounted; they journeyed on through rough and miry ways, and ever when this horse of Katharine's stumbled, he would storm and swear at the poor jaded beast, who could scarce crawl under his burthen, as if he had been the most passionate man alive.

At length, after a weary journey, during which Katharine had heard nothing but the wild ravings of Petruchio at the servant and the horses, they arrived at his house. Petruchio welcomed her kindly to her home, but he resolved she should have neither rest nor food that night. The tables were spread, and supper soon served; but Petruchio, pretending to find fault with every dish, threw the meat about the floor, and ordered the servants to remove it away; and all this he did, as he said, in love for his Katharine, that she might not eat meat that was not well dressed. And when Katharine, weary and supperless, retired to rest, he found the same fault with the bed, throwing the pillows and bed-clothes about the room, that she was forced to sit down in a chair, where if she chanced to drop asleep, she was presently awakened by the loud voice of her husband, storming at the servants for the ill-making of his wife's bridal-bed.

The next day Petruchio pursued the same course, still speaking kind words to Katharine, but when she attempted to eat, finding fault with everything that was set before her, throwing the breakfast on the floor as he had done the supper; and Katharine, the haughty Katharine, was fain to beg the servants would bring her secretly a morsel of food; but they being instructed by Petruchio, replied, they dared not give her anything unknown to their master. 'Ah,' said she, 'did he marry me to famish me? Beggars that come to my father's door have food given them. But I, who never knew what it was to entreat for anything, am starved for want of food, giddy for want of sleep, with oaths kept waking, and with brawling fed; and that which vexes me more than all, does it under the name of perfect love, pretending that if I sleep or eat, it were present death to me.' Here the soliloquy was interrupted by the entrance of Petruchio: he, not meaning she should be quite starved, had brought her a small portion of meat, and he said to her, 'How fares my sweet Kate? Here, love, you see how diligent I am, I have dressed your meat myself. I am sure this kindness merits thanks. What, not a word? Nay, then you love not the meat, and all the pains I have taken is to no purpose.' He then ordered the servant to take the dish away. Extreme hunger, which had abated the pride of Katharine, made her say, though angered to the heart, 'I pray you let it stand.' But this was not all Petruchio intended to bring her to, and he replied, 'The poorest service is repaid with thanks, and so shall mine before you touch the meat.' On this Katharine brought out a reluctant 'I thank you, sir.' And now he suffered her to make a slender meal, saying, 'Much good may it do your gentle heart, Kate; eat apace! And now, my honey love, we will return to your father's house, and revel it as bravely as the best, with silken coats and caps and golden rings, with ruffs and scarfs and fans and double change of finery;' and to make her believe he really intended to give her these gay things, he called in a tailor and a haberdasher, who brought some new clothes he had ordered for her, and then giving her plate to the servant to take away, before she had half satisfied her hunger, he said, 'What, have you dined?' The haberdasher presented a cap saying, 'Here is the cap your worship bespoke;' on which Petruchio began to storm afresh, saying the cap was moulded in a porringer, and that it was no bigger than a cockle or walnut shell, desiring the haberdasher to take it away and make it bigger. Katharine said, 'I will have this; all gentlewomen wear such caps as these.' – 'When you are gentle,' replied Petruchio, 'you shall have one too, and not till then.' The meat Katharine had eaten had a little revived her fallen spirits, and she said, 'Why, sir, I trust I may have leave to speak, and speak I will: I am no child, no babe; your betters have endured to hear me say my mind; and if you cannot, you had better stop your ears.' Petruchio would not hear these angry words, for he had happily discovered a better way of managing his wife than keeping up a jangling argument with her; therefore his answer was, 'Why, you say true; it is a paltry cap, and I love you for not liking it.' – 'Love me, or love me not,' said Katharine, 'I like the cap, and I will have this cap or none.' – 'You say you wish to see the gown,' said Petruchio, still affecting to misunderstand her. The tailor then came forward and showed her a fine gown he had made for her. Petruchio, whose intent was that she should have neither cap nor gown, found as much fault with that. 'O mercy, Heaven!' said he, 'what stuff is here! What, do you call this a sleeve? it is like a demi-cannon, carved up and down like an apple tart.' The tailor said, 'You bid me make it according to the fashion of the times;' and Katharine said, she never saw a better fashioned gown. This was enough for Petruchio, and privately desiring these people might be paid for their goods, and excuses made to them for the seemingly strange treatment he bestowed upon them, he with fierce words and furious gestures drove the tailor and the haberdasher out of the room; and then turning to Katharine, he said, 'Well, come, my Kate, we will go to your father's even in these mean garments we now wear.' And then he ordered his horses, affirming they should reach Baptista's house by dinner-time, for that it was but seven o'clock. Now it was not early morning, but the very middle of the day, when he spoke this; therefore Katharine ventured to say, though modestly, being almost overcome by the vehemence of his manner, 'I dare assure you, sir, it is two o'clock, and will be supper-time before we get there.' But Petruchio meant that she should be so completely subdued, that she should assent to everything he said, before he carried her to her father; and therefore, as if he were lord even of the sun, and could command the hours, he said it should be what time he pleased to have it, before he set forward; 'For,' he said, 'whatever I say or do, you still are crossing it. I will not go to-day, and when I go, it shall be what o'clock I say it is.' Another day Katharine was forced to practise her newly-found obedience, and not till he had brought her proud spirit to such a perfect subjection, that she dared not remember there was such a word as contradiction, would Petruchio allow her to go to her father's house; and even while they were upon their journey thither, she was in danger of being turned back again, only because she happened to hint it was the sun, when he affirmed the moon shone brightly at noonday. 'Now, by my mother's son,' said he, 'and that is myself, it shall be the moon, or stars, or what I list, before I journey to your father's house.' He then made as if he were going back again; but Katharine, no longer Katharine the Shrew, but the obedient wife, said, 'Let us go forward, I pray, now we have come so far, and it shall be the sun, or moon, or what you please, and if you please to call it a rush candle henceforth, I vow it shall be so for me.' This he resolved to prove, therefore he said again, 'I say, it is the moon.' – 'I know it is the moon,' replied Katharine. 'You lie, it is the blessed sun,' said Petruchio. 'Then it is the blessed sun,' replied Katharine; 'but sun it is not, when you say it is not. What you will have it named, even so it is, and so it ever shall be for Katharine.' Now then he suffered her to proceed on her journey; but further to try if this yielding humour would last, he addressed an old gentleman they met on the road as if he had been a young woman, saying to him, 'Good morrow, gentle mistress;' and asked Katharine if she had ever beheld a fairer gentlewoman, praising the red and white of the old man's cheeks, and comparing his eyes to two bright stars; and again he addressed him, saying, 'Fair lovely maid, once more good day to you!' and said to his wife, 'Sweet Kate, embrace her for her beauty's sake.' The now completely vanquished Katharine quickly adopted her husband's opinion, and made her speech in like sort to the old gentleman, saying to him, 'Young budding virgin, you are fair, and fresh, and sweet: whither are you going, and where is your dwelling? Happy are the parents of so fair a child.' – 'Why, how now, Kate,' said Petruchio; 'I hope you are not mad. This is a man, old and wrinkled, faded and withered, and not a maiden, as you say he is.' On this Katharine said, 'Pardon me, old gentleman; the sun has so dazzled my eyes, that everything I look on seemeth green. Now I perceive you are a reverend father: I hope you will pardon me for my sad mistake.' – 'Do, good old grandsire,' said Petruchio, 'and tell us which way you are travelling. We shall be glad of your good company, if you are going our way.' The old gentleman replied, 'Fair sir, and you, my merry mistress, your strange encounter has much amazed me. My name is Vincentio, and I am going to visit a son of mine who lives at Padua.' Then Petruchio knew the old gentleman to be father of Lucentio, a young gentleman who was to be married to Baptista's younger daughter, Bianca, and he made Vincentio very happy, by telling him the rich marriage his son was about to make: and they all journeyed on pleasantly together till they came to Baptista's house, where there was a large company assembled to celebrate the wedding of Bianca and Lucentio, Baptista having willingly consented to the marriage of Bianca when he had got Katharine off his hands.

When they entered, Baptista welcomed them to the wedding feast, and there was present also another newly married pair.

Lucentio, Bianca's husband, and Hortensio, the other new married man, could not forbear sly jests, which seemed to hint at the shrewish disposition of Petruchio's wife, and these fond bridegrooms seemed highly pleased with the mild tempers of the ladies they had chosen, laughing at Petruchio for his less fortunate choice. Petruchio took little notice of their jokes till the ladies were retired after dinner, and then he perceived Baptista himself joined in the laugh against him: for when Petruchio affirmed that his wife would prove more obedient than theirs, the father of Katharine said, 'Now, in good sadness, son Petruchio, I fear you have got the veriest shrew of all.' 'Well,' said Petruchio, 'I say no, and therefore for assurance that I speak the truth, let us each one send for his wife, and he whose wife is most obedient to come at first when she is sent for, shall win a wager which we will propose.' To this the other two husbands willingly consented, for they were quite confident that their gentle wives would prove more obedient than the headstrong Katharine; and they proposed a wager of twenty crowns, but Petruchio merrily said, he would lay as much as that upon his hawk or hound, but twenty times as much upon his wife. Lucentio and Hortensio raised the wager to a hundred crowns, and Lucentio first sent his servant to desire Bianca would come to him. But the servant returned, and said, 'Sir, my mistress sends you word she is busy and cannot come.' – 'How,' said Petruchio, 'does she say she is busy and cannot come? Is that an answer for a wife?' Then they laughed at him, and said, it would be well if Katharine did not send him a worse answer. And now it was Hortensio's turn to send for his wife; and he said to his servant, 'Go, and entreat my wife to come to me.' 'Oh ho! entreat her!' said Petruchio. 'Nay, then, she needs must come.' – 'I am afraid, sir,' said Hortensio, 'your wife will not be entreated.' But presently this civil husband looked a little blank, when the servant returned without his mistress; and he said to him, 'How now! Where is my wife?' – 'Sir,' said the servant, 'my mistress says, you have some goodly jest in hand, and therefore she will not come. She bids you come to her.' – 'Worse and worse!' said Petruchio; and then he sent his servant, saying, 'Sirrah, go to your mistress, and tell her I command her to come to me.' The company had scarcely time to think she would not obey this summons, when Baptista, all in amaze, exclaimed, 'Now, by my *holidame*, here comes Katharine!' and she entered, saying meekly to Petruchio, 'What is your will, sir, that you send for me?' – 'Where is your sister and Hortensio's wife?' said he. Katharine replied, 'They sit conferring by the parlour fire.' – 'Go, fetch them hither!' said Petruchio. Away went Katharine without reply to perform her husband's command. 'Here is a wonder,' said Lucentio, 'if you talk of a wonder.' – 'And so it is,' said Hortensio; 'I marvel what it bodes.' – 'Marry, peace it bodes,' said Petruchio, 'and love, and quiet life, and right supremacy; and, to be short, everything that is sweet and happy.' Katharine's father, overjoyed to see this reformation in his daughter, said, 'Now, fair befall thee, son Petruchio! you have won the wager, and I will add another twenty thousand crowns to her dowry, as if she were another daughter, for she is changed as if she had never been.' – 'Nay,' said Petruchio, 'I will win the wager better yet, and show more signs of her new-built virtue and obedience.' Katharine now entering with the two ladies, he continued, 'See where she comes, and brings your froward wives as prisoners to her womanly persuasion. Katharine, that cap of yours does not become you; off with that bauble, and throw it under foot.' Katharine instantly took off her cap, and threw it down. 'Lord!' said Hortensio's wife, 'may I never have a cause to sigh till I am brought to such a silly pass!' And Bianca, she too said, 'Fie, what foolish duty call you this?' On this Bianca's husband said to her, 'I wish your duty were as foolish too! The wisdom of your duty, fair

Bianca, has cost me a hundred crowns since dinner-time.' – 'The more fool you,' said Bianca, 'for laying on my duty.' – 'Katharine,' said Petruchio, 'I charge you tell these headstrong women what duty they owe their lords and husbands.' And to the wonder of all present, the reformed shrewish lady spoke as eloquently in praise of the wifelike duty of obedience, as she had practised it implicitly in a ready submission to Petruchio's will. And Katharine once more became famous in Padua, not as heretofore, as Katharine the shrew, but as Katharine the most obedient and duteous wife in Padua.

ALL'S WELL THAT ENDS WELL

BERTRAM, Count of Rousillon, had newly come to his title and estate, by the death of his father. The King of France loved the father of Bertram, and when he heard of his death, he sent for his son to come immediately to his royal court in Paris, intending, for the friendship he bore the late count, to grace young Bertram with his especial favour and protection.

Bertram was living with his mother, the widowed countess, when Lafeu, an old lord of the French court, came to conduct him to the king. The King of France was an absolute monarch, and the invitation to court was in the form of a royal mandate, or positive command, which no subject, of what high dignity soever, might disobey; therefore though the countess, in parting with this dear son, seemed a second time to bury her husband, whose loss she had so lately mourned, yet she dared not to keep him a single day, but gave instant orders for his departure. Lafeu, who came to fetch him, tried to comfort the countess for the loss of her late lord, and her son's sudden absence; and he said, in a courtier's flattering manner, that the king was so kind a prince, she would find in his majesty a husband, and he would be a father to her son; meaning only, that the good king would befriend the fortunes of Bertram. Lafeu told the countess that the king had fallen into a sad malady, which was pronounced by his physicians to be incurable. The lady expressed great sorrow on hearing this account of the king's ill health, and said, she wished the father of Helena (a young gentlewoman who was present in attendance upon her) were living, for that she doubted not he could have cured his majesty of his disease. And she told Lafeu something of the history of Helena, saying she was the only daughter of the famous physician Gerard de Narbon, and that he had recommended his daughter to her care when he was dying, so that since his death she had taken Helena under her protection; then the countess praised the virtuous disposition and excellent qualities of Helena, saying she inherited these virtues from her worthy father. While she was speaking, Helena wept in sad and mournful silence, which made the countess gently reprove her for too much grieving for her father's death.

Bertram now bade his mother farewell. The countess parted with this dear son with tears and many blessings, and commended him to the care of Lafeu, saying, 'Good my lord, advise him, for he is an unseasoned courtier.'

Bertram's last words were spoken to Helena, but they were words of mere civility, wishing her happiness; and he concluded his short farewell to her with saying, 'Be comfortable to my mother, your mistress, and make much of her.'

Helena had long loved Bertram, and when she wept in sad and mournful silence, the tears she shed were not for Gerard de Narbon. Helena loved her father, but in the present feeling of a deeper love, the object of which she was about to lose, she had forgotten the very form and features of her dead father, her imagination presenting no image to her mind but Bertram's.

Helena had long loved Bertram, yet she always remembered that he was the Count of Rousillon, descended from the most ancient family in France. She of humble birth. Her parents of no note at all. His ancestors all noble. And therefore she looked up to the high-born Bertram as to her master and to her dear lord, and dared not form any wish but to live his servant, and so living to die his vassal. So great the distance seemed to her between his height of dignity and her lowly fortunes, that she would say, 'It were all one that I should love a bright particular star, and think to wed it, Bertram is so far above me.'

Bertram's absence filled her eyes with tears and her heart with sorrow; for though she loved without hope, yet it was a pretty comfort to her to see him every hour, and Helena would sit and look upon his dark eye, his arched brow, and the curls of his fine hair, till she seemed to draw his portrait on the tablet of her heart, that heart too capable of retaining the memory of every line in the features of that loved face.

Gerard de Narbon, when he died, left her no other portion than some prescriptions of rare and well-proved virtue, which by deep study and long experience in medicine he had collected as sovereign and almost infallible remedies. Among the rest, there was one set down as an approved medicine for the disease under which Lafeu said the king at that time languished: and when Helena heard of the king's complaint, she, who till now had been so humble and so hopeless, formed an ambitious project in her mind to go herself to Paris, and undertake the cure of the king. But though Helena was the possessor of this choice prescription, it was unlikely, as the king as well as his physicians was of opinion that his disease was incurable, that they would give credit to a poor unlearned virgin, if she should offer to perform a cure. The firm hopes that Helena had of succeeding, if she might be permitted to make the trial, seemed more than ever her father's skill warranted, though he was the most famous physician of his time; for she felt a strong faith that this good medicine was sanctified by all the luckiest stars in heaven to be the legacy that should advance her fortune, even to the high dignity of being Count Rousillon's wife.

Bertram had not been long gone, when the countess was informed by her steward, that he had overheard Helena talking to herself, and that he understood from some words she uttered, she was in love with Bertram, and thought of following him to Paris. The countess dismissed the steward with thanks, and desired him to tell Helena she wished to speak with her. What she had just heard of Helena brought the remembrance of days long past into the mind of the countess; those days probably when her love for Bertram's father first began; and she said to herself, 'Even so it was with me when I was young. Love is a thorn that belongs to the rose of youth; for in the season of youth, if ever we are nature's children, these faults are ours, though then we think not they are faults.'

While the countess was thus meditating on the loving errors of her own youth, Helena entered, and she said to her, 'Helena, you know I am a mother to you.' Helena replied, 'You are my honourable mistress.'

'You are my daughter,' said the countess again: 'I say I am your mother. Why do you start and look pale at my words?' With looks of alarm and confused thoughts, fearing the countess suspected her love, Helena still replied, 'Pardon me, madam, you are not my mother; the Count Rousillon cannot be my brother, nor I your daughter.' 'Yet, Helena,' said the countess, 'you might be my daughter-in-law; and I am afraid that is what you mean to be, the words *mother* and *daughter* so disturb you. Helena, do you love my son?' 'Good madam, pardon me,' said the affrighted Helena. Again the countess repeated her question, 'Do you love my son?' 'Do not you love him, madam?' said Helena. The countess replied, 'Give me not this evasive answer, Helena. Come, come, disclose the state of your affections, for your love has to the full appeared.' Helena on her knees now owned her love, and with shame and terror implored the pardon of her noble mistress; and with words expressive of the sense she had of the inequality between their fortunes, she protested Bertram did not know she loved him, comparing her humble unaspiring love to a poor Indian, who adores the sun that looks upon his worshipper, but knows of him no more. The countess asked Helena if she had not lately an intent to go to Paris? Helena owned the design she had formed in her mind, when she heard Lafeu speak of the king's illness. 'This was your motive for wishing to go to Paris,' said the countess, 'was it? Speak truly.' Helena honestly answered, 'My lord your son made me to think of this; else Paris, and the medicine, and the king, had from the conversation of my thoughts been absent then.' The countess heard the whole of this confession without saying a word either of approval or of blame, but she strictly questioned Helena as to the probability of the medicine being useful to the king. She found that it was the most prized by Gerard de Narbon of all he possessed, and that he had given it to his daughter on his death-bed; and remembering the solemn promise she had made at that awful hour in regard to this young maid, whose destiny, and the life of the king himself, seemed to depend on the execution of a project (which though conceived by the fond suggestions of a loving maiden's thoughts, the countess knew not but it might be the unseen workings of Providence to bring to pass the recovery of the king, and to lay the foundation of the future fortunes of Gerard de Narbon's daughter), free leave she gave to Helena to pursue her own way, and generously furnished her with ample means and suitable attendants; and Helena set out for Paris with the blessings of the countess, and her kindest wishes for her success.

Helena arrived at Paris, and by the assistance of her friend the old Lord Lafeu, she obtained an audience of the king. She had still many difficulties to encounter, for the king was not easily prevailed on to try the medicine offered him by this fair young doctor. But she told him she was Gerard de Narbon's daughter (with whose fame the king was well acquainted), and she offered the precious medicine as the darling treasure which contained the essence of all her father's long experience and skill, and she boldly engaged to forfeit her life, if it failed to restore his majesty to perfect health in the space of two days. The king at length consented to try it, and in two days' time Helena was to lose her life if the king did not recover; but if she succeeded, he promised to give her the choice of any man throughout all France (the princes only excepted) whom she could like for a husband; the choice of a husband being the fee Helena demanded if she cured the king of his disease.

Helena did not deceive herself in the hope she conceived of the efficacy of her father's medicine. Before two days were at an end, the king was restored to perfect health, and he assembled all the young noblemen of his court together, in order to confer the promised reward of a husband upon his fair physician; and he desired Helena to look round on this youthful parcel of noble bachelors, and choose her husband. Helena was not slow to make her choice, for among these young lords she saw the Count Rousillon, and turning to Bertram, she said, 'This is the man. I dare not say, my lord, I take you, but I give me and my service ever whilst I live into your guiding power.' 'Why, then,' said the king, 'young Bertram, take her; she is your wife.' Bertram did not hesitate to declare his dislike to this present of the king's of the self-offered Helena, who, he said, was a poor physician's daughter, bred at his father's charge, and now living a dependent on his mother's bounty. Helena heard him speak these words of rejection and of scorn, and she said to the king, 'That you are well, my lord, I am glad. Let the rest go.' But the king would not suffer his royal command to be so slighted; for the power of bestowing their nobles in marriage was one of the many privileges of the kings of France; and that same day Bertram was married to Helena, a forced and uneasy marriage to Bertram, and of no promising hope to the poor lady, who, though she gained the noble husband she had hazarded her life to obtain, seemed to have won but a splendid blank, her husband's love not being a gift in the power of the King of France to bestow.

Helena was no sooner married, than she was desired by Bertram to apply to the king for him for leave of absence from court; and when she brought him the king's permission for his departure, Bertram told her that he was not prepared for this sudden marriage, it had much unsettled him, and therefore she must not wonder at the course he should pursue. If Helena wondered not, she grieved when she found it was his intention to leave her. He ordered her to go home to his mother. When Helena heard this unkind command, she replied, 'Sir, I can nothing say to this, but that I am your most obedient servant, and shall ever with true observance seek to eke out that desert, wherein my homely stars have failed to equal my great fortunes.' But this humble speech of Helena's did not at all move the haughty Bertram to pity his gentle wife, and he parted from her without even the common civility of a kind farewell.

Back to the countess then Helena returned. She had accomplished the purport of her journey, she had preserved the life of the king, and she had wedded her heart's dear lord, the Count Rousillon; but she returned back a dejected lady to her noble mother-in-law, and as soon as she entered the house she received a letter from Bertram which almost broke her heart.

The good countess received her with a cordial welcome, as if she had been her son's own choice, and a lady of a high degree, and she spoke kind words to comfort her for the unkind neglect of Bertram in sending his wife home on her bridal day alone. But this gracious reception failed to cheer the sad mind of Helena, and she said, 'Madam, my lord is gone, for ever gone.' She then read these words out of Bertram's letter: *When you can get the ring from my finger, which never shall come off, then call me husband, but in such a Then I write a Never.* 'This is a dreadful sentence!' said Helena. The countess begged her to have patience, and said, now Bertram was gone, she should be her child, and that she deserved a lord that twenty such rude boys as Bertram might tend upon, and hourly call her mistress. But in vain by respectful condescension and kind flattery his matchless mother tried to soothe the sorrows of her daughter-in-law.

Helena still kept her eyes fixed upon the letter, and cried out in an agony of grief, *Till I have no wife, I have nothing in France.* The countess asked her if she found those words in the letter? 'Yes, madam,' was all poor Helena could answer.

The next morning Helena was missing. She left a letter to be delivered to the countess after she was gone, to acquaint her with the reason of her sudden absence: in this letter she informed her that she was so much grieved at having driven Bertram from his native country and his home, that to atone for her offence, she had undertaken a pilgrimage to the shrine of St Jaques le Grand, and concluded with requesting the countess to inform her son that the wife he so hated had left his house for ever.

Bertram, when he left Paris, went to Florence, and there became an officer in the Duke of Florence's army, and after a successful war, in which he distinguished himself by many brave actions, Bertram received letters from his mother, containing the acceptable tidings that Helena would no more disturb him; and he was preparing to return home, when Helena herself, clad in her pilgrim's weeds, arrived at the city of Florence.

Florence was a city through which the pilgrims used to pass on their way to St Jaques le Grand; and when Helena arrived at this city, she heard that a hospitable widow dwelt there, who used to receive into her house the female pilgrims that were going to visit the shrine of that saint, giving them lodging and kind entertainment. To this good lady, therefore, Helena went, and the widow gave her a courteous welcome, and invited her to see whatever was curious in that famous city, and told her that if she would like to see the duke's army, she would take her where she might have a full view of it. 'And you will see a countryman of yours,' said the widow; 'his name is Count Rousillon, who has done worthy service in the duke's wars.' Helena wanted no second invitation, when she found Bertram was to make part of the show. She accompanied her hostess; and a sad and mournful pleasure it was to her to look once more upon her dear husband's face. 'Is he not a handsome man?' said the widow. 'I like him well,' replied Helena, with great truth. All the way they walked, the talkative widow's discourse was all of Bertram: she told Helena the story of Bertram's marriage, and how he had deserted the poor lady his wife, and entered into the duke's army to avoid living with her. To this account of her own misfortunes Helena patiently listened, and when it was ended, the history of Bertram was not yet done, for then the widow began another tale, every word of which sank deep into the mind of Helena; for the story she now told was of Bertram's love for her daughter.

Though Bertram did not like the marriage forced on him by the king, it seems he was not insensible to love, for since he had been stationed with the army at Florence, he had fallen in love with Diana, a fair young gentlewoman, the daughter of this widow who was Helena's hostess; and every night, with music of all sorts, and songs composed in praise of Diana's beauty, he would come under her window, and solicit her love; and all his suit to her was, that she would permit him to visit her by stealth after the family were retired to rest; but Diana would by no means be persuaded to grant this improper request, nor give any encouragement to his suit, knowing him to be a married man; for Diana had been brought up under the counsels of a prudent mother, who, though she was now in reduced circumstances, was well born, and descended from the noble family of the Capulets.

All this the good lady related to Helena, highly praising the virtuous principles of her discreet daughter, which she said were entirely owing to the excellent education and good advice she had given her; and she further said, that Bertram had been particularly importunate with Diana to admit him to the visit he so much desired that night, because he was going to leave Florence early the next morning.

Though it grieved Helena to hear of Bertram's love for the widow's daughter, yet from this story the ardent mind of Helena conceived a project (nothing discouraged at the ill success of her former one) to recover her truant lord. She disclosed to the widow that she was Helena, the deserted wife of Bertram, and requested that her kind hostess and her daughter would suffer this visit from Bertram to take place, and allow her to pass herself upon Bertram for Diana; telling them, her chief motive for desiring to have this secret meeting with her husband, was to get a ring from him, which he had said, if ever she was in possession of he would acknowledge her as his wife.

The widow and her daughter promised to assist her in this affair, partly moved by pity for this unhappy forsaken wife, and partly won over to her interest by the promises of reward which Helena made them, giving them a purse of money in earnest of her future favour. In the course of that day Helena caused information to be sent to Bertram that she was dead; hoping that when he thought himself free to make a second choice by the news of her death, he would offer marriage to her in the feigned character of Diana. And if she could obtain the ring and this promise too, she doubted not she should make some future good come of it.

In the evening, after it was dark, Bertram was admitted into Diana's chamber, and Helena was there ready to receive him. The flattering compliments and love discourse he addressed to Helena were precious sounds to her, though she knew they were meant for Diana; and Bertram was so well pleased with her, that he made her a solemn promise to be her husband, and to love her for ever; which she hoped would be prophetic of a real affection, when he should know it was his own wife, the despised Helena, whose conversation had so delighted him.

Bertram never knew how sensible a lady Helena was, else perhaps he would not have been so regardless of her; and seeing her every day, he had entirely overlooked her beauty; a face we are accustomed to see constantly, losing the effect which is caused by the first sight either of beauty or of plainness; and of her understanding it was impossible he should judge, because she felt such reverence, mixed with her love for him, that she was always silent in his presence: but now that her future fate, and the happy ending of all her love-projects, seemed to depend on her leaving a favourable impression on the mind of Bertram from this night's interview, she exerted all her wit to please him; and the simple graces of her lively conversation and the endearing sweetness of her manners so charmed Bertram, that he vowed she should be his wife. Helena begged the ring from his finger as a token of his regard, and he gave it to her; and in return for this ring, which it was of such importance to her to possess, she gave him another ring, which was one the king had made her a present of. Before it was light in the morning, she sent Bertram away; and he immediately set out on his journey towards his mother's house.

Helena prevailed on the widow and Diana to accompany her to Paris, their further assistance being necessary to the full accomplishment of the plan she had formed. When they arrived there, they found the king was gone upon a visit to the Countess of Rousillon, and Helena followed the king with all the speed she could make.

The king was still in perfect health, and his gratitude to her who had been the means of his recovery was so lively in his mind, that the moment he saw the Countess of Rousillon, he began to talk of Helena, calling her a precious jewel that was lost by the folly of her son; but seeing the subject distressed the countess, who sincerely lamented the death of Helena, he said, 'My good lady, I have forgiven and forgotten all.' But the good-natured old Lafeu, who was present, and could not bear that the memory of his favourite Helena should be so lightly passed over, said, 'This I must say, the young lord did great offence to his majesty, his mother, and his lady; but to himself he did the greatest wrong of all, for he has lost a wife whose beauty astonished all eyes, whose words took all ears captive, whose deep perfection made all hearts wish to serve her.' The king said, 'Praising what is lost makes the remembrance dear. Well – call him hither;' meaning Bertram, who now presented himself before the king: and, on his expressing deep sorrow for the injuries he had done to Helena, the king, for his dead father's and his admirable mother's sake, pardoned him and restored him once more to his favour. But the gracious countenance of the king was soon changed towards him, for he perceived that Bertram wore the very ring upon his finger which he had given to Helena: and he well remembered that Helena had called all the saints in heaven to witness she would never part with that ring, unless she sent it to the king himself upon some great disaster befalling her; and Bertram, on the king's questioning him how he came by the ring, told an improbable story of a lady throwing it to him out of a window, and denied ever having seen Helena since the day of their marriage. The king, knowing Bertram's dislike to his wife, feared he had destroyed her: and he ordered his guards to seize Bertram, saying, 'I am wrapt in dismal thinking, for I fear the life of Helena was foully snatched.' At this moment Diana and her mother entered, and presented a petition to the king, wherein they begged his majesty to exert his royal power to compel Bertram to marry Diana, he having made a solemn promise of marriage. Bertram, fearing the king's anger, denied he had made any such promise; and then Diana produced the ring (which Helena had put into her hands) to confirm the truth of her words; and she said that she had given Bertram the ring he then wore, in exchange for that, at the time he vowed to marry her. On hearing this, the king ordered the guards to seize her also; and her account of the ring differing from Bertram's, the king's suspicions were confirmed: and he said, if they did not confess how they came by this ring of Helena's, they should be both put to death. Diana requested her mother might be permitted to fetch the jeweller of whom she bought the ring, which being granted, the widow went out, and presently returned leading in Helena herself.

The good countess, who in silent grief had beheld her son's danger, and had even dreaded that the suspicion of having destroyed his wife might possibly be true, finding her dear Helena, whom she loved with even a maternal affection, was still living, felt a delight she was hardly able to support; and the king, scarce believing for joy that it was Helena, said, 'Is this indeed the wife of Bertram that I see?' Helena, feeling herself yet an unacknowledged wife, replied, 'No, my good lord, it is but the shadow of a wife you see, the name and not the thing.' Bertram cried out, 'Both, both! O pardon!' – 'O my lord,' said Helena, 'when I personated this fair maid, I found you wondrous kind; and look, here is your letter!' reading to him in a joyful tone those words which she had once repeated so sorrowfully, *When from my finger you can get this ring*, – 'This is done; it was to me you gave the ring. Will you be mine, now you are doubly won?' Bertram replied, 'If you can make it plain that you were the lady I talked with that night, I will love you dearly ever, ever dearly.' This was no difficult task, for the widow and Diana came with Helena to prove this fact; and the king was so well pleased with Diana, for the friendly assistance she had rendered the dear lady he so truly valued for the service she had done him, that he promised her also a noble husband: Helena's history giving him a hint, that it was a suitable reward for kings to bestow upon fair ladies when they perform notable services.

Thus Helena at last found that her father's legacy was indeed sanctified by the luckiest stars in heaven; for she was now the beloved wife of her dear Bertram, the daughter-in-law of her noble mistress, and herself the Countess of Rousillon.

TWELFTH NIGHT

OR WHAT YOU WILL

SEBASTIAN and his sister Viola, a young gentleman and lady of Messaline, were twins, and (which was accounted a great wonder) from their birth they so much resembled each other, that, but for the difference in their dress, they could not be known apart. They were both born in one hour, and in one hour they were both in danger of perishing, for they were shipwrecked on the coast of Illyria, as they were making a sea-voyage together. The ship, on board of which they were, split on a rock in a violent storm, and a very small number of the ship's company escaped with their lives. The captain of the vessel, with a few of the sailors that were saved, got to land in a small boat, and with them they brought Viola safe on shore, where she, poor lady, instead of rejoicing at her own deliverance, began to lament her brother's loss; but the captain comforted her with the assurance that he had seen her brother, when the ship split, fasten himself to a strong mast, on which, as long as he could see anything of him for the distance, he perceived him borne up above the waves. Viola was much consoled by the hope this account gave her, and now considered how she was to dispose of herself in a strange country, so far from home; and she asked the captain if he knew anything of Illyria. 'Ay, very well, madam,' replied the captain, 'for I was born not three hours' travel from this place.' – 'Who governs here?' said Viola. The captain told her, Illyria was governed by Orsino, a duke noble in nature as well as dignity. Viola said, she had heard her father speak of Orsino, and that he was unmarried then. 'And he is so now,' said the captain; 'or was so very lately, for, but a month ago, I went from here, and then it was the general talk (as you know what great ones do, the people will prattle of) that Orsino sought the love of fair Olivia, a virtuous maid, the daughter of a count who died twelve months ago, leaving Olivia to the protection of her brother, who shortly after died also; and for the love of this dear brother, they say, she has abjured the sight and company of men.' Viola, who was herself in such sad affliction for her brother's loss, wished she could live with this lady, who so tenderly mourned a brother's death. She asked the captain if he could introduce her to Olivia, saying she would willingly serve this lady. But he replied, this would be a hard thing to accomplish, because the Lady Olivia would admit no person into her house since her brother's death, not even the duke himself. Then Viola formed another project in her mind, which was, in a man's habit, to serve the Duke Orsino as a page. It was a strange fancy in a young lady to put on male attire, and pass for a boy; but the forlorn and unprotected state of Viola, who was young and of uncommon beauty, alone, and in a foreign land, must plead her excuse.

She having observed a fair behaviour in the captain, and that he showed a friendly concern for her welfare, entrusted him with her design, and he readily engaged to assist her. Viola gave him money, and directed him to furnish her with suitable apparel, ordering her clothes to be made of the same colour and in the same fashion her brother Sebastian used to wear, and when she was dressed in her manly garb, she looked so exactly like her brother that some strange errors happened by means of their being mistaken for each other; for, as will afterwards appear, Sebastian was also saved.

Viola's good friend, the captain, when he had transformed this pretty lady into a gentleman, having some interest at court, got her presented to Orsino under the feigned name of Cesario. The duke was wonderfully pleased with the address and graceful deportment of this handsome youth, and made Cesario one of his pages, that being the office Viola wished to obtain: and she so well fulfilled the duties of her new station, and showed such a ready observance and faithful attachment to her lord, that she soon became his most favoured attendant. To Cesario Orsino confided the whole history of his love for the Lady Olivia. To Cesario he told the long and unsuccessful suit he had made to one who, rejecting his long services, and despising his person, refused to admit him to her presence; and for the love of this lady who had so unkindly treated him, the noble Orsino, forsaking the sports of the field and all manly exercises in which he used to delight, passed his hours in ignoble sloth, listening to the effeminate sounds of soft music, gentle airs, and passionate love-songs; and neglecting the company of the wise and learned lords with whom he used to associate, he was now all day long conversing with young Cesario. Unmeet companion no doubt his grave courtiers thought Cesario was for their once noble master, the great Duke Orsino.

It is a dangerous matter for young maidens to be the confidants of handsome young dukes; which Viola too soon found to her sorrow, for all that Orsino told her he endured for Olivia, she presently perceived she suffered for the love of him; and much it moved her wonder, that Olivia could be so regardless of this her peerless lord and master, whom she thought no one could behold without the deepest admiration, and she ventured gently to hint to Orsino, that it was a pity he should affect a lady who was so blind to his worthy qualities; and she said, 'If a lady were to love you, my lord, as you love Olivia (and perhaps there may be one who does), if you could not love her in return, would you not tell her that you could not love, and must she not be content with this answer?' But Orsino would not admit of this reasoning, for he denied that it was possible for any woman to love as he did. He said, no woman's heart was big enough to hold so much love, and therefore it was unfair to compare the love of any lady for him, to his love for Olivia. Now, though Viola had the utmost deference for the duke's opinions, she could not help thinking this was not quite true, for she thought her heart had full as much love in it as Orsino's had; and she said, 'Ah, but I know, my lord.' – 'What do you know, Cesario?' said Orsino. 'Too well I know,' replied Viola, 'what love women may owe to men. They are as true of heart as we are. My father had a daughter loved a man, as I perhaps, were I a woman, should love your lordship.' – 'And what is her history?' said Orsino. 'A blank, my lord,' replied Viola: 'she never told her love, but let concealment, like a worm in the bud, feed on her damask cheek. She pined in thought, and with a green and yellow melancholy, she sat like Patience on a monument, smiling at Grief.' The duke inquired if this lady died of her love, but to this question Viola returned an evasive answer; as probably she had feigned the story, to speak words expressive of the secret love and silent grief she suffered for Orsino.

While they were talking, a gentleman entered whom the duke had sent to Olivia, and he said, 'So please you, my lord, I might not be admitted to the lady, but by her handmaid she returned you this answer: Until seven years hence, the element itself shall not behold her face; but like a cloistress she will walk veiled, watering her chamber with her tears for the sad remembrance of her dead brother.' On hearing this, the duke exclaimed, 'O she that has a heart of this fine frame, to pay this debt of love to a dead brother, how will she love, when the rich golden shaft has touched her heart!' And then he said to Viola, 'You know, Cesario, I have told you all the secrets of my heart; therefore, good youth, go to Olivia's house. Be not denied access; stand at her doors, and tell her, there your fixed foot shall grow till you have audience.' – 'And if I do speak to her, my lord, what then?' said Viola. 'O then;' replied Orsino, 'unfold to her the passion of my love. Make a long discourse to her of my dear faith. It will well become you to act my woes, for she will attend more to you than to one of graver aspect.'

Away then went Viola; but not willingly did she undertake this courtship, for she was to woo a lady to become a wife to him she wished to marry: but having undertaken the affair, she performed it with fidelity; and Olivia soon heard that a youth was at her door who insisted upon being admitted to her presence. 'I told him,' said the servant, 'that you were sick: he said he knew you were, and therefore he came to speak with you. I told him that you were asleep: he seemed to have a foreknowledge of that too, and said, that therefore he must speak with you. What is to be said to him, lady? for he seems fortified against all denial, and will speak with you, whether you will or no.' Olivia, curious to see who this peremptory messenger might be, desired he might be admitted; and throwing her veil over her face, she said she would once more hear Orsino's embassy, not doubting but that he came from the duke, by his importunity. Viola, entering, put on the most manly air she could assume, and affecting the fine courtier language of great men's pages, she said to the veiled lady, 'Most radiant, exquisite, and matchless beauty, I pray you tell me if you are the lady of the house; for

I should be sorry to cast away my speech upon another; for besides that it is excellently well penned, I have taken great pains to learn it.' – 'Whence come you, sir?' said Olivia. 'I can say little more than I have studied,' replied Viola; 'and that question is out of my part.' – 'Are you a comedian?' said Olivia. 'No,' replied Viola; 'and yet I am not that which I play;' meaning that she, being a woman, feigned herself to be a man. And again she asked Olivia if she were the lady of the house. Olivia said she was; and then Viola, having more curiosity to see her rival's features, than haste to deliver her master's message, said 'Good madam, let me see your face.' With this bold request Olivia was not averse to comply; for this haughty beauty, whom the Duke Orsino had loved so long in vain, at first sight conceived a passion for the supposed page, the humble Cesario.

When Viola asked to see her face, Olivia said, 'Have you any commission from your lord and master to negotiate with my face?' And then, forgetting her determination to go veiled for seven long years, she drew aside her veil, saying, 'But I will draw the curtain and show the picture. Is it not well done?' Viola replied, 'It is beauty truly mixed; the red and white upon your cheeks is by Nature's own cunning hand laid on. You are the most cruel lady living, if you will lead these graces to the grave, and leave the world no copy.' – 'O, sir,' replied Olivia, 'I will not be so cruel. The world may have an inventory of my beauty. As, *item*, two lips, indifferent red; *item*, two grey eyes, with lids to them; one neck; one chin; and so forth. Were you sent here to praise me?' Viola replied, 'I see what you are: you are too proud, but you are fair. My lord and master loves you. O such a love could but be recompensed, though you were crowned the queen of beauty: for Orsino loves you with adoration and with tears, with groans that thunder love, and sighs of fire.' – 'Your lord,' said Olivia, 'knows well my mind. I cannot love him; yet I doubt not he is virtuous; I know him to be noble and of high estate, of fresh and spotless youth. All voices proclaim him learned, courteous, and valiant; yet I cannot love him, he might have taken his answer long ago.' – 'If I did love you as my master does,' said Viola, 'I would make me a willow cabin at your gates, and call upon your name; I would write complaining sonnets on Olivia, and sing them in the dead of night; your name should sound among the hills, and I would make

Echo, the babbling gossip of the air, cry out *Olivia*. O you should not rest between the elements of earth and air, but you should pity me.' – 'You might do much,' said Olivia: 'what is your parentage?' Viola replied, 'Above my fortunes, yet my state is well. I am a gentleman.' Olivia now reluctantly dismissed Viola, saying, 'Go to your master, and tell him, I cannot love him. Let him send no more, unless perchance you come again to tell me how he takes it.' And Viola departed, bidding the lady farewell by the name of Fair Cruelty. When she was gone, Olivia repeated the words, *Above my fortunes, yet my state is well. I am a gentleman.* And she said aloud, 'I will be sworn he is; his tongue, his face, his limbs, action, and spirit, plainly show he is a gentleman.' And then she wished Cesario was the duke; and perceiving the fast hold he had taken on her affections, she blamed herself for her sudden love: but the gentle blame which people lay upon their own faults has no deep root; and presently the noble Lady Olivia so far forgot the inequality between her fortunes and those of this seeming page, as well as the maidenly reserve which is the chief ornament of a lady's character, that she resolved to court the love of young Cesario, and sent a servant after him with a diamond ring, under the pretence that he had left it with her as a present from Orsino. She hoped by thus artfully making Cesario a present of the ring, she should give him some intimation of her design; and truly it did make Viola suspect; for knowing that Orsino had sent no ring by her, she began to recollect that Olivia's looks and manners were expressive of admiration, and she presently guessed her master's mistress had fallen in love with her. 'Alas,' said she, 'the poor lady might as well love a dream. Disguise I see is wicked, for it has caused Olivia to breathe as fruitless sighs for me as I do for Orsino.'

Viola returned to Orsino's palace, and related to her lord the ill success of the negotiation, repeating the command of Olivia, that the duke should trouble her no more. Yet still the duke persisted in hoping that the gentle Cesario would in time be able to persuade her to show some pity, and therefore he bade him he should go to her again the next day. In the meantime, to pass away the tedious interval, he commanded a song which he loved to be sung; and he said, 'My good Cesario, when I heard that song last night, methought it did relieve my passion much.

Mark it, Cesario, it is old and plain. The spinsters and the knitters when they sit in the sun, and the young maids that weave their thread with bone, chant this song. It is silly, yet I love it, for it tells of the innocence of love in the old time.'

SONG

Come away, come away, Death,
And in sad cypress let me be laid;
Fly away, fly away, breath,
I am slain by a fair cruel maid.
My shroud of white stuck all with yew, O prepare it!
My part of death no one so true did share it.
Not a flower, not a flower sweet,
On my black coffin let there be strewn:
Not a friend, not a friend greet
My poor corpse, where my bones shall be thrown.
A thousand thousand sighs to save, lay me O where
Sad true lover never find my grave, to weep there!

Viola did not fail to mark the words of the old song, which in such true simplicity described the pangs of unrequited love, and she bore testimony in her countenance of feeling what the song expressed. Her sad looks were observed by Orsino, who said to her, 'My life upon it, Cesario, though you are so young, your eye has looked upon some face that it loves: has it not, boy?' – 'A little, with your leave,' replied Viola. 'And what kind of woman, and of what age is she?' said Orsino. 'Of your age and of your complexion, my lord,' said Viola; which made the duke smile to hear this fair young boy loved a woman so much older than himself, and of a man's dark complexion; but Viola secretly meant Orsino, and not a woman like him.

When Viola made her second visit to Olivia, she found no difficulty in gaining access to her. Servants soon discover when their ladies delight to converse with handsome young messengers; and the instant Viola arrived, the gates were thrown wide open, and the duke's page was shown into Olivia's apartment with great respect; and when Viola told Olivia that she was come once more to plead in her lord's behalf, this lady said, 'I desired you never to speak of him again; but if you would undertake another suit, I had rather hear you solicit, than music from the spheres.' This was pretty plain speaking, but Olivia soon explained herself still more plainly, and openly confessed her love; and when she saw displeasure with perplexity expressed in Viola's face, she said, 'O what a deal of scorn looks beautiful in the contempt and anger of his lip! Cesario, by the roses of the spring, by maidhood, honour, and by truth, I love you so, that, in spite of your pride, I have neither wit nor reason to conceal my passion.' But in vain the lady wooed; Viola hastened from her presence, threatening never more to come to plead Orsino's love; and all the reply she made to Olivia's fond solicitation was, a declaration of a resolution *Never to love any woman.*

No sooner had Viola left the lady than a claim was made upon her valour. A gentleman, a rejected suitor of Olivia, who had learned how that lady had favoured the duke's messenger, challenged him to fight a duel. What should poor Viola do, though she carried a manlike outside, had a true woman's heart, and feared to look on her own sword?

When she saw her formidable rival advancing towards her with his sword drawn, she began to think of confessing that she was a woman; but she was relieved at once from her terror, and the shame of such a discovery, by a stranger that was passing by, who made up to them, and as if he had been long known to her, and were her dearest friend, said to her opponent, 'If this young gentleman has done offence, I will take the fault on me; and if you offend him, I will for his sake defy you.' Before Viola had time to thank him for his protection, or to inquire the reason of his kind interference, her new friend met with an enemy where his bravery was of no use to him; for the officers of justice coming up in that instant, apprehended the stranger in the duke's name, to answer for an offence he had committed some years before: and he said to Viola, 'This comes with seeking you:' and then he asked her for a purse, saying, 'Now my necessity makes me ask for my purse, and it grieves me much more for what I cannot do for you, than for what befalls myself. You stand amazed, but be of comfort.' His words did indeed amaze Viola, and she protested she knew him not, nor had ever received a purse from him; but for the kindness he had just shown her, she offered him a small sum of money, being nearly the whole she possessed. And now the stranger spoke severe things, charging her with ingratitude and unkindness. He said, 'This youth, whom you see here, I snatched from the jaws of death, and for his sake alone I came to Illyria, and have fallen into this danger.' But the officers cared little for hearkening to the complaints of their prisoner, and they hurried him off, saying, 'What is that to us?' And as he was carried away, he called Viola by the name of Sebastian, reproaching the supposed Sebastian for disowning his friend, as long as he was within hearing. When Viola heard herself called Sebastian, though the stranger was taken away too hastily for her to ask an explanation, she conjectured that this seeming mystery might arise from her being mistaken for her brother; and she began to cherish hopes that it was her brother whose life this man said he had preserved. And so indeed it was. The stranger, whose name was Antonio, was a sea-captain. He had taken Sebastian up into his ship, when, almost exhausted with fatigue, he was floating on the mast to which he had fastened himself in the storm. Antonio conceived such a friendship for Sebastian, that he resolved to accompany him whithersoever he went, and when the youth expressed a curiosity to visit Orsino's court, Antonio, rather than part from him, came to Illyria, though he knew, if his person should be known there, his life would be in danger, because in a sea-fight he had once dangerously wounded the Duke Orsino's nephew. This was the offence for which he was now made a prisoner.

Antonio and Sebastian had landed together but a few hours before Antonio met Viola. He had given his purse to Sebastian, desiring him to use it freely if he saw anything he wished to purchase, telling him he would wait at the inn, while Sebastian went to view the town; but Sebastian not returning at the time appointed, Antonio had ventured out to look for him, and Viola being dressed the same, and in face so exactly resembling her brother, Antonio drew his sword (as he thought) in defence of the youth he had saved, and when Sebastian (as he supposed) disowned him, and denied him his own purse, no wonder he accused him of ingratitude.

Viola, when Antonio was gone, fearing a second invitation to fight, slunk home as fast as she could. She had not been long gone, when her adversary thought he saw her return; but it was her brother Sebastian, who happened to arrive at this place, and he said, 'Now, sir, have I met with you again? There's for you;' and struck him a blow. Sebastian was no coward; he returned the blow with interest, and drew his sword.

A lady now put a stop to this duel, for Olivia came out of the house, and she too mistaking Sebastian for Cesario, invited him to come into her house, expressing much sorrow at the rude attack he had met with. Though Sebastian was as much surprised at the courtesy of this lady as at the rudeness of his unknown foe, yet he went very willingly into the house, and Olivia was delighted to find Cesario (as she thought him) become more sensible of her attentions; for though their features were exactly the same, there was none of the contempt and anger to be seen in his face, which she had complained of when she told her love to Cesario.

Sebastian did not at all object to the fondness the lady lavished on him. He seemed to take it in very good part, yet he wondered how it had come to pass, and he was rather inclined to think Olivia was not in her right senses; but perceiving that she was mistress of a fine house, and that she ordered her affairs and seemed to govern her family discreetly, and that in all but her sudden love for him she appeared in the full possession of her reason, he well approved of the courtship; and Olivia finding Cesario in this good humour, and fearing he might change his mind, proposed that, as she had a priest in the house, they should be instantly married. Sebastian assented to this proposal; and when the marriage ceremony was over, he left his lady for a short time, intending to go and tell his friend Antonio the good fortune that he had met with. In the meantime Orsino came to visit Olivia: and at the moment he arrived before Olivia's house, the officers of justice brought their prisoner, Antonio, before the duke. Viola was with Orsino, her master; and when Antonio saw Viola, whom he still imagined to be Sebastian, he told the duke in what manner he had rescued this youth from the perils of the sea; and after fully relating all the kindness he had really shown to Sebastian, he ended his complaint with saying, that for three months, both day and night, this ungrateful youth had been with him. But now the Lady Olivia coming forth from her house, the duke could no longer attend to Antonio's story; and he said, 'Here comes the countess: now Heaven walks on earth! but for thee, fellow, thy words are madness. Three months has this youth attended on me:' and then he ordered Antonio to be taken aside. But Orsino's heavenly countess soon gave the duke cause to accuse Cesario as much of ingratitude as Antonio had done, for all the words he could hear Olivia speak were words of kindness to Cesario: and when he found his page had obtained this high place in Olivia's favour, he threatened him with all the terrors of his just revenge; and as he was going to depart, he called Viola to follow him, saying, 'Come, boy, with me. My thoughts are ripe for mischief.' Though it seemed in his jealous rage he was going to doom Viola to instant death, yet her love made her no longer a coward, and she said she would most joyfully suffer death to give her master ease. But Olivia would not so lose her husband, and she cried, 'Where goes my Cesario?' Viola replied, 'After him I love more than my life.' Olivia, however prevented their departure by loudly proclaiming that Cesario was her husband, and sent for the priest, who declared that not two hours had passed since he had married the Lady Olivia to this young man. In vain Viola protested she was not married to Olivia; the evidence of that lady and the priest made Orsino believe that his page had robbed him of the treasure he prized above his life. But thinking that it was past recall, he was bidding farewell to his faithless mistress, and the *young dissembler*, her husband, as he called Viola, warning her never to come in his sight again, when (as it seemed to them) a miracle appeared! for another Cesario entered, and addressed Olivia as his wife. This new Cesario was Sebastian, the real husband of Olivia; and when their wonder had a little ceased at seeing two persons with the same face, the same voice, and the same habit, the brother and sister began to question each other; for Viola could scarce be persuaded that her brother was living, and Sebastian knew not how to account for the sister he supposed drowned being found in the habit of a young man. But Viola presently acknowledged that she was indeed Viola, and his sister, under that disguise.

When all the errors were cleared up which the extreme likeness between this twin brother and sister had occasioned, they laughed at the Lady Olivia for the pleasant mistake she had made in falling in love with a woman; and Olivia showed no dislike to her exchange, when she found she had wedded the brother instead of the sister.

The hopes of Orsino were for ever at an end by this marriage of Olivia, and with his hopes, all his fruitless love seemed to vanish away, and all his thoughts were fixed on the event of his favourite, young Cesario, being changed into a fair lady. He viewed Viola with great attention, and he remembered how very handsome he had always thought Cesario was, and he concluded she would look very beautiful in a woman's attire; and then he remembered how often she had said *she loved him*, which at the time seemed only the dutiful expressions of a faithful page; but now he guessed that something more was meant, for many of her pretty sayings, which were like riddles to him, came now into his mind, and he no sooner remembered all these things than he resolved to make Viola his wife; and he said to her (he still could not help calling her *Cesario* and *boy*), 'Boy, you have said to me a thousand times that you should never love a woman like to me, and for the faithful service you have done for me so much beneath your soft and tender breeding, and since you have called me master so long, you shall now be your master's mistress, and Orsino's true duchess.'

Olivia, perceiving Orsino was making over that heart, which she had so ungraciously rejected, to Viola, invited them to enter her house, and offered the assistance of the good priest, who had married her to Sebastian in the morning, to perform the same ceremony in the remaining part of the day for Orsino and Viola. Thus the twin brother and sister were both wedded on the same day: the storm and shipwreck, which had separated them, being the means of bringing to pass their high and mighty fortunes. Viola was the wife of Orsino, the Duke of Illyria, and Sebastian the husband of the rich and noble countess, the Lady Olivia.

THE WINTER'S TALE

LEONTES, King of Sicily, and his queen, the beautiful and virtuous Hermione, once lived in the greatest harmony together. So happy was Leontes in the love of this excellent lady, that he had no wish ungratified, except that he sometimes desired to see again, and to present to his queen, his old companion and school-fellow, Polixenes, King of Bohemia. Leontes and Polixenes were brought up together from their infancy, but being, by the death of their fathers, called to reign over their respective kingdoms, they had not met for many years, though they frequently interchanged gifts, and loving embassies.

At length, after repeated invitations, Polixenes came from Bohemia to the Sicilian court, to make his friend Leontes a visit.

At first this visit gave nothing but pleasure to Leontes. He recommended the friend of his youth to the queen's particular attention, and seemed in the presence of his dear friend and old companion to have his felicity quite completed. They talked over old times; their school-days and their youthful pranks were remembered, and recounted to Hermione, who always took a cheerful part in these conversations.

When, after a long stay, Polixenes was preparing to depart, Hermione, at the desire of her husband, joined her entreaties to his that Polixenes would prolong his visit.

And now began this good queen's sorrow; for Polixenes refusing to stay at the request of Leontes, was won over by Hermione's gentle and persuasive words to put off his departure for some weeks longer. Upon this, although Leontes had so long known the integrity and honourable principles of his friend Polixenes, as well as the excellent disposition of his virtuous queen, he was seized with an ungovernable jealousy. Every attention Hermione showed to Polixenes, though by her husband's particular desire, and merely to please him, increased the unfortunate king's jealousy; and from being a loving and a true friend, and the best and fondest of husbands, Leontes became suddenly a savage and inhuman monster. Sending for Camillo, one of the lords of his court, and telling him of the suspicion he entertained, he commanded him to poison Polixenes.

Camillo was a good man; and he, well knowing that the jealousy of Leontes had not the slightest foundation in truth, instead of poisoning Polixenes, acquainted him with the king his master's orders, and agreed to escape with him out of the Sicilian dominions; and Polixenes, with the assistance of Camillo, arrived safe in his own kingdom of Bohemia, where Camillo lived from that time in the king's court, and became the chief friend and favourite of Polixenes.

The flight of Polixenes enraged the jealous Leontes still more; he went to the queen's apartment, where the good lady was sitting with her little son Mamillius, who was just beginning to tell one of his best stories to amuse his mother, when the king entered, and taking the child away, sent Hermione to prison.

Mamillius, though but a very young child, loved his mother tenderly; and when he saw her so dishonoured, and found she was taken from him to be put into a prison, he took it deeply to heart, and drooped and pined away by slow degrees, losing his appetite and his sleep, till it was thought his grief would kill him.

The king, when he had sent his queen to prison, commanded Cleomenes and Dion, two Sicilian lords, to go to Delphos, there to inquire of the oracle at the temple of Apollo, if his queen had been unfaithful to him.

When Hermione had been a short time in prison, she was brought to bed of a daughter; and the poor lady received much comfort from the sight of her pretty baby, and she said to it, 'My poor little prisoner, I am as innocent as you are.'

Hermione had a kind friend in the noble-spirited Paulina, who was the wife of Antigonus, a Sicilian lord; and when the lady Paulina heard her royal mistress was brought to bed, she went to the prison where Hermione was confined; and she said to Emilia, a lady who attended upon Hermione, 'I pray you, Emilia, tell the good queen, if her majesty dare trust me with her little babe, I will carry it to the king, its father; we do not know how he may soften at the sight of his innocent child.' 'Most worthy madam,' replied Emilia, 'I will acquaint the queen with your noble offer; she was wishing to-day that she had any friend who would venture to present the child to the king.' 'And tell her,' said Paulina, 'that I will speak boldly to Leontes in her defence.' 'May you be for ever blessed,' said Emilia, 'for your kindness to our gracious queen!' Emilia then went to Hermione, who joyfully gave up her baby to the care of Paulina, for she had feared that no one would dare venture to present the child to its father.

Paulina took the new-born infant, and forcing herself into the king's presence, notwithstanding her husband, fearing the king's anger, endeavoured to prevent her, she laid the babe at its father's feet, and Paulina made a noble speech to the king in defence of Hermione, and she reproached him severely for his inhumanity, and implored him to have mercy on his innocent wife and child. But Paulina's spirited remonstrances only aggravated Leontes' displeasure, and he ordered her husband Antigonus to take her from his presence.

When Paulina went away, she left the little baby at its father's feet, thinking when he was alone with it, he would look upon it, and have pity on its helpless innocence.

The good Paulina was mistaken: for no sooner was she gone than the merciless father ordered Antigonus, Paulina's husband, to take the child, and carry it out to sea, and leave it upon some desert shore to perish.

Antigonus, unlike the good Camillo, too well obeyed the orders of Leontes; for he immediately carried the child on ship-board, and put out to sea, intending to leave it on the first desert coast he could find.

So firmly was the king persuaded of the guilt of Hermione, that he would not wait for the return of Cleomenes and Dion, whom he had sent to consult the oracle of Apollo at Delphos; but before the queen was recovered from her lying-in, and from her grief for the loss of her precious baby, he had her brought to a public trial before all the lords and nobles of his court. And when all the great lords, the judges, and all the nobility of the land were assembled together to try Hermione, and that unhappy queen was standing as a prisoner before her subjects to receive their judgement, Cleomenes and Dion entered the assembly, and presented to the king the answer of the oracle, sealed up; and Leontes commanded the seal to be broken, and the words of the oracle to be read aloud, and these were the words: '*Hermione is innocent, Polixenes blameless, Camillo a true subject, Leontes a jealous tyrant, and the king shall live without an heir if that which is lost be not found.*' The king would give no credit to the words of the oracle: he said it was a falsehood invented by the queen's friends, and he desired the judge to proceed in the trial of the queen; but while Leontes was speaking, a man entered and told him that the Prince Mamillius, hearing his mother was to be tried for her life, struck with grief and shame, had suddenly died.

Hermione, upon hearing of the death of this dear affectionate child, who had lost his life in sorrowing for her misfortune, fainted; and Leontes, pierced to the heart by the news, began to feel pity for his unhappy queen, and he ordered Paulina, and the ladies who were her attendants, to take her away, and use means for her recovery. Paulina soon returned, and told the king that Hermione was dead.

When Leontes heard that the queen was dead, he repented of his cruelty to her; and now that he thought his ill-usage had broken Hermione's heart, he believed her innocent; and now he thought the words of the oracle were true, as he knew 'if that which was lost was not found,' which he concluded was his young daughter, he should be without an heir, the young Prince Mamillius being dead; and he would give his kingdom now to recover his lost daughter: and Leontes gave himself up to remorse, and passed many years in mournful thoughts and repentant grief.

The ship in which Antigonus carried the infant princess out to sea was driven by a storm upon the coast of Bohemia, the very kingdom of the good King Polixenes. Here Antigonus landed, and here he left the little baby.

Antigonus never returned to Sicily to tell Leontes where he had left his daughter, for as he was going back to the ship, a bear came out of the woods, and tore him to pieces; a just punishment on him for obeying the wicked order of Leontes.

The child was dressed in rich clothes and jewels; for Hermione had made it very fine when she sent it to Leontes, and Antigonus had pinned a paper to its mantle, and the name of *Perdita* written thereon, and words obscurely intimating its high birth and untoward fate.

This poor deserted baby was found by a shepherd. He was a humane man, and so he carried the little Perdita home to his wife, who nursed it tenderly; but poverty tempted the shepherd to conceal the rich prize he had found: therefore he left that part of the country, that no one might know where he got his riches, and with part of Perdita's jewels he bought herds of sheep, and became a wealthy shepherd. He brought up Perdita as his own child, and she knew not she was any other than a shepherd's daughter.

The little Perdita grew up a lovely maiden; and though she had no better education that that of a shepherd's daughter, yet so did the natural graces she inherited from her royal mother shine forth in her untutored mind, that no one from her behaviour would have known she had not been brought up in her father's court.

Polixenes, the King of Bohemia, had an only son, whose name was Florizel. As this young prince was hunting near the shepherd's dwelling, he saw the old man's supposed daughter; and the beauty, modesty, and queen-like deportment of Perdita caused him instantly to fall in love with her. He soon, under the name of Doricles, and in the disguise of a private gentleman, became a constant visitor at the old shepherd's house. Florizel's frequent absences from court alarmed Polixenes; and setting people to watch his son, he discovered his love for the shepherd's fair daughter.

Polixenes then called for Camillo, the faithful Camillo, who had preserved his life from the fury of Leontes, and desired that he would accompany him to the house of the shepherd, the supposed father of Perdita.

Polixenes and Camillo, both in disguise, arrived at the old shepherd's dwelling while they were celebrating the feast of sheep-shearing; and though they were strangers, yet at the sheep-shearing every guest being made welcome, they were invited to walk in, and join in the general festivity.

Nothing but mirth and jollity was going forward. Tables were spread and great preparations were making for the rustic feast. Some lads and lasses were dancing on the green before the house, while others of the young men were buying ribands, gloves, and such toys, of a pedlar at the door.

While this busy scene was going forward, Florizel and Perdita sat quietly in a retired corner, seemingly more pleased with the conversation of each other, than desirous of engaging in the sports and silly amusements of those around them.

The king was so disguised that it was impossible his son could know him: he therefore advanced near enough to hear the conversation. The simple yet elegant manner in which Perdita conversed with his son did not a little surprise Polixenes: he said to Camillo, 'This is the prettiest low-born lass I ever saw; nothing she does or says but looks like something greater than herself, too noble for this place.'

Camillo replied, 'Indeed she is the very queen of curds and cream.'

'Pray, my good friend,' said the king to the old shepherd, 'what fair swain is that talking with your daughter?' 'They call him Doricles,' replied the shepherd. 'He says he loves my daughter; and, to speak truth, there is not a kiss to choose which loves the other best. If young Doricles can get her, she shall bring him that he little dreams of;' meaning the remainder of Perdita's jewels; which, after he had bought herds of sheep with part of them, he had carefully hoarded up for her marriage portion.

Polixenes then addressed his son. 'How now, young man!' said he: 'your heart seems full of something that takes off your mind from feasting. When I was young, I used to load my love with presents; but you have let the pedlar go, and have brought your lass no toy.'

The young prince, who little thought he was talking to the king his father, replied, 'Old sir, she prizes not such trifles; the gifts which Perdita expects from me are locked up in my heart.' Then turning to Perdita, he said to her, 'O hear me, Perdita, before this ancient gentleman, who it seems was once himself a lover; he shall hear what I profess.' Florizel then called upon the old stranger to be a witness to a solemn promise of marriage which he made to Perdita, saying to Polixenes, 'I pray you, mark our contract.'

'Mark your divorce, young sir,' said the king, discovering himself. Polixenes then reproached his son for daring to contract himself to this low-born maiden, calling Perdita 'shepherd's-brat, sheep-hook,' and other disrespectful names; and threatening, if ever she suffered his son to see her again, he would put her, and the old shepherd her father, to a cruel death.

The king then left them in great wrath, and ordered Camillo to follow him with Prince Florizel.

When the king had departed, Perdita, whose royal nature was roused by Polixenes' reproaches, said, 'Though we are all undone, I was not much afraid; and once or twice I was about to speak, and tell him plainly that the selfsame sun which shines upon his palace, hides not his face from our cottage, but looks on both alike.' Then sorrowfully she said, 'But now I am awakened from this dream, I will queen it no further. Leave me, sir; I will go milk my ewes and weep.'

The kind-hearted Camillo was charmed with the spirit and propriety of Perdita's behaviour; and perceiving that the young prince was too deeply in love to give up his mistress at the command of his royal father, he thought of a way to befriend the lovers, and at the same time to execute a favourite scheme he had in his mind.

Camillo had long known that Leontes, the King of Sicily, was become a true penitent; and though Camillo was now the favoured friend of King Polixenes, he could not help wishing once more to see his late royal master and his native home. He therefore proposed to Florizel and Perdita that they should accompany him to the Sicilian court, where he would engage Leontes should protect them, till, through his mediation, they could obtain pardon from Polixenes, and his consent to their marriage.

To this proposal they joyfully agreed; and Camillo, who conducted everything relative to their flight, allowed the old shepherd to go along with them.

The shepherd took with him the remainder of Perdita's jewels, her baby clothes, and the paper which he had found pinned to her mantle.

After a prosperous voyage, Florizel and Perdita, Camillo and the old shepherd, arrived in safety at the court of Leontes. Leontes, who still mourned his dead Hermione and his lost child, received Camillo with great kindness, and gave a cordial welcome to Prince Florizel. But Perdita, whom Florizel introduced as his princess, seemed to engross all Leontes' attention: perceiving a resemblance between her and his dead queen Hermione, his grief broke out afresh, and he said, such a lovely creature might his own daughter have been, if he had not so cruelly destroyed her. 'And then, too,' said he to Florizel, 'I lost the society and friendship of your brave father, whom I now desire more than my life once again to look upon.'

When the old shepherd heard how much notice the king had taken of Perdita, and that he had lost a daughter, who was exposed in infancy, he fell to comparing the time when he found the little Perdita, with the manner of its exposure, the jewels and other tokens of its high birth; from all which it was impossible for him not to conclude that Perdita and the king's lost daughter were the same.

Florizel and Perdita, Camillo and the faithful Paulina, were present when the old shepherd related to the king the manner in which he had found the child, and also the circumstance of Antigonus' death, he having seen the bear seize upon him. He showed the rich mantle in which Paulina remembered Hermione had wrapped the child; and he produced a jewel which she remembered Hermione had tied about Perdita's neck, and he gave up the paper which Paulina knew to be the writing of her husband; it could not be doubted that Perdita was Leontes' own daughter: but oh! the noble struggles of Paulina, between sorrow for her husband's death, and joy that the oracle was fulfilled, in the king's heir, his long-lost daughter being found. When Leontes heard that Perdita was his daughter, the great sorrow that he felt that Hermione was not living to behold her child, made him that he could say nothing for a long time, but, 'O thy mother, thy mother!'

Paulina interrupted this joyful yet distressful scene, with saying to Leontes, that she had a statue newly finished by that rare Italian master, Julio Romano, which was such a perfect resemblance of the queen, that would his majesty be pleased to go to her house and look upon it, he would be almost ready to think it was Hermione herself. Thither then they all went; the king anxious to see the semblance of his Hermione, and Perdita longing to behold what the mother she never saw did look like.

When Paulina drew back the curtain which concealed this famous statue, so perfectly did it resemble Hermione, that all the king's sorrow was renewed at the sight: for a long time he had no power to speak or move.

'I like your silence, my liege,' said Paulina, 'it the more shows your wonder. Is not this statue very like your queen?'

At length the king said, 'O, thus she stood, even with such majesty, when I first wooed her. But yet, Paulina, Hermione was not so aged as this statue looks.' Paulina replied, 'So much the more the carver's excellence, who has made the statue as Hermione would have looked had she been living now. But let me draw the curtain, sire, lest presently you think it moves.'

The king then said, 'Do not draw the curtain; Would I were dead! See, Camillo, would you not think it breathed? Her eye seems to have motion in it.' 'I must draw the curtain, my liege,' said Paulina. 'You are so transported, you will persuade yourself the statue lives.' 'O sweet Paulina,' said Leontes, 'make me think so twenty years together! Still methinks there is an air comes from her. What fine chisel could ever yet cut breath? Let no man mock me, for I kiss her.' 'Good my lord, forbear!' said Paulina. 'The ruddiness upon her lip is wet; you will stain your own with oily painting. Shall I draw the curtain?' 'No, not these twenty years,' said Leontes.

Perdita, who all this time had been kneeling, and beholding in silent admiration the statue of her matchless mother, said now, 'And so long could I stay here, looking upon my dear mother.'

'Either forbear this transport,' said Paulina to Leontes, 'and let me draw the curtain; or prepare yourself for more amazement. I can make the statue move indeed; ay, and descend from off the pedestal, and take you by the hand. But then you will think, which I protest I am not, that I am assisted by some wicked powers.'

'What you can make her do,' said the astonished king, 'I am content to look upon. What you can make her speak, I am content to hear; for it is as easy to make her speak as move.'

Paulina then ordered some slow and solemn music, which she had prepared for the purpose, to strike up; and, to the amazement of all the beholders, the statue came down from off the pedestal, and threw its arms around Leontes' neck. The statue then began to speak, praying for blessings on her husband, and on her child, the newly-found Perdita.

No wonder that the statue hung upon Leontes' neck, and blessed her husband and her child. No wonder; for the statue was indeed Hermione herself, the real, the living queen.

Paulina had falsely reported to the king the death of Hermione, thinking that the only means to preserve her royal mistress' life; and with the good Paulina, Hermione had lived ever since, never choosing Leontes should know she was living, till she heard Perdita was found; for though she had long forgiven the injuries which Leontes had done to herself, she could not pardon his cruelty to his infant daughter.

His dead queen thus restored to life, his lost daughter found, the long-sorrowing Leontes could scarcely support the excess of his own happiness.

Nothing but congratulations and affectionate speeches were heard on all sides. Now the delighted parents thanked Prince Florizel for loving their lowly-seeming daughter; and now they blessed the good old shepherd for preserving their child. Greatly did Camillo and Paulina rejoice that they had lived to see so good an end of all their faithful services.

And as if nothing should be wanting to complete this strange and unlooked-for joy, King Polixenes himself now entered the palace.

When Polixenes first missed his son and Camillo, knowing that Camillo had long wished to return to Sicily, he conjectured he should find the fugitives here; and, following them with all speed, he happened to just arrive at this, the happiest moment of Leontes' life.

Polixenes took a part in the general joy; he forgave his friend Leontes the unjust jealousy he had conceived against him, and they once more loved each other with all the warmth of their first boyish friendship. And there was no fear that Polixenes would now oppose his son's marriage with Perdita. She was no 'sheep-hook' now, but the heiress of the crown of Sicily.

Thus have we seen the patient virtues of the long-suffering Hermione rewarded. That excellent lady lived many years with her Leontes and her Perdita, the happiest of mothers and of queens.

Tragedies

TROILUS AND CRESSIDA

◆◆◆◆◆◆◆◆◆◆◆◆◆◆

It was a morning in summer, seven years after the army of the Greeks had landed at Troy to seek Helen, beautiful queen of Menelaus of Sparta, who had been carried off by a Trojan prince. Sun was high over the Greek camp, with its tents and huts like innumerable haycocks; over the rivers Scamander and Simois; over the wide plain that took four hours to cross on foot; and over the massive walls, ramparts, and towers of the high-built six-gated city where King Priam ruled. Even now the long war showed no sign of ending. By day the warriors would do battle on the plain; at night the Trojan sentinels spied far off the twinkling watch-fires of the Greeks. By day the glint of sun on cuirass and blade; by night the glow of the fires. By day the clangour of weapons; by night the neighing of horse and the challenge of a sentinel. So it had been for seven full years, and in this mid-morning there appeared to be no reason why the war should cease.

As Prince Troilus, one of the noble sons of Priam, stood by the palace in the upper city, he found little pleasure in the practice of war. He thought not of Helen, who was the subject of the broil, and who wished nothing better than to stay in Troy, but of Cressida (daughter of the traitorous Trojan priest Calchas, now with the Greeks), who lived at the house of Pandarus, her uncle. He told her uncle so as he began to put off the armour he had only just donned. He was, he said, madly in love with Cressida, though they had never spoken together; and the crafty Pandarus, who was well aware of this, and who was the only link between Troilus and his niece, feigned to be angry so that Troilus would seek even more ardently what he could not have. 'I will leave all as I found it, and there an end,' said Pandarus, going off in pretended tetchiness while Troilus, listening to the war sounds on the plain, said ruefully to himself, 'I cannot fight for Helen: that is too starved a subject for my sword. My thoughts are Cressida's. For me her bed is India; there she lies, a pearl. Between our Ilium and where Cressid is, let it be called a wild and wandering flood: myself a merchant and this Pandarus my doubtful hope, my convoy, and my ship.' As he reflected thus, a Trojan general Aeneas came by, rallying him on his absence from the field, and Troilus, re-arming hastily, went down with him to battle.

That evening, in a street of Troy, Cressida was talking to her servant, and hearing how Prince Hector sought the death of the Greek Ajax who had struck him down in the previous day's battle. Pandarus, coming up to them, began to tease Cressida about the differences between Troilus and Hector, and to rouse her jealousy by suggesting that Helen herself loved Troilus. But Cressida had as swift a wit as her uncle. They were still talking when the sound of the trumpets interrupted them as the Trojan warriors came in from the fight; and Pandarus, going up to a terrace with his niece, began to tell her about the lords who passed below, their names and their qualities. Here was Aeneas, one of the flowers of Troy – but she must wait for Prince Troilus. Here was Antenor; there the brave Hector; there Paris; worthy men all, but where was Troilus? Prince Helenus passed; Prince Deiphobus; then, at length, Troilus himself, hailed now by Pandarus as 'the prince of chivalry. Had I a sister were a grace, or a daughter a goddess, he should take his choice. O admirable man! – Paris is dirt to him!'

'There is among the Greeks,' said Cressida slyly, 'Achilles, a better man than Troilus.'

'Achilles!' scoffed Pandarus. 'The man is a porter, a drayman, a very camel.'

'Well, well!' sighed Cressida. A page hastened with word from Troilus that his lord would speak instantly with Pandarus, and the crafty man hurried off, saying, 'I will be with you, niece, by and by, to bring a token from Troilus.' Left to herself, the capricious girl murmured that though she saw far more in Troilus than all of the praise Pandarus bestowed on him, she would still hold aloof a while. 'Things won are done; joy's soul lies in the doing.'

Later that month, in the dog-days of a long truce, the Greek generals met in their camp round a table before the tent of Agamemnon, their leader. Troy, he said, stood yet after a seven years' siege; but was not this a trial ordained by Jove to test the constancy of the Greeks? Ulysses, Prince of Ithaca, believed that the Greeks suffered because of internal envies and ambitions, and because each man thought poorly of the one above him. 'When degree is shaken, which is the ladder to all high designs, the enterprise is sick.' Troy stood, not because the Trojans were strong, but because their enemy was weak: such a man as the great Achilles remained all day in his tent, gibing at his fellows. Nestor, the oldest of the Greeks, added that Ajax had grown similarly self-willed and listened to the scurrilous railing of the man Thersites, just as Achilles listened to the mocking Patroclus who was always with him.

The generals were still at the core of their debate when a trumpet rang out, and Aeneas appeared by the tent as a messenger from Troy. He came, he told them, from Hector, weary now of the boredom of a truce. Hence this message from him to the Greeks in conference:

'Kings, princes, lords! If there be one of you here, among the flower of Greece, that holds his honour higher than his ease, that knows his valour and knows not his fear, to him this challenge. Hector proclaims he has a lady who is wiser, fairer, truer, than any Greek has known, or ever will. To-morrow, then, midway between these tents and the walls of Troy, he sounds his trumpet-peal. If it should rouse a Grecian that is true in love, Hector will fight with him upon that theme. If no one comes, he'll say in Troy when he returns that not a woman in the realm of Greece is worth a splintered lance.'

It was the kind of chivalrous challenge in which the Greeks delighted. Agamemnon said that it should be told to all; and ancient Nestor swore that, if nobody accepted the summons, he would answer it himself. With this, Agamemnon led Aeneas to feast at his pavilion. Ulysses and Nestor, remaining, debated earnestly. Hector's challenge, they agreed, could be meant for one man only, Achilles; and Ulysses saw in it a way to force the sulking Greek to come to himself. They would put it about the camp that Ajax was the better man, and that he must meet Hector. This by itself would anger Achilles. If Ajax emerged safely, he would be praised by all; if not, nothing was lost, for Achilles, they knew, was the greater and his time was yet to come. Here was a stratagem to prick his pride. Ulysses said, as he and Nestor went off to tell Agamemnon, 'Hit or miss, Ajax employed plucks down Achilles' plume.'

That night, in the hilltop palace of Priam, the Trojan King and his sons pondered on a message from the Greeks: one of many that had been brought during the progress of the interminable war. In the latest message the Greeks said that if Helen were delivered to their hands, no more would be said or done. Hector declared at once that Helen should be returned: she was not worth what she had cost. But Troilus held that it would be base, having once praised their brother Paris for a noble prize, to say now that they had stolen what they feared to keep. Helen was a pearl whose price had launched more than a thousand ships and turned armed kings to merchants.

While they were still in eager argument, they heard the voice of the young prophetess Cassandra, a princess of Troy. 'Cry, Trojans, cry!' The long-drawn wail came nearer until at length Cassandra burst into the room, raving wildly, her hair dishevelled about her. 'Cry, Trojans, cry! Lend me ten thousand eyes, and I will fill them with prophetic tears. Our firebrand brother Paris burns us all. Cry, Trojans, cry! a Helen and a woe. Cry, cry! Troy burns – or else let Helen go!'

She ran out into the palace corridor while all at their evening tasks shivered to hear the tones of mad Cassandra. Within, Hector flung out at Troilus, 'You hear our sister?' But Troilus replied firmly that all Cassandra's prophecies could not alter for him the course of a war that had engaged their honours. Prince Paris, whose action had begun the conflict seven years earlier, said now that he could never retract what he had done. Would it not be shame to them and treasonous to Helen to yield her up? Well might they fight for her, a woman in the world unparalleled!

Hector reflected upon this. Though he believed that, morally, Helen should be returned to King Menelaus, he admitted that it meant much to their personal honour to keep her safe. And Troilus, listening to him, cried gladly, 'Why, worthy Hector, she is a theme of honour and renown, a spur to valiant and magnanimous deeds, the courage that may now beat down our foe and set our names in record.' Hearing this, Hector said at last, 'I am yours.'

In the camp of the Greeks that night, Agamemnon, Ulysses, and the rest were preparing for their lesson to Achilles who lay, apparently 'ill-disposed', within the closed flaps of his tent. 'He is sick because he is proud,' mocked Ajax. 'You may call it melancholy if you favour the man; but, by my head, it is pride.' A messenger went to Achilles from Agamemnon: 'Tell him we are come to speak with him. Say we think him over-proud and under-honest. We prefer to heed an active dwarf before a sleeping giant.' Further, to make sure that Achilles realised what was thought of him, Ulysses himself went out to the tent where the warrior sulked.

On returning, he said that Achilles would not go to the field tomorrow and gave no reason for it: he was proud beyond all reason. At once the lords joined in praising Ajax, and in saying how much worthier he was than Achilles. Diomedes whispered to Nestor, 'Look now at Ajax. How his silence drinks up this applause!' Before long they had got Ajax to believe that he, and he alone, was the grand champion of the Greeks. 'For he that taught you to fight,' said Ulysses to him, 'there is but one reward. Mars should divide eternity in twain and give him half.'

Love was the theme within the strong walls of Troy that evening, where musicians played to Helen and Paris and their guests, and Pandarus, who had called with a message from Troilus, sang his favourite song of 'Love, love, nothing but love.' This, too, was the story later that night when Prince Troilus walked in the orchard beside the house of Pandarus, preparing for the sight of Cressida that had at last been promised. 'O gentle Pandarus,' he said, 'from Cupid's shoulder pluck his painted wings and fly with me to Cressid.' Pandarus agreed to bring his niece immediately; and while he was away, Troilus was lost in an ecstasy of hope: 'Expectation whirls me round. The imaginary relish is so strong that it enchants my sense.' Within minutes Cressida, white-robed, was there. 'Come,' said Pandarus cheerfully, 'why need you blush, Prince Troilus? Swear the oaths now to her that you have sworn to me. Come, speak to her. Kiss her.' Troilus said simply, 'You have bereft me of all words'; and Pandarus, excusing himself for a moment to get a fire lighted within, left them together. 'Will you walk in, my lord?' said Cressida demurely. 'O Cressida,' replied Troilus, 'how often have I wished me thus! Faith needs the fewest words.'

'Boldness comes to me now,' Cressida whispered, 'and it brings me heart. Prince Troilus, I have loved you night and day for many weary months.'

'Why was my Cressid then so hard to win?'

'Hard to seem won,' Cressida answered. 'I was won, my lord, by the first glance you gave me; until now I have kept my love in bounds, though I wished myself a man, or else that we women had man's privilege of speaking first.'

Troilus, clasping her hands and gazing down at her, told her with deep seriousness that in the world to come, true youths in love would take him for example. When they were tired of saying 'As true as steel' or 'As true as sun to day', 'As true as Troilus' would crown their verse and form a solemn vow. Cressida, moved to sincerity, cried in answer that if she were false or swerved a hair from truth, then when time was old and had forgot itself, when waterdrops had worn the stones of Troy and blind oblivion swallowed cities up, her name would be the pattern for false maids in love. When men had said 'As false as air, as water, wind, or sandy earth,' then let them say – to reach the heart of falsehood – 'As false as Cressid'.

Pandarus, who had been listening anxiously, took each by a hand and said, 'There's a bargain made. If either of you prove false, now that I have taken such pains to join you, let every go-between be called, to the world's end, a Pandarus; let all constant men be named Troilus, and all false women Cressida. Say amen.' And Troilus and Cressida, hand in hand, responded, 'Amen.'

They did not know that down in the enemy camp, Cressida's Trojan father Calchas was asking that night for his service to the Greeks to be repaid. The Greeks, he said, had just taken a prisoner Antenor, much loved in Troy. If this man were sent back in exchange for Cressida, Calchas would regard that as payment for all his work. It was so agreed: Diomedes should take Antenor to Troy and bring back Cressida. This settled, the Greek lords continued their mocking of Achilles. One by one they passed him as he stood at the entrance to his tent, some ignoring him entirely, while others gave only a disdainful nod. Agamemnon, Nestor, Menelaus, Ajax, all went by; and Achilles stood puzzled and offended. Last to arrive was Ulysses, his head bent upon the book he was reading. Achilles engaged him in talk, and Ulysses spoke subtly of Ajax and the chance he would have with Hector on the morrow. 'How some men creep into fortune,' he said, 'while others are forgotten!' Achilles said gloomily, 'I do believe it. The lords passed me by as misers do by beggars. I had neither good word nor look. Ulysses, are my deeds forgotten?'

Ulysses studied Achilles gravely. Good deeds, he said, were forgotten as soon as done. It was perseverance that kept honour bright; a man who worked no more would hang merely as rusty armour upon a wall. Time was like a fashionable host that slightly shook the hand of a parting guest, but turned with arms outstretched to hail a newcomer.

Achilles was staring in surprise; and Ulysses pressed home his argument. Virtue, he said, could not live upon the past: all things, beauty or wit, high birth, vigour, deserving deeds, love, friendship, charity – all of these fell victim to the envious tongue of time. Great Achilles must not wonder then that the Greeks began to worship Ajax, for things in motion sooner caught the eye than those that did not stir. But he might still regain his place if once he ceased to entomb himself within his tent and to hide from Greece his glories.

Saluting Achilles, Ulysses turned to his book again and moved on, while the warrior thought over what had been said to him, 'My mind is troubled like a fountain stirred, and I myself see not the bottom of it.'

In the cold, faint daybreak of the next morning Diomedes was in Troy upon his mission to return Antenor and to receive in exchange the fair Cressida. Paris, who conducted Diomedes to the house of Pandarus, feared they would be unwelcome visitors to his brother Troilus who was staying there; and Aeneas, whom they met briefly in the street, seconded him. 'Troilus,' he said, 'had rather Troy were borne to Greece than his Cressida borne from Troy.' Bidding Aeneas go first and break the news as gently as he could, Paris led Diomedes by torchlight among the narrow ways towards the house of Pandarus.

Aeneas, in high haste, was duly there before them to speak to Troilus. Half-breathless, he said, 'I scarce have time to salute you, Prince. Close at hand are Paris your brother with the Grecian Diomedes and our Antenor. It is for Antenor's sake that we must yield to Diomedes the lady Cressida for conduct to her father. Alas, my lord, within the hour.'

'How my achievements mock me!' Troilus cried as he ran out with Aeneas; and Pandarus said in utter dismay, 'Is it possible? no sooner got than lost.' Cressida, coming in to him, asked what was the matter, why he sighed so profoundly, and where Troilus was; but her uncle was so distraught that she had to beg him on her knees to tell her coherently what had happened. Pandarus at length told her that she was to be exchanged for Antenor and must be gone from Troilus; whereupon Cressida, as sincere as she had ever been, fell to weeping and to crying again what she had said on the previous night, 'O you gods divine! Make Cressid's name the very crown of falsehood, if ever she leave Troilus! Uncle, let me go in and weep. I will not go from Troy.'

But the sun was rising and the hour at hand for the delivery of Cressida to Diomedes. Troilus came to her where she wept in her room, with Pandarus endeavouring to comfort her. 'Is it true,' she asked, 'that I must go from Troy? Is it possible?' And Troilus, as stricken as she was, said that the parting must be sudden. Though they had spent on each other so many thousand sighs, they now had scarce time for one, or for a single tearful kiss. Urging her to be true of heart, and Cressida swearing to be so, Troilus gave her a sleeve as a token, and she gave to him a glove. He swore to bribe the Greek sentinels and to visit her nightly, and yet once more – while she cried out at his repetition – he begged her to be true and not to be tempted by the Grecian youths. 'Do you think I will?' exclaimed Cressida, to which, after a moment, he answered sadly, 'No, but sometimes we are devils to ourselves.'

Paris summoned them now, and Troilus told him to enter with the Greek Diomedes. Cressida of a sudden paused in her lament as she perceived the handsome Greek who bowed courteously to her, and Troilus said with all the meaning at his command, 'Diomedes, deal fairly with her. If ever you are at mercy of my sword, say Cressid's name, and you will be safe as Priam is in Ilium.' Diomedes laughed lightly: 'Lady Cressid, your beauty is enough. You shall command me wholly.' The speech had a ring that Troilus distrusted. He confronted Diomedes while the sun sparkled upon the Trojan wall: 'She is as far above your praise as you are unworthy to be called her servant. Then keep her well. If you do not, though the great Achilles be your guard, I'll cut your throat.' Diomedes replied with quick arrogance; but it was time for them to reach the city gate. Indeed they had barely done this before the warning of Hector's trumpet showed that the Trojan warrior was ready to speed his challenge to the plain.

Before Hector arrived, Cressida was in the Greek camp with Diomedes. One after another, the generals, Ulysses excepted, saluted her with a kiss. To all of them, her woes for a moment forgotten, she replied readily and sharply, bandying wit with wit. When she had gone, Nestor praised her as a woman of quick sense; but Ulysses shook his wise head. It was enough, he said, to look at Cressida to know that she was false. 'There's language in her eye, her cheek, her lip.' He did not speak further because a Trojan trumpet announced the approach of Hector prepared for battle. After the formal courtesies of chivalry, he entered the lists with Ajax, and the champions made themselves ready. Agamemnon, beckoning Ulysses to him, asked the name of the Trojan with Hector, the youth who looked so melancholy. Ulysses told him that it was Troilus, youngest son of Priam, a true knight not yet mature but firm in word and deed.

Meanwhile, the fighting had begun. Evenly matched at first, it did not continue long, for Ajax, though a Greek, was Hector's cousin, and Hector would not fight in earnest against one of his own kin. This being so, Ajax invited Hector to feast with him and to visit the Grecian tents. When Agamemnon had saluted Hector and Troilus, and Menelaus and old Nestor had added their greeting, Ulysses came slowly up to the Trojan warrior.

'I wonder now,' he said, 'how yonder city stands when you are here with us – its base and pillar?'

'Ah,' said Hector, 'I know you, lord Ulysses, well. Many have died since first I saw you as an ambassador of Troy.'

'I prophesied then what would come,' Ulysses answered. 'One day your walls and towers will crumble to their base.'

Hector said with Trojan pride, 'I must not believe you. They stand yet; and, lord Ulysses, the fall of every Trojan stone will cost a drop of Grecian blood. The end crowns all; and Time one day must end it.'

Achilles had left his tent to gaze at Hector. Now he swaggered up to the Trojan, asking the heavens to tell him where one day he would strike Hector's death-blow. Replying with a similar brag, Hector prayed Achilles to come to the open field for there had been wars enough since he had ceased to fight. At this Achilles declared that to-morrow he would meet him in deadly war; that night they would be friends. To welcoming music the Greeks conducted Hector into the tent of Agamemnon; but Troilus, lingering with Ulysses, asked where the priest Calchas was housed. Ulysses said that it was at the tent of Menelaus whither Diomedes – who now thought of nothing but fair Cressida – was going that very night. 'Sweet lord,' said Troilus, 'will you bring me thither when we have parted from Agamemnon?' Ulysses said that he would do so: 'Had Cressida no lover in Troy that wails her absence?' And Troilus responded bravely, 'She was beloved; she loved; she is, and doth.'

It was very late when the Trojan guests left the tent of Agamemnon. In the light of torch and lantern, and guided by their hosts, they traversed the intricate pattern of the Greek encampment and found the great tent where Achilles welcomed them. But only Hector, with Ajax and Nestor the veteran, accepted the hospitality of Achilles. Troilus, in the company of Ulysses, had slipped off in pursuit of Diomedes as he bore a single torch to the place where Cressida lodged.

There they heard Diomedes call Cressida out to him. There, too, standing where the torch could not shine upon them, they saw Cressida greet Diomedes with pleasure, and heard her say archly, 'Sweet honey Greek, tempt me no more to folly,' and then coax and tease him and stroke his cheek, while Diomedes, half-angry, half-allured, lingered irresolutely. All this while Ulysses was in fear lest Troilus should disclose himself in rage. They overheard Diomedes say, 'Give me some token,' and Cressida, 'I'll fetch you one,' and when she had returned from the tent with her chosen pledge, she handed to Diomedes the sleeve that Troilus had given to her that very morning.

'O beauty!' cried Troilus, 'where is thy faith?' Ulysses, with a quiet 'My lord!', brought him to himself. For a few minutes Cressida hesitated, troubled by conscience, at first taking back the pledge, remembering Troilus, and saying 'He loved me', and then at last yielding it to Diomedes but refusing to say whose it had been. 'To-morrow,' said

Diomedes, 'I will wear it upon my helm and grieve his spirit that dares not challenge it.' They arranged an assignation; and Diomedes and his single torch faded into the night among the tents while the fickle Cressida stood in momentary contemplation: 'Troilus farewell! one eye yet looks on thee, but with my heart the other eye doth see.' She entered the tent, and there was nothing but the silent night.

'All's done, my lord,' said Ulysses softly. Troilus broke into a fierce and frightening passion, raving on to the last cry of 'O Cressid! O false Cressid! false! false! false! Let all untruths stand by your perjured name, and they'll seem glorious.' Ulysses begged him again to control himself, for a torchbearer had advanced to them. It proved to be Aeneas seeking for the prince who must return now to Troy. Troilus had spent his fury. Looking for the last time at the tent where Cressida lay, he said slowly, 'Farewell, revolted fair! And Diomed, stand fast—and wear a castle on thy head!'

In Troy, Hector's wife Andromache, who all night had dreamed of disaster, was imploring him not to fight that day, and Cassandra joined in the plea. Though Hector resisted entreaty, in his turn he begged Troilus not to take the field. They were still in dispute when King Priam added his own command. Again Hector refused. Below, on the plain, the day's battle had begun. Hector went forward to it. Just as Troilus was about to follow, crying, 'Proud Diomed, believe I come to lose my arm or win my sleeve,' Pandarus brought a letter from Cressida. 'What does she say?' he asked. Troilus looked at the letter. 'Words, words,' he answered, 'mere words; no message from the heart.' Tearing the paper into small pieces, he mounted his horse and rode to the field.

It would be a sad day for the chivalry of Troy. In the beginning it seemed that the Greeks had been forced to retreat. Hector performed such deeds of valour that by noon Agamemnon was calling for men to reinforce his wavering army. Then all was changed. Both Achilles, savage at the death of his best friend Patroclus, and Ajax, who from sheer pride had refused to arm that day, came thundering out to war. With Achilles were his dreaded Myrmidons, his personal troops, pitiless and grim of aspect, that followed him wherever he might move. The battle became fiercely even. Troilus, fighting like Hector's brother, came many times face to face with Diomedes, but neither could gain an advantage, though Troilus lost his horse to the Greek.

At the battle's height Achilles summoned the Myrmidons about him: 'Mark what I say – and attend my every step. Strike not until Hector is found. Then encircle him with your weapons and show no mercy.' It was near sunset when Hector, weary and alone, sat down to rest. He took off his helmet and hung his shield behind him; and he was lying there, unarmed, when Achilles and the Myrmidons, who had marked his every movement, stole upon him and ringed him with their swords. Hector, looking up, knew that his life was ended. 'I am unarmed,' he said. 'Take no advantage, Greek.' But Achilles, with savage jubilation, responded merely, 'Strike, fellows, strike! This is the man I seek.' Moving together, the sable-armoured Myrmidons advanced on Hector and thrust their swords into his defenceless body; and, as he fell dead, Achilles shouted in triumph, 'So, Ilium, fall thou next. Now Troy, sink down! On, Myrmidons! Cry it round the field: Achilles hath this mighty Hector slain.'

It was twilight, and trumpeters had summoned the armies to retire. Achilles sheathed his sword. 'Come,' he ordered, 'tie the body to my horse's tail and let me drag the Trojan through the field.' Within a few minutes, waving his sword, he rode off on his grey charger, the Myrmidons massing behind him as they shouted, 'Achilles hath slain Hector!' and 'Achilles! Achilles!'

It had already been noised round the field that Hector was dead. When the news reached Agamemnon, he said very simply, 'If it is true, great Troy is ours and these sharp wars are ended.'

Despair lay heavily upon the Trojans as they clustered in the gloom. Troilus stared up at the lights upon the hill of Troy. 'Hector is gone,' he said in dazed grief. 'What word is this for Priam? What word for our sorrowing city? . . . Hector is dead. There is no more to say.' He shook his sword at the distant twinkling cluster of the Greek tents. 'Achilles, coward! No space of earth shall free you from my hate. I'll haunt you like a wicked conscience still.'

'Come, my lord!' said Aeneas.

Troilus turned with drooping head. 'Ay, strike up our march to Troy. Hope of revenge must hide this deadly woe.' As the Trojans set their silent course towards the city, the figure of Pandarus appeared from the dark plain, calling to Troilus, 'Hear you, hear you!' And Troilus repelled him with a bitter exclamation, 'Ignominy and shame pursue you and live for ever with your name!'

The weary soldiers had reached the shadow of the city wall. The only noise was the measured tramp of marching feet. Presently the immense gate of Troy clanged shut behind the stragglers, and they heard, borne faintly from the distance, a sound as of women weeping.

CORIOLANUS

ONE blusterous morning in ancient Rome, a company of citizens thronged a street, bearing staves and clubs and crying out against the famine in the city, and the patricians who allowed it to exist while their own storehouses were crammed with grain.

The burly man who led the mutineers shouted in a voice that was full and reverberating, 'You are resolved rather to die than to famish. Caius Marcius is chief enemy to the people. Then let us kill him and we shall have corn at our own price. If the patricians who get too much corn would but give to us their overplus while it is wholesome, they would be humane. But they will not do so, so let us revenge ourselves with our weapons. The gods know that I speak this in hunger for bread, not in thirst for revenge.'

Another citizen spoke. 'Would you proceed especially against Caius Marcius?' There was an answering roar: 'Against him first: he is a very dog to the common people.'

'But,' said the man, 'consider, friends, what services he has done for his country.' The first citizen replied, 'Very well, we would be content to applaud him for it. But he is merely proud. He has not toiled for his country, but only to please his mother and himself.'

'Still,' urged the second citizen, 'you must not say he is covetous.'

'If I must not,' replied the other hotly, 'I do not lack further accusations. He has faults more than enough.' They listened for a moment to a distant cry. 'The other side of the city is risen. Why do we stay here prating? Come to the Capitol.'

There entered the street, as he spoke, a white-haired patrician whom the second citizen hailed as 'Worthy Menenius Agrippa, one that has always loved the people.' Even the first citizen had to say grudgingly that the man was honest enough.

Menenius Agrippa considered the angry faces: 'What work is in hand, my countrymen, and where go you with bats and clubs?' Immediately the second citizen retorted that for a full fortnight the

Senate had known what they intended to do. Poor suitors had strong breaths; it should be realised also that they had strong arms.

Menenius Agrippa tried to reason with them. The patricians, he said, had most charitable care of the needy, and the commoners might as well strike at heaven with their staves as lift them now against the Roman state. The gods, not the patricians, had caused the famine. Were it not better then to kneel to the gods than to attack men who cared as fathers for those who cursed them as enemies?

It was an unfortunate moment to say this. While Menenius was still speaking, the patrician Caius Marcius, a noble, arrogant man, as handsome as a marble figure and himself marble-proud, walked disdainfully down the street. He studied the crowd with contempt. 'What's the matter, you dissentious rogues? What would you have, you curs that like not peace or war? You are no surer than a coal of fire upon the ice, a hailstone in the sun. He that depends on your favours must swim with fins of lead. Every minute you change your minds, calling a man noble that was once your hate, or vile whom you had loved . . . What do they seek now, Menenius?'

'For corn at their own rates. They say the city is well stored with it.'

'*They* say,' exclaimed Marcius with emphatic irony. 'They sit by the fire and presume to know what's done in the Capitol. Why, if the nobility would let me use my sword, I'd make a heap of dead.'

The citizens, pressed back to the walls, watched these men talking. 'Where is the other troop?' Menenius asked. Marcius replied that it had been dispersed. Its members had vented their complaints and the Senate had granted them a strange petition: five tribunes to act as their voices. One was Junius Brutus, another Sicinius Velutus; he knew not the others, but the rabble should have unroofed the city before they had so prevailed with him. He raised his hand: 'Go, get you home, you fragments!'

They were dispersing moodily when a messenger sped along the street with news that the Volsces were in arms, commanded by Tullus Aufidius. Almost at once the senators, passing by, ordered Marcius to attend upon the Roman general Cominius; and, pointing to the swarm of citizens, Marcius exclaimed in anger, 'The Volsces have much corn. Take these rats hither to gnaw the granaries.' Quickly the citizens stole away: soon everyone had gone but the newly-honoured tribunes who cried out against Marcius and his intolerable scorn. 'Such a nature,' said Sicinius Velutus, 'disdains the shadow that he treads upon at noon.' Smouldering with discontent, they followed the senators.

Immediately Marcius left Rome upon his Volscian campaign. In his house, after some weeks had passed, his mother Volumnia and his wife Virgilia sat at needlework. Volumnia was a redoubtable Roman matron, fearing nothing. Her daughter-in-law, of a softer mould, had a settled melancholy that caused Volumnia to say, 'I beg you, daughter, sing, or express yourself more cheerfully. If my son were my husband, I should rejoice in the absence wherein he gains his honour. As a boy I sent him, my only son, to the cruel war from which he returned wearing the garland of honour. Had I a dozen sons, and none less dear than Marcius, I had rather eleven died nobly for their country than that one should idle his life away at home.'

'Heaven keep my lord from fell Aufidius!' said Virgilia. Her mother-in-law retorted, 'He'll beat Aufidius' head below his knee and tread upon his neck.'

Virgilia's friend, Valeria, called now to take her out of doors; but Virgilia answered that until her husband came back she would not pass the threshold. Still Valeria insisted, while Volumnia listened in impatience. 'Go with me,' Valeria said, 'and I'll tell you excellent news of your husband. I heard a senator speak it last night. Cominius has taken one part of our Roman power against the army of the Volsces. But your lord and Titus Lartius are besieging the city of Corioli and mean that the war shall be brief. Now, I pray you, go with us. Sweet lady Virgilia, come, forget this solemn mood.'

'Let her be,' said Volumnia. 'She will be poor company for us.' And Virgilia, as she desired, was left alone.

While she worried about her absent husband, Marcius was doing deeds of high valour at Corioli. Unaided, he entered the gate of the city. When the place was won he insisted on taking his men against the neighbouring Volscian army led by Aufidius. Finally, in full battle, he met Aufidius hand to hand and had almost beaten him down when other Volscians ran to their shamed general's help. That night Marcius stood before the Romans, his arm in a scarf, while Cominius praised him:

'If I were to tell you of your deeds to-day, you'd not believe it; but I shall report them, Marcius, in Rome. Even the dull tribunes that hate your honour must say against their hearts: "We thank the gods our Rome has such a soldier." '

Marcius put all compliment aside. 'No more,' he said. 'Even my mother grieves me when she praises me. I have done as all of you have done—what I can, and for my country.' Again Cominius promised that Rome should hear of his deeds, and that a tenth of the day's booty would be his. Marcius refused it, and it was while he still shrugged off his honours that the trumpets of the army pealed and the soldiers, crying 'Marcius! Marcius!', flung up their caps and lances. 'May those same instruments that you profane never sound more,' he shouted wrathfully. 'Must drum and trumpet in the field prove flatterers!'

Cominius, knowing his man, paid no heed. Advancing, he spoke to the assembled legions. 'Be it known to all the world, as it is to us, that Caius Marcius wears the garland of the war. In token of his feats I give to him my noble steed and all that goes with it. And from this hour, for what he did to-day before Corioli, we call him, with all the applause and clamour of our host, Caius Marcius Coriolanus. Now bear that addition nobly.'

Once more the trumpets and drums. Then the army's roar of 'Coriolanus!' rose to the drifting clouds.

'I will go wash,' said the new-made Coriolanus. 'When my face is fair, you will see whether I blush or not . . . Still, I thank you.'

The noise of the cheering was heard far off by Tullus Aufidius, the Volscian, as he glowered upon his defeat. Five times he had fought with Coriolanus; five times he had been the loser. But he swore that if ever they met again, beard to beard, one of them should die. He would spare no craft to revenge himself. 'Wherever I find him, be it at my very hearth, my sword shall pay this score.'

For the time the wars were done. In Rome Menenius Agrippa and the tribunes of the people were still talking of Marcius. When the tribunes complained of his pride and his arrogance, Menenius threw back his head in despair: 'Pride! You talk of pride! O that you could turn your eyes towards the nape of your necks and see yourselves through and through.'

'What then, sir?' demanded Junius Brutus unwisely.

'Why,' said Menenius, 'you would discover two as proud, violent testy magistrates, alias fools, as there are in the city of Rome.'

'You are known well enough too,' said Sicinius Velutus sourly.

'I am known,' rejoined Menenius, 'as a whimsical patrician that loves his cup of hot wine without water in it. I am easily offended. I rise late. What I think, I utter. But then you know neither me nor yourselves nor anything.' As the tribunes walked sulkily aside, Volumnia bore down upon Menenius. 'Honourable friend,' she said, 'my boy Marcius approaches. For the love of Juno, let's go. Look, here's a letter from him; the state has another, his wife another, and I think there is one at home for you.'

'I will make my very house reel to-night,' said Menenius, as excited as she. 'Is he not wounded? He has usually come home wounded.' Virgilia cried, 'O no, no, no!' but Volumnia answered that Marcius was indeed wounded and she thanked the gods for it. Agreeing, Menenius asked anxiously if Marcius had brought victory home in his pocket, and Volumnia said that he bore it on his brows, for he came the third time back with the oaken garland. The Senate had letters from Cominius that gave to Marcius the whole honour of the war; he had outdone his former deeds doubly.

Menenius glanced round to make sure that the tribunes had heard every word of this, and that they knew Marcius was returning. Volumnia talked on. Her son had been wounded in the shoulder and the left arm. Before the last expedition he had had twenty-five wounds. Now it would be twenty-seven, every gash an enemy's grave.

Trumpets shrilled. Between the generals Cominius and Titus Lartius walked the hero of the wars, crowned with his oaken wreath. Behind, in long marching order, were the soldiers of Rome. They halted, and into the open came a herald. 'Know, Rome,' he cried, 'that all alone Marcius did fight within Corioli gates. There his new name was won. Salute him with it now! Welcome to Rome, renownèd Coriolanus!'

Coriolanus, in customary embarrassment, said, 'Pray, no more!' Cominius pointed to his mother, and Coriolanus, who deferred to her beyond any person in the world, knelt at her feet. As she lifted him, she motioned to Virgilia who stood speechless by her side. Coriolanus, embracing his wife lovingly, said to her, 'My gracious silence, hail! O, my dear, such eyes the widows of Corioli have, and mothers that lack sons.'

'The gods crown thee!' put in Menenius. Coriolanus gripped his hand: 'And live you yet?' Menenius, repeating 'A thousand, thousand welcomes!', added in his loudest voice, 'You generals are men that Rome should dote on. Yet, by the faith of men, we have some old crabtrees here at home that will not find you worthy.' The tribunes of the people did not speak until the procession had swept forward to the Capitol. Then their glances met. For a while every tongue held the name of Coriolanus; clearly he would be consul, and if he were elected, patrician of the patricians as he was, the people's officers might well sleep during his term of office. Only one hope lived: that Coriolanus might give to the commoners cause to remember their malice against him, for if he did, his new-born honours would fade as if they had never been. Had he not said once that, were he to stand for consul, he would never appear in the market-place wearing the prescribed gown of humility, showing his wounds, and begging from the people their votes for his election? If he still refused the ancient rite, then might he be destroyed. Meanwhile the tribunes would remind the commoners of the hatred Coriolanus had shown for them; some day his insolence must set the people blazing, and the blaze would destroy him for ever.

The tribunes were conferring malevolently when a messenger reached them to say that they were needed at the Capitol, for it was thought that Coriolanus would be consul. The nobles bowed to him as if he were Jove's statue, and the commons made a thunder that none before had heard.

In the Capitol the senators, Cominius as consul, had taken their places. Coriolanus waited, standing; and the tribunes of the people sat apart. First, Menenius Agrippa rose to desire Cominius, as their present consul and as general in the late Volscian war, to proclaim to them the deeds of Coriolanus; and another senator wished that the tribunes of the people might listen kindly and report in that vein to the commoners. Junius Brutus replied shortly that they would be happy to do this if Coriolanus would think more warmly of the people than he had done before. Coriolanus himself had wandered away, saying that he would rather have his wounds again than hear how he had got them.

When he was out of sight Cominius began to praise him without reserve. If it were held that valour, of all virtues, were the chief, then in the world no man could stand by Coriolanus. At sixteen years he went out to fight against Tarquin and struck him to the knee. For his feats that day he was brow-bound with the oak. Since then he had fought in seventeen battles. At Corioli where he made even the coward turn terror into sport, from face to foot he was a thing of blood. Alone he had entered the gate of Corioli, fought his way from the city, and then again struck it like a planet. Until the Romans called both field and city theirs he had never paused to rest his driving sword. His deeds were this man's life: he cared for nothing else.

The speech done, Coriolanus was summoned again, and Menenius Agrippa rose joyfully: 'The Senate are well pleased to make thee consul.' Coriolanus inclined his head: 'I owe them still my life and services.'

So much was completed; but there remained yet an ancient custom for which the tribunes waited. Before final election the man named as consul had to show himself in the rough gown of humility and beg the people's voice as they passed by him in the market-place. Coriolanus begged that this custom should be put aside; and at once Sicinius Velutus rose to say that the people would not give up a single jot of ceremony. Urged by Menenius not to stir up needless opposition, Coriolanus unwillingly consented.

After an hour he walked into the forum with Menenius. Wearing with distaste the humble gown, he was ready to do his part. Before he appeared, the citizens, talking among themselves with animation, had agreed that if only Coriolanus would incline to the people, there was no worthier man for the office. Now he took his stand, and they prepared to pass by him in ones and twos while he made the traditional request.

Menenius was finding it hard to keep his friend calm and to impress upon him that at all costs he must be courteous. With some doubt the old man left the forum. There, as the first citizens moved by self-consciously, Coriolanus said curtly, 'You know the cause of my standing here?' 'What has brought you to it?' said one of the men; and Coriolanus answered, 'My own desert, nay, not my own desire.' A second citizen said plainly, 'You must think, sir, that if we give you anything, we hope to gain by you.' Coriolanus flashed back, 'Well, then, I pray, your price of the consulship?'

'The price is, to ask it kindly.'

Coriolanus spoke with quite unnatural calm: 'Kindly, sir, I beg you to let me have it.' He paused before saying rapidly, 'I have wounds to show – which shall be yours in private. Your good voice, sir?'

'You shall have it,' said one of the citizens. 'Then I have your alms,' rapped Coriolanus. 'Adieu!' The two citizens went perplexed away. 'But that is something odd,' one of them mused. The other hesitated: 'If I were to give my voice again – but it is no matter.'

So the ceremony proceeded, Coriolanus treating every passer-by with servility that was exaggerated or irony that was mocking. 'Rather than fool it so,' he muttered, 'let the high office and the honours go to a man that could approve this task.' But at least half of it was over, and soon all was ended. Menenius reappeared, with the frowning tribunes. Coriolanus had received the popular voice. Nothing remained but a formal gathering at the Senate House.

Or so it seemed. But now the tribunes, deeply embittered, were setting out to reverse the election. It was not difficult. They listened to the plebeians saying how Coriolanus had mocked them even while he begged their voices; and how, using them scornfully, he had refused to show his wounds. At once Sicinius Velutus and Junius Brutus asked why the man had not been rejected. He had been the people's enemy. He had spoken against their liberties and charters, and if he continued to be their foe they had cursed themselves in choosing him.

By this time the fickle crowd was changing. Coriolanus was not yet confirmed; he must be denied. The tribunes ordered it to be spread about that he was no man for consul, that he still held the people in contempt, and that an ignorant election must be swiftly revoked. The plebeians heard and obeyed. Very soon, in a rabble ominously sullen, they converged upon the Capitol from every side.

Unaware of all this, Coriolanus was near his home with the patricians, studying fresh news of impending war. The Volscians, still under the command of Tullus Aufidius, looked for the right moment to advance again on Rome; Aufidius himself was in his city of Antium with the heads of the Volscian state. When he spoke, during a parley, with the Roman general Titus Lartius he had declared that, of all people on the earth, he hated Coriolanus most. His passion rising, Coriolanus longed for a cause to seek Aufidius in Antium, and he was saying so to Titus Lartius when the tribunes met them in mid-street and warned them not to pass. It would be dangerous, Junius Brutus said: the people were incensed and would not have Coriolanus as their consul.

The man's easily-roused anger swelled to high tide. When, he exclaimed, the patricians of Rome deferred to the rank-scented multitude, they merely nourished the seed of insolence and rebellion.

Catching delightedly at his words, the tribunes promised to let the people know of them. With unguarded contempt Coriolanus railed on. The plebeians had not deserved the stored corn that was given to them. When summoned to the wars, few of them would go; those that did showed most valour in their mutiny.

So he raged in fiery declamation against the rabble until Sicinius Velutus shouted, 'He has spoken like a traitor, and shall answer as traitors do,' and Junius Brutus ordered: 'Let him be apprehended.'

'Go, call the people,' said Sicinius to an officer. He confronted Coriolanus: 'In the name of the people I arrest you as a foe to the public weal.'

'Hence, old goat!' blazed Coriolanus. 'Hence, rotten thing, or I shall shake your bones out of your garments.'

Within minutes they were surrounded by a screaming, shouting crowd whose main cry was 'Down with him! Down with him!' At length some order was restored, though the mob was still perilously restive near Coriolanus who had relapsed into imperious calm. The tribunes spoke briefly. Sicinius demanded that Coriolanus should be sentenced to death; Junius Brutus, on behalf of the people, pronounced the sentence; and Sicinius ordered that he should be cast forthwith from the summit of the steep Tarpeian Rock. 'Yield, Marcius, yield!' thundered the mob. It was then that Coriolanus, breaking a contemptuous silence, drew his sword: 'I'll die here. Some among you have beheld me fighting. Then meet me now yourselves.' In a few moments the tribunes and the people were beaten off, and Menenius said quickly, 'Coriolanus, get to your house. Away, or all will be nought.' But

Coriolanus was intent on nothing but battle: 'On fair ground I could beat forty of them.' Menenius implored him to go with Cominius, saying to a senator as Coriolanus swung on his heel without a further glance at the mob, 'His nature is too noble for the world. His heart's his mouth.'

Again the mob pressed forward; again Sicinius cried that Coriolanus should be thrown from the Tarpeian Rock; again Menenius sought to allay this fury. Let them consider: Coriolanus had been bred in war since he could draw a sword; he was unschooled in tactful terms. Would it not be better to bring him to the Forum and to mark there how he answered the charges against him? To this course the tribunes agreed; and Menenius swore to fetch Coriolanus to them.

In his house Coriolanus stormed on, vowing that he would not treat the plebeians differently whatever death they might ordain for him. Only one thing puzzled him now: his mother had been as disdainful as he was, so why did she wish him to be milder? Volumnia spoke sternly: 'I would you had put your power well on before you risked it thus.' Menenius, profoundly troubled, entered from the tribunes. Coriolanus must retract what he had spoken; there was no other way. All present, his mother and his friends, begged him to do so; Volumnia told him to kneel before the people, to tell him that he was their soldier, and, being bred to war, lacked a soft and winning tongue.

It seemed of a sudden that he was persuaded. Bitter yet, he kept control: 'I'll play with them for their loves, and come home the friend of every trade in Rome. Do not fear, mother. I'll return as consul, or never trust me further in the way of flattery.' And he looked back at them from the door: 'The word is *mildly*.'

The tribunes awaited him in the Forum, their plan prepared. Immediately they would accuse him of seeking tyrannical power. If he evaded the charge, then they would insist upon his hatred of the people and claim that the spoils of the Volscian war had not been distributed. An officer was told to assemble the people and to warn them that when they heard Sicinius cry, 'It shall be so in the name and right of the commons,' they should respond either 'Fine!' or 'Death!' or 'Banishment!' according to the tribune's word. Further, once the shout had been raised, it must continue in a confused uproar until sentence had been carried out. 'Put him to anger straight,' said Junius Brutus to his partner. 'Once he is roused, he speaks what is in his heart.'

Coriolanus was carefully, self-consciously, controlled as he entered in the ranks of the patricians and formally besought the gods to keep Rome in safety. A vast mob had collected. Sicinius Velutus demanded that Coriolanus should submit there and then to the people's voice and yield to lawful censure.

As Coriolanus answered, Menenius saw in his eye a familiar and deadly glint. Why, having been passed with full voice for consul, did they wish to dishonour him? Sicinius thrust back: 'We charge you with seeking tyrannous power for which you are a traitor to the people.'

Menenius felt his restraining hand pushed away. 'The fires of the lowest hell enfold the people!' cried Coriolanus. 'Call me their traitor, injurious tribune! You lie!'

The people shouted with a single terrifying voice, 'To the Rock! To the Rock!' Menenius tried to speak; but Coriolanus, past all care, said, 'I would not buy their mercy at the price of one fair word.' It was left to Sicinius Velutus to proclaim: 'In the name of the people, and in the power of us the tribunes, we banish him from our city, never more to enter the gates of Rome. In the people's name, I say it shall be so.' Behind him was the thunder of 'It shall be so! It shall be so! He is banished, and it shall be so!' Though Cominius opened his mouth, every word was obscured by the full chanted roar, 'It shall be so! It shall be so!'

Then for one moment the tones of Coriolanus were raised above all else like a storm-wind: 'You common cry of curs, whose breath I hate as reek of the rotten fens; whose loves I prize as the dead carcases of unburied men that do corrupt my air, I banish *you.*' His voice wavered: 'Despising, for you, this city, thus I turn my back . . . There is a world elsewhere.' And he passed from their sight.

A short time later, at a city gate, he said farewell to his mother and his weeping wife, to Menenius Agrippa, to Cominius, and to the young nobility of Rome: 'A brief farewell. The beast with many heads butts me away. My mother, where is your ancient courage? Farewell, my wife, I'll do better yet. My old and true Menenius, my friends of noble touch, when I have gone bid me farewell and smile. While I remain above the ground, you shall hear from me still.' He turned and walked through the gate. Presently he rode away into the quiet evening.

Within the city the tribunes, in high glee, had dismissed the people. But they could not escape from Volumnia who met them with the cry, 'The hoarded plagues of the gods requite your love!' and lashed them with her words until they fled in dismay. 'Come,' she said then to Virgilia. 'Come, let's go. Lament as I do, in anger Juno-like.'

Some weeks passed. Upon an evening in the Volscian city of Antium, lights glowed from every window in the house of Tullus Aufidius where the general feasted the nobles of the state. Wearing mean apparel and with his face muffled, Coriolanus came to find the man who had been his unrelenting enemy. 'If he slay me,' he said to himself, 'he does fair justice, but if he receives me well I'll do much for his country.' He entered the house and lingered in its wide hall. Attendants hurried to and fro with food and wine. Music sounded within, and voices called for service. One of the attendants caught sight of the meanly-clothed stranger and stopped, telling him that the porter should have forbidden him entry. Other servitors approached with threats; Coriolanus was surrounded and asked curiously where he dwelt. Replying 'Under the canopy – in the city of kites and crows,' he struck the men from him angrily just as the magnificent figure of the Volscian Aufidius strode into the hall, saying, 'Where is this fellow?'

Puzzled, he looked Coriolanus up and down: 'Speak, man, what is your name? I know you not.' Unmoving, Coriolanus began to reply: 'My name is Caius Marcius who hath done to you particularly, and to all the Volsces, great hurt and mischief. Witness my surname Coriolanus—.'

'Coriolanus!' In astonishment Tullus Aufidius clapped his hand upon his sword-hilt, but Coriolanus went on, 'Only that name remains. The cruelty and envy of the people drove me from Rome. The dastard nobles have forsaken me. I come to you now not out of hope to save my life, for if I feared death, Aufidius, of all men would I have avoided you. It is for revenge I come. Use then my misery that this revengeful mood may do you service, for I will fight against my cankered country with all the spleen of the under-fiends. If you dare not accept my offer, kill me where I stand.'

With a cry, Tullus Aufidius embraced him. 'Each word has weeded from my heart a root of ancient envy. Let me twine my arms about you – about that body I sought so often to destroy. Marcius, our army waits. I had proposed once more to fight with you; but now, most absolute sir, if you will lead your own revenges against Rome, be general here with me. First, come in; let me commend you to our senators and those who shall acclaim you. A thousand welcomes, and more a friend than ever enemy – though, Marcius, that was much.'

It was not long before the Volscians, under the joint command of Marcius and Aufidius, marched resolutely upon Rome. The city had been placid and unprepared. The tribunes were lazily complacent. No news had come of Coriolanus. Old Menenius, sad and loyal, had waited to hear from him. Now he heard more than he had bargained, for news arrived on a sultry morning that the Volscians were driving towards Rome, burning and destroying, with the revengeful Coriolanus as their leader. If this were so, the city could have no hope; a man so scorned would never relent. The fickle mob, learning the news, began to say that Coriolanus should never have been banished; but it was far too late for easy repentance. Cominius went out to plead with his old comrade and found him inflexible, sitting in armour of gold, his eye red as if it would burn Rome. He would hear nothing of his private friends; he had no mercy to the city that had cast him off. Even Menenius whom he had loved more than any other man, could not shake his will. Going alone as an ambassador, the old patrician wept before Coriolanus, saying, 'My son, my son, you are preparing fire for us. Look, here is water to quench it. I beseech you to pardon Rome and your pleading countrymen.' Coriolanus replied to him: 'Wife, mother, child, I know not. Menenius, I will not hear another word.' Rome was on the edge.

Tullus Aufidius had become jealous of the power of Coriolanus and resentful of his haughty bearing among the Volscians. The man, he said, must not be allowed to hold his place when Rome had fallen, as fall it inevitably must, for it was now not a day's march distant. Coriolanus and Aufidius were in council when they heard shouting from soldiers outside their tent. There, walking towards them between the guards and habited in deepest black, were Virgilia, Volumnia who led her grandson Young Marcius, and, behind them, Valeria. Touched though he was by this unexpected sight, and by his mother's bow to him – 'as if Olympus to a molehill should in supplication nod' – Coriolanus swore to himself to remain obdurate through the hardest test of all.

To Virgilia's 'My lord and husband!' he replied coldly, 'These eyes are not the same I wore in Rome.' But he embraced her and knelt as a son before his mother. Volumnia, raising him, sank to her own knees, something he had never known. Half-dazed, he acknowledged the kneeling Valeria and his young son; then when Volumnia said they came as suitors to him, he turned back, begging them to speak no more. Volumnia, who had risen, would not be put by. They were, she said, more unfortunate than any living women. Whatever happened now must be calamity: either Coriolanus must tread upon a ruined Rome or be led a prisoner through the streets. If he conquered Rome, his name would be remembered only as the destroyer of his own country. And she cried, 'Speak to me, son. Do you think it is honourable for a noble man still to remember wrongs? Daughter, speak to him; he cares not for your tears. Speak, my grandson; perhaps your childishness will move him more than our reasons can. There is no man in the world that owes more to his mother, yet here must I speak unheeded . . . So, you turn away. Once more, ladies, let us shame him with our knees . . . Yet no reply. This is the end: we will back to Rome and die among our neighbours. Let us go!' Volumnia faced him with the contempt that she herself had taught him: 'Sir, dismiss us now. I am hushed until Rome be on fire, and then I'll speak a little.'

The women waited, sombre in the burning noon among the martial glitter of the camp. All round them was very still. Aufidius and the Volscian officers behind Coriolanus had not shifted a foot. He himself, unable to hide his agonised longing, had borne it until he could bear no more. Now, as he clasped Volumnia's hand, he broke down, suddenly and unashamed: 'O, mother, mother, what have you done? O you have won a happy victory for Rome – but for your son, believe it, O believe it, most dangerous is this yielding!'

Volumnia, who had heard almost disbelievingly, saw the tears on her son's cheek and wept in her relief: so did Virgilia and Valeria. Coriolanus spoke to the Volscian leader: 'Aufidius, were you in my place, would you have granted less?' Aufidius said softly, 'I was moved'; but his eyes belied it. He did not answer when Coriolanus went on, 'What peace you'd make, advise me. For my part, I'll not to Rome. I'll back with you. Stand with me in this cause.' Even while he spoke he knew that Aufidius was once more the implacable enemy of old. He turned to his wife and mother: 'Ladies, you deserve to have a temple built you. All the swords in Italy, and her confederate arms, could not have made this peace.'

While Volumnia and the rest were being greeted in Rome with the noise of drum and fife and trumpet, the crowd's joyful acclamation, and the strewing of flowers along their path, the Volscian army remained in its camp to await the making of a treaty. This accomplished, it began its slow march back to Corioli. Tullus Aufidius, reaching the city first, convened his conspirators. Already he had written to the Volscian lords his account of what had passed. Coriolanus, he said, must die.

Soon, at the head of the army, the crowd cheering it home as it marched beneath the gold insignia of the Volsces, Coriolanus entered the market-place of Corioli and thus addressed the waiting senators: 'Hail, lords, I am returned your soldier, no more a lover of my country than when I left it. I have led your wars even to the gates of Rome, and there we made peace with no less honour to the Volscian realm than shame unto the Romans.'

The senators listened motionless. Pausing uncertainly, Coriolanus proceeded, 'Our spoils are great. Here I deliver, signed by the consul and patricians, and with the Senate's seal, what Rome has yielded to us.' He held up the parchment, and Tullus Aufidius exclaimed, 'Read it not, noble lords. Tell the traitor in the highest degree how he has abused your powers.'

Coriolanus started. 'Traitor!'

'Ay, traitor Marcius – Caius Marcius! Who would grace you with your stolen name – Coriolanus, here in Corioli? You lords of the state, this man has given up your city – I say your city – Rome, unto his wife and mother, breaking his oath and resolution like a twist of rotten silk.'

'Hear'st thou, Mars!' exclaimed Coriolanus; and Aufidius said bitterly, 'Name not the god, you boy of tears.'

Coriolanus could see no pity in any face. He was overwhelmed by enemies. But trapped though he might be, he would die as he had lived, in Roman pride, and he lifted his voice in a last brag: 'Cut me to pieces, Volscians. Men and lads, stain all your edges on me!' And he leapt towards Aufidius. 'You called me boy! Here, like an eagle in a dovecote, I fluttered your Volscians – in Corioli!' His sword flashed. 'Alone I did it.'

All was in storm. The people closed in menacingly, shouting, 'Tear him to pieces!', 'He killed my son,' 'He killed my father.' A senator was heard to say helplessly, 'The man is noble.' But everything was obliterated by the staccato chorus of the conspirators: 'Kill, kill, kill, kill him!' On the last word their swords struck as one, and Coriolanus was stabbed to the ground. Aufidius placed his foot upon the corpse. But, as he stood there, panting, an old senator rose with an authoritative command: 'Bear hence the body, and let it be regarded as the noblest that ever herald followed.'

Aufidius had lowered his sword. 'My rage,' he said, 'is gone, and I am lost in sorrow. Take him up. Though in Corioli he has done much wrong, yet he shall have a noble memory.' With three of his officers he raised the body of Coriolanus; and slowly, to the notes of a dead march, they bore it upon their shoulders to the place of burial.

ROMEO AND JULIET

◆◆◆◆◆◆◆◆◆

The two chief families in Verona were the rich Capulets and the Montagues. There had been an old quarrel between these families, which was grown to such a height, and so deadly was the enmity between them, that it extended to the remotest kindred, to the followers and retainers of both sides, insomuch that a servant of the house of Montague could not meet a servant of the house of Capulet, nor a Capulet encounter with a Montague by chance, but fierce words and sometimes bloodshed ensued; and frequent were the brawls from such accidental meetings, which disturbed the happy quiet of Verona's streets.

Old Lord Capulet made a great supper, to which many fair ladies and many noble guests were invited. All the admired beauties of Verona were present, and all comers were made welcome if they were not of the house of Montague. At this feast of Capulets, Rosaline, beloved of Romeo, son to the old Lord Montague, was present; and though it was dangerous for a Montague to be seen in this assembly, yet Benvolio, a friend of Romeo, persuaded the young lord to go to this assembly in the disguise of a mask, that he might see his Rosaline, and seeing her, compare her with some choice beauties of Verona, who (he said) would make him think his swan a crow. Romeo had small faith in Benvolio's words; nevertheless, for the love of Rosaline, he was persuaded to go. For Romeo was a sincere and passionate lover, and one that lost his sleep for love, and fled society to be alone, thinking on Rosaline, who disdained him, and never requited his love, with the least show of courtesy or affection; and Benvolio wished to cure his friend of this love by showing him diversity of ladies and company. To this feast of Capulets then young Romeo with Benvolio and their friend

Mercutio went masked. Old Capulet bid them welcome, and told them that ladies who had their toes unplagued with corns would dance with them. And the old man was light hearted and merry, and said that he had worn a mask when he was young, and could have told a whispering tale in a fair lady's ear. And they fell to dancing, and Romeo was suddenly struck with the exceeding beauty of a lady who danced there, who seemed to him to teach the torches to burn bright, and her beauty to show by night like a rich jewel worn by a blackamoor; beauty too rich for use, too dear for earth! like a snowy dove trooping with crows (he said), so richly did her beauty and perfections shine above the ladies her companions. While he uttered these praises, he was overheard by Tybalt, a nephew of Lord Capulet, who knew him by his voice to be Romeo. And this Tybalt, being of a fiery and passionate temper, could not endure that a Montague should come under cover of a mask, to fleer and scorn (as he said) at their solemnities. And he stormed and raged exceedingly, and would have struck young Romeo dead. But his uncle, the old Lord Capulet, would not suffer him to do any injury at that time, both out of respect to his guests, and because Romeo had borne himself like a gentleman, and all tongues in Verona bragged of him to be a virtuous and well-governed youth. Tybalt, forced to be patient against his will, restrained himself, but swore that this vile Montague should at another time dearly pay for his intrusion.

The dancing being done, Romeo watched the place where the lady stood; and under favour of his masking habit, which might seem to excuse in part the liberty, he presumed in the gentlest manner to take her by the hand, calling it a shrine, which if he profaned by touching it, he was a blushing pilgrim, and would kiss it for atonement. 'Good pilgrim,' answered the lady, 'your devotion shows by far too mannerly and too courtly: saints have hands, which pilgrims may touch, but kiss not.' – 'Have not saints lips, and pilgrims too?' said Romeo. 'Ay,' said the lady, 'lips which they must use in prayer.' – 'O then, my dear saint,' said Romeo, 'hear my prayer, and grant it, lest I despair.' In such like allusions and loving conceits they were engaged, when the lady was called away to her mother. And Romeo inquiring who her mother was, discovered that the lady whose peerless beauty he was so much struck with, was young Juliet, daughter and heir to the Lord

Capulet, the great enemy of the Montagues; and that he had unknowingly engaged his heart to his foe. This troubled him, but it could not dissuade him from loving. As little rest had Juliet, when she found that the gentleman that she had been talking with was Romeo and a Montague, for she had been suddenly smit with the same hasty and inconsiderate passion for Romeo, which he had conceived for her; and a prodigious birth of love it seemed to her, that she must love her enemy, and that her affections should settle there, where family considerations should induce her chiefly to hate.

It being midnight, Romeo with his companions departed; but they soon missed him, for, unable to stay away from the house where he had left his heart, he leaped the wall of an orchard which was at the back of Juliet's house. Here he had not been long, ruminating on his new love, when Juliet appeared above at a window, through which her exceeding beauty seemed to break like the light of the sun in the east; and the moon, which shone in the orchard with a faint light, appeared to Romeo as if sick and pale with grief at the superior lustre of this new sun. And she, leaning her cheek upon her hand, he passionately wished himself a glove upon that hand, that he might touch her cheek. She all this while thinking herself alone, fetched a deep sigh, and exclaimed, 'Ah me!' Romeo, enraptured to hear her speak, said softly, and unheard by her, 'O speak again, bright angel, for such you appear, being over my head, like a winged messenger from heaven whom mortals fall back to gaze upon.' She, unconscious of being overheard, and full of the new passion which that night's adventure had given birth to, called upon her lover by name (whom she supposed absent): 'O Romeo, Romeo!' said she, 'wherefore art thou Romeo? Deny thy father, and refuse thy name, for my sake; or if thou wilt not, be but my sworn love, and I no longer will be a Capulet.' Romeo, having this encouragement, would fain have spoken, but he was desirous of hearing more; and the lady continued her passionate discourse with herself (as she thought), still chiding Romeo for being Romeo and a Montague, and wishing him some other name, or that he would put away that hated name, and for that name which was no part of himself, he should take all herself. At this loving word Romeo could no longer refrain, but taking up the dialogue as if her words had been addressed to him personally, and not merely in fancy, he bade her call him Love, or by whatever other name she pleased, for he was no longer Romeo, if that name was displeasing to her. Juliet, alarmed to hear a man's voice in the garden, did not at first know who it was, that by favour of the night and darkness had thus stumbled upon the discovery of her secret; but when he spoke again, though her ears had not yet drunk a hundred words of that tongue's uttering, yet so nice is a lover's hearing, that she immediately knew him to be young Romeo, and she expostulated with him on the danger to which he had exposed himself by climbing the orchard walls, for if any of her kinsmen should find him there, it would be death to him being a Montague. 'Alack,' said Romeo, 'there is more peril in your eye, than in twenty of their swords. Do you but look kind upon me, lady, and I am proof against their enmity. Better my life should be ended by their hate, than that hated life should be prolonged, to live without your love.' – 'How came you into this place,' said Juliet, 'and by whose direction?' – 'Love directed me,' answered Romeo: 'I am no pilot, yet wert thou as far apart from me, as that vast shore which is washed with the farthest sea, I should venture for such merchandise.' A crimson blush came over Juliet's face, yet unseen by Romeo by reason of the night, when she reflected upon the discovery which she had made, yet not meaning to make it, of her love to Romeo. She would fain have recalled her words, but that was impossible: fain would she have stood upon form, and have kept her lover at a distance, as the custom of discreet ladies is, to frown and be perverse, and give their suitors harsh denials at first; to stand off, and affect a coyness or indifference, where they most love, that their lovers may not think them too lightly or too easily won; for the difficulty of attainment increases the value of the object. But there was no room in her case for denials, or puttings off, or any of the customary arts of delay and protracted courtship. Romeo had heard from her own tongue, when she did not dream that he was near her, a confession of her love. So with an honest frankness, which the novelty of her situation excused, she confirmed the truth of what he had before heard, and addressing him by the name of *fair Montague* (love can sweeten a sour name), she begged him not to impute her easy yielding to levity or an unworthy mind, but that he must lay the fault of it (if it were a fault) upon the accident of the night which had so strangely discovered her thoughts. And she added, that though her behaviour to him might not be sufficiently prudent, measured by the custom of her sex, yet that she would prove more true than many whose prudence was dissembling, and their modesty artificial cunning.

Romeo was beginning to call the heavens to witness, that nothing was farther from his thoughts than to impute a shadow of dishonour to such an honoured lady, when she stopped him, begging him not to swear; for although she joyed in him, yet she had no joy of that night's contract: it was too rash, too unadvised, too sudden. But he being urgent with her to exchange a vow of love with him that night, she said that she already had given him hers before he requested it; meaning, when he overheard her confession; but she would retract what she then bestowed, for the pleasure of giving it again, for her bounty was as infinite as the sea, and her love as deep. From this loving conference she was called away by her nurse, who slept with her, and thought it time for her to be in bed, for it was near to daybreak; but hastily returning, she said three or four words more to Romeo, the purport of which was, that if his love was indeed honourable, and his purpose marriage, she would send a messenger to him to-morrow, to appoint a time for their marriage, when she would lay all her fortunes at his feet, and follow him as her lord through the world. While they were settling this point, Juliet was repeatedly called for by her nurse, and went in and returned, and went and returned again, for she seemed as jealous of Romeo going from her, as a young girl of her bird, which she will let hop a little from her hand, and pluck it back with a silken thread; and Romeo was as loath to part as she; for the sweetest music to lovers is the sound of each other's tongues at night. But at last they parted, wishing mutually sweet sleep and rest for that night.

The day was breaking when they parted, and Romeo, who was too full of thoughts of his mistress and that blessed meeting to allow him to sleep, instead of going home, bent his course to a monastery hard by, to find Friar Lawrence. The good friar was already up at his devotions, but seeing young Romeo abroad so early, he conjectured rightly that he had not been abed that night, but that some distemper of youthful affection had kept him waking. He was right in imputing the cause of

Romeo's wakefulness to love, but he made a wrong guess at the object, for he thought that his love for Rosaline had kept him waking. But when Romeo revealed his new passion for Juliet, and requested the assistance of the friar to marry them that day, the holy man lifted up his eyes and hands in a sort of wonder at the sudden change in Romeo's affections, for he had been privy to all Romeo's love for Rosaline, and his many complaints of her disdain: and he said, that young men's love lay not truly in their hearts, but in their eyes. But Romeo replying, that he himself had often chidden him for doting on Rosaline, who could not love him again, whereas Juliet both loved and was beloved by him, the friar assented in some measure to his reasons; and thinking that a matrimonial alliance between young Juliet and Romeo might happily be the means of making up the long breach between the Capulets and the Montagues; which no one more lamented than this good friar, who was a friend to both the families and had often interposed his mediation to make up the quarrel without effect; partly moved by policy, and partly by his fondness for young Romeo, to whom he could deny nothing, the old man consented to join their hands in marriage.

Now was Romeo blessed indeed, and Juliet, who knew his intent from a messenger which she had despatched according to promise, did not fail to be early at the cell of Friar Lawrence, where their hands were joined in holy marriage; the good friar praying the heavens to smile upon that act, and in the union of this young Montague and young Capulet to bury the old strife and long dissensions of their families.

The ceremony being over, Juliet hastened home, where she stayed impatient for the coming of night, at which time Romeo promised to come and meet her in the orchard, where they had met the night before; and the time between seemed as tedious to her, as the night before some great festival seems to an impatient child, that has got new finery which it may not put on till the morning.

That same day, about noon, Romeo's friends, Benvolio and Mercutio, walking through the streets of Verona, were met by a party of the Capulets with the impetuous Tybalt at their head. This was the same angry Tybalt who would have fought with Romeo at old Lord Capulet's feast. He, seeing Mercutio, accused him bluntly of associating with Romeo, a Montague. Mercutio, who had as much fire and youthful blood in him as Tybalt, replied to this accusation with some sharpness; and in spite of all Benvolio could say to moderate their wrath, a quarrel was beginning, when Romeo himself passing that way, the fierce Tybalt turned from Mercutio to Romeo, and gave him the disgraceful appellation of villain. Romeo wished to avoid a quarrel with Tybalt above all men, because he was the kinsman of Juliet, and much beloved by her; besides, this young Montague had never thoroughly entered into the family quarrel, being by nature wise and gentle, and the name of a Capulet, which was his dear lady's name, was now rather a charm to allay resentment, than a watchword to excite fury. So he tried to reason with Tybalt, whom he saluted mildly by the name of *good Capulet*, as if he, though a Montague, had some secret pleasure in uttering that name: but Tybalt, who hated all Montagues as he hated hell, would hear no reason, but drew his weapon; and Mercutio, who knew not of Romeo's secret motive for desiring peace with Tybalt, but looked upon his present forbearance as a sort of calm dishonourable submission, with many disdainful words provoked Tybalt to the prosecution of his first quarrel with him; and Tybalt and Mercutio fought, till Mercutio fell, receiving his death's wound while Romeo and Benvolio were vainly endeavouring to part the combatants. Mercutio being dead, Romeo kept his temper no longer, but returned the scornful appellation of villain which Tybalt had given him; and they fought till Tybalt was slain by Romeo. This deadly broil falling out in the midst of Verona at noonday, the news of it quickly brought a crowd of citizens to the spot, and among them the old Lords Capulet and Montague, with their wives; and soon after arrived the prince himself, who being related to Mercutio, whom Tybalt had slain, and having had the peace of his government often disturbed by these brawls of Montagues and Capulets, came determined to put the law in strictest force against those who should be found to be offenders. Benvolio, who had been eye-witness to the fray, was commanded by the prince to relate the origin of it; which he did, keeping as near the truth as he could without injury to Romeo, softening and excusing the part which his friends took in it. Lady Capulet, whose extreme grief for the loss of her kinsman Tybalt made her keep no bounds in her revenge, exhorted the prince to do strict justice upon his murderer, and to pay no attention to Benvolio's representation, who being Romeo's friend and a Montague spoke partially. Thus she pleaded against her new son-in-law, but she knew not yet that he was her son-in-law and Juliet's husband. On the other hand was to be seen Lady Montague pleading for her child's life, and arguing with some justice that Romeo had done nothing worthy of punishment in taking the life of Tybalt, which was already forfeited to the law by his having slain Mercutio. The prince, unmoved by the passionate exclamations of these women, on a careful examination of the facts, pronounced his sentence, and by that sentence Romeo was banished from Verona.

Heavy news to young Juliet, who had been but a few hours a bride, and now by this decree seemed everlastingly divorced! When the tidings reached her, she at first gave way to rage against Romeo, who had slain her dear cousin: she called him a beautiful tyrant, a fiend angelical, a ravenous dove, a lamb with a wolf's nature, a serpent-heart hid with a flowering face, and other like contradictory names, which denoted the struggles in her mind between her love and her resentment: but in the end love got the mastery, and the tears which she shed for grief that Romeo had slain her cousin, turned to drops of joy that her husband lived whom Tybalt would have slain. Then came fresh tears, and they were altogether of grief for Romeo's banishment. That word was more terrible to her than the death of many Tybalts.

Romeo, after the fray, had taken refuge in Friar Lawrence's cell, where he was first made acquainted with the prince's sentence, which seemed to him far more terrible than death. To him it appeared there was no world out of Verona's walls, no living out of the sight of Juliet. Heaven was there where Juliet lived, and all beyond was purgatory, torture, hell. The good friar would have applied the consolation of philosophy to his griefs: but this frantic young man would hear of none, but like a madman he tore his hair, and threw himself all along upon the ground, as he said, to take the measure of his grave. From this unseemly state he was roused by a message from his dear lady, which a little revived him; and then the friar took the advantage to expostulate with him on the unmanly weakness which he had shown. He had slain

Tybalt, but would he also slay himself, slay his dear lady, who lived but in his life? The noble form of man, he said, was but a shape of wax, when it wanted the courage which should keep it firm. The law had been lenient to him, that instead of death, which he had incurred, had pronounced by the prince's mouth only banishment. He had slain Tybalt, but Tybalt would have slain him: there was a sort of happiness in that. Juliet was alive, and (beyond all hope) had become his dear wife; therein he was most happy. All these blessings, as the friar made them out to be, did Romeo put from him like a sullen misbehaved wench. And the friar bade him beware, for such as despaired (he said) died miserable. Then when Romeo was a little calmed, he counselled him that he should go that night and secretly take his leave of Juliet, and thence proceed straightways to Mantua, at which place he should sojourn, till the friar found fit occasion to publish his marriage, which might be a joyful means of reconciling their families; and then he did not doubt but the prince would be moved to pardon him, and he would return with twenty times more joy than he went forth with grief. Romeo was convinced by these wise counsels of the friar, and took his leave to go and seek his lady, proposing to stay with her that night, and by daybreak pursue his journey alone to Mantua; to which place the good friar promised to send him letters from time to time, acquainting him with the state of affairs at home.

That night Romeo passed with his dear wife, gaining secret admission to her chamber, from the orchard in which he had heard her confession of love the night before. That had been a night of unmixed joy and rapture; but the pleasures of this night, and the delight which these lovers took in each other's society, were sadly allayed with the prospect of parting, and the fatal adventures of the past day. The unwelcome daybreak seemed to come too soon, and when Juliet heard the morning song of the lark, she would have persuaded herself that it was the nightingale, which sings by night; but it was too truly the lark which sang, and a discordant and unpleasing note it seemed to her; and the streaks of day in the east too certainly pointed out that it was time for these lovers to part. Romeo took his leave of his dear wife with a heavy heart, promising to write to her from Mantua every hour in the day; and when he had descended from her chamber-window, as he stood below her on the ground, in that sad foreboding state of mind in which she was, he appeared to her eyes as one dead in the bottom of a tomb. Romeo's mind misgave him in like manner: but now he was forced hastily to depart, for it was death for him to be found within the walls of Verona after daybreak.

This was but the beginning of the tragedy of this pair of star-crossed lovers. Romeo had not been gone many days, before the old Lord Capulet proposed a match for Juliet. The husband he had chosen for her, not dreaming that she was married already, was Count Paris, a gallant, young, and noble gentleman, no unworthy suitor to the young Juliet, if she had never seen Romeo.

The terrified Juliet was in a sad perplexity at her father's offer. She pleaded her youth unsuitable to marriage, the recent death of Tybalt, which had left her spirits too weak to meet a husband with any face of joy, and how indecorous it would show for the family of the Capulets to be celebrating a nuptial feast, when his funeral solemnities were hardly over: she pleaded every reason against the match, but the true one, namely, that she was married already. But Lord Capulet was deaf to all her excuses, and in a peremptory manner ordered her to get ready, for by the following Thursday she should be married to Paris: and having found her a husband, rich, young, and noble, such as the proudest maid in Verona might joyfully accept, he could not bear that out of affected coyness, as he construed her denial, she should oppose obstacles to her own good fortune.

In this extremity Juliet applied to the friendly friar, always her counsellor in distress, and he asking her if she had resolution to undertake a desperate remedy, and she answering that she would go into the grave alive rather than marry Paris, her own dear husband living; he directed her to go home, and appear merry, and give her consent to marry Paris, according to her father's desire, and on the next night, which was the night before the marriage, to drink off the contents of a phial which he then gave her, the effect of which would be that for two-and-forty hours after drinking it she should appear cold and lifeless; and when the bridegroom came to fetch her in the morning, he would find her to appearance dead; that then she would be borne, as the manner in that country was, uncovered on a bier, to be buried in the family vault; that if she could put off womanish fear, and consent to this terrible trial, in forty-two hours after swallowing the liquid (such was its certain operation) she would be sure to awake, as from a dream; and before she should awake, he would let her husband know their drift, and he should come in the night, and bear her thence to Mantua. Love, and the dread of marrying Paris, gave young Juliet strength to undertake this horrible adventure; and she took the phial of the friar, promising to observe his directions.

Going from the monastery, she met the young Count Paris, and modestly dissembling, promised to become his bride. This was joyful news to the Lord Capulet and his wife. It seemed to put youth into the old man; and Juliet, who had displeased him exceedingly, by her refusal of the count, was his darling again, now she promised to be obedient. All things in the house were in a bustle against the approaching nuptials. No cost was spared to prepare such festival rejoicings as Verona had never before witnessed.

On the Wednesday night Juliet drank off the potion. She had many misgivings lest the friar, to avoid the blame which might be imputed to him for marrying her to Romeo, had given her poison; but then he was always known for a holy man: then lest she should awake before the time that Romeo was to come for her; whether the terror of the place, a vault full of dead Capulets' bones, and where Tybalt, all bloody, lay festering in his shroud, would not be enough to drive her distracted: again she thought of all the stories she had heard of spirits haunting the places where their bodies were bestowed. But then her love for Romeo, and her aversion for Paris returned, and she desperately swallowed the draught, and became insensible.

When young Paris came early in the morning with music to awaken his bride, instead of a living Juliet, her chamber presented the dreary spectacle of a lifeless corse. What death to his hopes! What confusion then reigned through the whole house! Poor Paris lamenting his bride, whom most detestable death had beguiled him of, had divorced from him even before their hands were joined. But still more piteous it was to hear the mournings of the old Lord and Lady Capulet, who having but this one, one poor loving child to rejoice and solace in, cruel death had snatched her from their sight, just as these careful parents were on the point of seeing her advanced (as they thought) by a promising and advantageous match. Now all things that were ordained for the festival were turned from their properties to do the office of a black funeral. The wedding cheer served for a sad burial feast, the bridal hymns were changed for sullen dirges, the sprightly instruments to melancholy bells, and the flowers that should have been strewed in the bride's path now served but to strew her corse. Now, instead of a priest to marry her, a priest was needed to bury her; and she was borne to church indeed, not to augment the cheerful hopes of the living, but to swell the dreary numbers of the dead.

Bad news, which always travels faster than good, now brought the dismal story of his Juliet's death to Romeo, at Mantua, before the messenger could arrive, who was sent from Friar Lawrence to apprise him that these were mock funerals only, and but the shadow and representation of death, and that his dear lady lay in the tomb but for a short while, expecting when Romeo would come to release her from that dreary mansion. Just before, Romeo had been unusually joyful and light-hearted. He had dreamed in the night that he was dead (a strange dream, that gave a dead man leave to think), and that his lady came and found him dead, and breathed such life with kisses in his lips, that he revived, and was an emperor! And now that a messenger came from Verona, he thought surely it was to confirm some good news which his dreams had presaged. But when the contrary to this flattering vision appeared, and that it was his lady who was dead in truth, whom he could not revive by any kisses, he ordered horses to be got ready, for he determined that night to visit Verona, and to see his lady in her tomb. And as mischief is swift to enter into the thoughts of desperate men, he called to mind a poor apothecary, whose shop in Mantua he had lately passed, and from the beggarly appearance of the man, who seemed famished, and the wretched show in his shop of empty boxes ranged on dirty shelves, and other tokens of extreme wretchedness, he had said at the time (perhaps having some misgivings that his own disastrous life might haply meet with a conclusion so desperate), 'If a man were to need poison, which by the law of Mantua it is death to sell, here lives a poor wretch who would sell it him.' These words of his now came into his mind, and he sought out the apothecary, who after some pretended scruples, Romeo offering him gold, which his poverty could not resist, sold him a poison, which, if he swallowed, he told him, if he had the strength of twenty men, would quickly despatch him.

With this poison he set out for Verona, to have a sight of his dear lady in her tomb, meaning, when he had satisfied his sight, to swallow the poison, and be buried by her side. He reached Verona at midnight, and found the churchyard, in the midst of which was situated the ancient tomb of the Capulets. He had provided a light, and a spade, and wrenching iron, and was proceeding to break open the monument, when he was interrupted by a voice, which by the name of *vile Montague*, bade him desist from his unlawful business. It was the young Count Paris, who had come to the tomb of Juliet at that unseasonable time of night, to strew flowers and to weep over the grave of her that should have been his bride. He knew not what an interest Romeo had in the dead, but knowing him to be a Montague, and (as he supposed) a sworn foe to all the Capulets, he judged that he was come by night to do some villainous shame to the dead bodies; therefore in an angry tone he bade him desist; and as a criminal, condemned by the laws of Verona to die if he were found within the walls of the city, he would have apprehended him. Romeo urged Paris to leave him, and warned him by the fate of Tybalt, who lay buried there, not to provoke his anger, or draw down another sin upon his head, by forcing him to kill him. But the count in scorn refused his warning, and laid hands on him as a felon, which Romeo resisting, they fought, and Paris fell. When Romeo, by the help of a light, came to see who it was that he had slain, that it was Paris, who (he learned in his way from Mantua) should have married Juliet, he took the dead youth by the hand, as one whom misfortune had made a companion, and said that he would bury him in a triumphal grave, meaning in Juliet's grave, which he now opened: and there lay his lady, as one whom death had no power upon to change a feature or complexion, in her matchless beauty; or as if Death were amorous, and the lean abhorred monster kept her there for his delight; for she lay yet fresh and blooming, as she had fallen to sleep when she swallowed that benumbing potion; and near her lay Tybalt in his bloody shroud, whom Romeo seeing, begged pardon of his lifeless corse, and for Juliet's sake called him *cousin*, and said that he was about to do him a favour by putting his enemy to death. Here Romeo took his last leave of his lady's lips, kissing them; and here he shook the burden of his cross stars from his weary body, swallowing that poison which the apothecary had sold him, whose operation was fatal and real, not like that dissembling potion which Juliet had swallowed, the effect of which was now nearly expiring, and she about to awake to complain that Romeo had not kept his time, or that he had come too soon.

For now the hour was arrived at which the friar had promised that she should awake; and he, having learned that his letters which he had sent to Mantua, by some unlucky detention of the messenger, had never reached Romeo, came himself, provided with a pickaxe and lantern, to deliver the lady from her confinement; but he was surprised to find a light already burning in the Capulets' monument, and to see swords and blood near it, and Romeo and Paris lying breathless by the monument.

Before he could entertain a conjecture, to imagine how these fatal accidents had fallen out, Juliet awoke out of her trance, and seeing the friar near her, she remembered the place where she was, and the occasion of her being there, and asked for Romeo, but the friar, hearing a noise, bade her come out of that place of death, and of unnatural sleep, for a greater power than they could contradict had thwarted their intents; and being frightened by the noise of people coming, he fled: but when Juliet saw the cup closed in her true love's hands, she guessed that poison had been the cause of his end, and she would have swallowed the dregs if any had been left, and she kissed his still warm lips to try if any poison yet did hang upon them; then hearing a nearer noise of people coming, she quickly unsheathed a dagger which she wore, and stabbing herself, died by her true Romeo's side.

The watch by this time had come up to the place. A page belonging to Count Paris, who had witnessed the fight between his master and Romeo, had given the alarm, which had spread among the citizens, who went up and down the streets of Verona confusedly exclaiming, A Paris! a Romeo! a Juliet! as the rumour had imperfectly reached them, till the uproar brought Lord Montague and Lord Capulet out of their beds, with the prince, to inquire into the causes of the disturbance. The friar had been apprehended by some of the watch, coming from the churchyard, trembling, sighing, and weeping, in a suspicious manner. A great multitude being assembled at the Capulets' monument, the friar was demanded by the prince to deliver what he knew of these strange and disastrous accidents.

And there, in the presence of the old Lords Montague and Capulet, he faithfully related the story of their children's fatal love, the part he took in promoting their marriage, in the hope in that union to end the long quarrels between their families: how Romeo, there dead, was husband to Juliet; and Juliet, there dead, was Romeo's faithful wife; how before he could find a fit opportunity to divulge their marriage, another match was projected for Juliet, who, to avoid the crime of a second marriage, swallowed the sleeping draught (as he advised), and all thought her dead; how meantime he wrote to Romeo, to come and take her thence when the force of the potion should cease, and by what unfortunate miscarriage of the messenger the letters never reached Romeo: further than this the friar could not follow the story, nor knew more than that coming himself, to deliver Juliet from that place of death, he found the Count Paris and Romeo slain. The remainder of the transactions was supplied by the narration of the page who had seen Paris and Romeo fight, and by the servant who came with Romeo from Verona, to whom this faithful lover had given letters to be delivered to his father in the event of his death, which made good the friar's words, confessing his marriage with Juliet, imploring the forgiveness of his parents, acknowledging the buying of the poison of the poor apothecary, and his intent in coming to the monument, to die, and lie with Juliet. All these circumstances agreed together to clear the friar from any hand he could be supposed to have in these complicated slaughters, further than as the unintended consequences of his own well meant, yet too artificial and subtle contrivances.

And the prince, turning to these old lords, Montague and Capulet, rebuked them for their brutal and irrational enmities, and showed them what a scourge Heaven had laid upon such offences, that it had found means even through the love of their children to punish their unnatural hate.

And these old rivals, no longer enemies, agreed to bury their long strife in their children's graves; and Lord Capulet requested Lord

Montague to give him his hand, calling him by the name of brother, as if in acknowledgement of the union of their families, by the marriage of the young Capulet and Montague; saying that Lord Montague's hand (in token of reconcilement) was all he demanded for his daughter's jointure: but Lord Montague said he would give him more, for he would raise her a statue of pure gold, that while Verona kept its name, no figure should be so esteemed for its richness and workmanship as that of the true and faithful Juliet. And Lord Capulet in return said that he would raise another statue to Romeo. So did these poor old lords, when it was too late, strive to outgo each other in mutual courtesies: while so deadly had been their rage and enmity in past times, that nothing but the fearful overthrow of their children (poor sacrifices to their quarrels and dissensions) could remove the rooted hates and jealousies of the noble families.

TIMON OF ATHENS

◆◆◆◆◆◆◆◆◆◆◆◆◆◆◆◆◆◆◆◆◆◆◆◆◆◆◆◆◆◆◆◆◆◆◆◆

TIMON, a lord of Athens, in the enjoyment of a princely fortune, affected a humour of liberality which knew no limits. His almost infinite wealth could not flow in so fast, but he poured it out faster upon all sorts and degrees of people. Not the poor only tasted of his bounty, but great lords did not disdain to rank themselves among his dependants and followers. His table was resorted to by all the luxurious feasters, and his house was open to all comers and goers at Athens. His large wealth combined with his free and prodigal nature to subdue all hearts to his love; men of all minds and dispositions tendered their services to Lord Timon, from the glass-faced flatterer, whose face reflects as in a mirror the present humour of his patron, to the rough and unbending cynic, who affecting a contempt of men's persons, and an indifference to worldly things, yet could not stand out against the gracious manners and munificent soul of Lord Timon, but would come (against his nature) to partake of his royal entertainments, and return most rich in his own estimation if he had received a nod or a salutation from Timon.

If a poet had composed a work which wanted a recommendatory introduction to the world, he had no more to do but to dedicate it to Lord Timon, and the poem was sure of sale, besides a present purse from the patron, and daily access to his house and table. If a painter had a picture to dispose of, he had only to take it to Lord Timon, and pretend to consult his taste as to the merits of it; nothing more was wanting to persuade the liberal-hearted lord to buy it. If a jeweller had a stone of price, or a mercer rich costly stuffs, which for their costliness lay upon his hands, Lord Timon's house was a ready mart always open, where they might get off their wares or their jewellery at any price, and the good-natured lord would thank them into the bargain, as if they had done him a piece of courtesy in letting him have the refusal of such precious commodities. So that by this means his house was thronged with superfluous purchases, of no use but to swell uneasy and ostentatious pomp; and his person was still more inconveniently beset with a crowd of these idle visitors, lying poets, painters, sharking tradesmen, lords, ladies, needy courtiers, and expectants, who continually filled his lobbies, raining their fulsome flatteries in whispers in his ears, sacrificing to him with adulation as to a God, making sacred the very stirrup by which he mounted his horse, and seeming as though they drank the free air but through his permission and bounty.

Some of these daily dependants were young men of birth, who (their means not answering to their extravagance) had been put in prison by creditors, and redeemed thence by Lord Timon; these young prodigals thenceforward fastened upon his lordship, as if by common sympathy he were necessarily endeared to all such spendthrifts and loose livers, who, not being able to follow him in his wealth, found it easier to copy him in prodigality and copious spending of what was their own. One of these flesh-flies was Ventidius, for whose debts, unjustly contracted, Timon but lately had paid down the sum of five talents.

But among this confluence, this great flood of visitors, none were more conspicuous than the makers of presents and givers of gifts. It was fortunate for these men if Timon took a fancy to a dog or a horse, or any piece of cheap furniture which was theirs. The thing so praised, whatever it was, was sure to be sent the next morning with the compliments of the giver for Lord Timon's acceptance, and apologies for the unworthiness of the gift; and this dog or horse, or whatever it might be, did not fail to produce from Timon's bounty, who would not be outdone in gifts, perhaps twenty dogs or horses, certainly presents of far richer worth, as these pretended donors knew well enough, and that their false presents were but the putting out of so much money at large and speedy interest. In this way Lord Lucius had lately sent to Timon a present of four milk-white horses, trapped in silver, which this cunning lord had observed Timon upon some occasion to commend; and another lord, Lucullus, had bestowed upon him in the same pretended way of free gift a brace of greyhounds, whose make and fleetness Timon had been heard to admire; these presents the easy-hearted lord accepted without suspicion of the dishonest views of the presenters; and the givers of course were rewarded with some rich return, a diamond or some jewel of twenty times the value of their false and mercenary donation.

Sometimes these creatures would go to work in a more direct way, and with gross and palpable artifice, which yet the credulous Timon was too blind to see, would affect to admire and praise something that Timon possessed, a bargain that he had bought, or some late purchase, which was sure to draw from this yielding and soft-hearted lord a gift of the thing commended, for no service in the world done for it but the easy expense of a little cheap and obvious flattery. In this way Timon but the other day had given to one of these mean lords the bay courser which he himself rode upon, because his lordship had been pleased to say that it was a handsome beast and went well; and Timon knew that no man ever justly praised what he did not wish to possess. For Lord Timon weighted his friends' affection with his own, and so fond was he of bestowing, that he could have dealt kingdoms to these supposed friends, and never have been weary.

Not that Timon's wealth all went to enrich these wicked flatterers; he could do noble and praiseworthy actions; and when a servant of his once loved the daughter of a rich Athenian, but could not hope to obtain her by reason that in wealth and rank the maid was so far above him, Lord Timon freely bestowed upon his servant three Athenian talents, to make his fortune equal with the dowry which the father of the young maid demanded of him who should be her husband. But for the most part, knaves and parasites had the command of his fortune, false friends whom he did not know to be such, but because they flocked around his person, he thought they must needs love him; and because they smiled and flattered him, he thought surely that his conduct was approved by all the wise and good. And when he was feasting in the midst of all these flatterers and mock friends, when they were eating him up, and draining his fortunes dry with large draughts of richest wines drunk to his health and prosperity, he could not perceive the difference of a friend from a flatterer, but to his deluded eyes (made proud with the sight) it seemed a precious comfort to have so many like brothers commanding one another's fortunes (though it was his own fortune which paid all the costs), and with joy they would run over at the spectacle of such, as it appeared to him, truly festive and fraternal meeting.

But while he thus outwent the very heart of kindness, and poured out his bounty, as if Plutus, the god of gold, had been but his steward; while thus he proceeded without care or stop, so senseless of expense that he would neither inquire how he could maintain it, nor cease his wild flow of riot; his riches, which were not infinite, must needs melt away before a prodigality which knew no limits. But who should tell him so? his flatterers? they had an interest in shutting his eyes. In vain did his honest steward Flavius try to represent to him his condition, laying his accounts before him, begging of him, praying of him, with an importunity that on any other occasion would have been unmannerly in a servant, beseeching him with tears to look into the state of his affairs. Timon would still put him off, and turn the discourse to something else; for nothing is so deaf to remonstrance as riches turned to poverty, nothing is so unwilling to believe its situation, nothing so incredulous to its own true state, and hard to give credit to a reverse. Often had this good steward, this honest creature, when all the rooms of Timon's great house have been choked up with riotous feeders at his master's cost, when the floors have wept with drunken spilling of wine, and every apartment has blazed with lights and resounded with music and feasting, often had he retired by himself to some solitary spot, and wept faster than the wine ran from the wasteful casks within, to see the mad bounty of his lord, and to think, when the means were gone which brought him praises from all sorts of people, how quickly the breath would be gone of which the praise was made; praises won in feasting would be lost in fasting, and at one cloud of winter-showers these flies would disappear.

But now the time was come that Timon could shut his ears no longer to the representations of this faithful steward. Money must be had; and when he ordered Flavius to sell some of his land for that purpose, Flavius informed him, what he had in vain endeavoured at several times before to make him listen to, that most of his land was already sold or forfeited, and that all he possessed at present was not enough to pay the one half of what he owed. Struck with wonder at this presentation, Timon hastily replied, 'My lands extend from Athens to Lacedaemon.' 'O my good lord,' said Flavius, 'the world is but a world, and has bounds; were it all yours to give in a breath, how quickly were it gone!'

Timon consoled himself that no villainous bounty had yet come from him, that if he had given his wealth away unwisely, it had not been bestowed to feed his vices, but to cherish his friends; and he bade the kind-hearted steward (who was weeping) to take comfort in the assurance that his master could never lack means, while he had so many noble friends; and this infatuated lord persuaded himself that he had nothing to do but to send and borrow, to use every man's fortune (that had ever tasted his bounty) in this extremity, as freely as his own. Then with a cheerful look, as if confident of the trial, he severally despatched messengers to Lord Lucius, to Lords Lucullus and Sempronius, men upon whom he had lavished his gifts in past times without measure or moderation; and to Ventidius, whom he had lately released out of prison by paying his debts, and who, by the death of his father, was now come into the possession of an ample fortune, and well enabled to requite Timon's courtesy: to request of Ventidius the return of those five talents which he had paid for him, and of each of those noble lords the loan of fifty talents; nothing doubting that their gratitude would supply his wants (if he needed it) to the amount of five hundred times fifty talents.

Lucullus was the first applied to. This mean lord had been dreaming overnight of a silver bason and cup, and when Timon's servant was announced, his sordid mind suggested to him that this was surely a making out of his dream, and that Timon had sent him such a present: but when he understood the truth of the matter, and that Timon wanted money, the quality of his faint and watery friendship showed itself, for with many protestations he vowed to the servant that he had long foreseen the ruin of his master's affairs, and many a time had he come to dinner to tell him of it, and had come again to supper to try to persuade him to spend less, but he would take no counsel nor warning by his coming: and true it was that he had been a constant attender (as he said) at Timon's feasts, as he had in greater things tasted his bounty; but that he ever came with that intent, or gave good counsel or reproof to Timon, was a base unworthy lie, which he suitably followed up with meanly offering the servant a bribe, to go home to his master and tell him that he had not found Lucullus at home.

As little success had the messenger who was sent to Lord Lucius. This lying lord, who was full of Timon's meat, and enriched almost to bursting with Timon's costly presents, when he found the wind changed, and the fountain of so much bounty suddenly stopped, at first could hardly believe it; but on its being confirmed, he affected great regret that he should not have it in his power to serve Lord Timon, for unfortunately (which was a base falsehood) he had made a great purchase the day before, which had quite disfurnished him of the means at present, the more beast he, he called himself, to put it out of his power to serve so good a friend; and he counted it one of his greatest afflictions that his ability should fail him to pleasure such an honourable gentleman.

Who can call any man friend that dips in the same dish with him? just of this metal is every flatterer. In the recollection of everybody Timon had been a father to this Lucius, had kept up his credit with his purse; Timon's money had gone to pay the wages of his servants, to pay the hire of the labourers who had sweat to build the fine houses which Lucius's pride had made necessary to him: yet, oh! the monster which man makes himself when he proves ungrateful! this Lucius now denied to Timon a sum, which, in respect of what Timon had bestowed on him, was less than charitable men afford to beggars.

Sempronius, and every one of these mercenary lords to whom Timon applied in their turn, returned the same evasive answer or direct denial; even Ventidius, the redeemed and now rich Ventidius, refused to assist him with the loan of those five talents which Timon had not lent but generously given him in his distress.

Now was Timon as much avoided in his poverty as he had been courted and resorted to in his riches. Now the same tongues which had been loudest in his praises, extolling him as bountiful, liberal, and open handed, were not ashamed to censure that very bounty as folly, that liberality as profuseness, though it had shown itself folly in nothing so truly as in the selection of such unworthy creatures as themselves for its objects. Now was Timon's princely mansion forsaken, and become a shunned and hated place, a place for men to pass by, not a place, as formerly, where every passenger must stop and taste of his wine and good cheer; now, instead of being thronged with feasting and tumultuous guests, it was beset with impatient and clamorous creditors, usurers, extortioners, fierce and intolerable in their demands, pleading bonds, interest, mortgages; iron-hearted men that would take no denial nor putting off, that Timon's house was now his jail, which he could not pass, nor go in nor out for them; one demanding his due of fifty talents, another bringing in a bill of five thousand crowns, which if he would tell out his blood by drops, and pay them so, he had not enough in his body to discharge, drop by drop.

In this desperate and irremediable state (as it seemed) of his affairs, the eyes of all men were suddenly surprised at a new and incredible lustre which this setting sun put forth. Once more Lord Timon proclaimed a feast, to which he invited his accustomed guests, lords, ladies, all that was great or fashionable in Athens. Lords Lucius and Lucullus came, Ventidius, Sempronius, and the rest. Who more sorry now than these fawning wretches, when they found (as they thought) that Lord Timon's poverty was all pretence, and had been only put on to make trial of their loves, to think that they should not have seen through the artifice at the time, and have had the cheap credit of obliging his lordship? yet who more glad to find the fountain of that noble bounty, which they had thought dried up, still fresh and running? They came dissembling, protesting, expressing deepest sorrow and shame, that when his lordship sent to them, they should have been so unfortunate as to want the present means to oblige so honourable a friend. But Timon begged them not to give such trifles a thought, for he had altogether forgotten it. And these base fawning lords, though they had denied him money in his adversity, yet could not refuse their presence at this new blaze of his returning prosperity. For the swallow follows not summer more willingly than men of these dispositions follow the good fortunes of the great, nor more willingly leaves winter than these shrink from the first appearance of a reverse; such summer birds are men. But now with music and state the banquet of smoking dishes was served up; and when the guests had a little done admiring whence the bankrupt Timon could find means to furnish so costly a feast, some doubting whether the scene which they saw was real, as scarce trusting their own eyes; at a signal given, the dishes were uncovered, and Timon's drift appeared: instead of those varieties and far-fetched dainties which they expected, that Timon's epicurean table in past times had so liberally presented, now appeared under the covers of these dishes a preparation more suitable to Timon's poverty, nothing but a little smoke and lukewarm water, fit feast for this knot of mouth-friends, whose professions were indeed smoke, and their hearts lukewarm and slippery as the water with which Timon welcomed his astonished guests, bidding them, 'Uncover, dogs, and lap;' and before they could recover their surprise, sprinkling it in their faces, that they might have enough, and throwing dishes and all after them, who now ran huddling out, lords, ladies, with their caps snatched up in haste, a splendid confusion, Timon pursuing them, still calling them what they were, 'smooth smiling parasites, destroyers under the mask of courtesy, affable wolves, meek bears, fools of fortune, feast-friends, time-flies.' They, crowding out to avoid him, left the house more willingly than they had entered it; some losing their gowns and caps, and some their jewels in the hurry, all glad to escape out of the presence of such a mad lord, and from the ridicule of his mock banquet.

This was the last feast which ever Timon made, and in it he took farewell of Athens and the society of men; for, after that, he betook himself to the woods, turning his back upon the hated city and upon all mankind, wishing the walls of that detestable city might sink, and the houses fall upon their owners, wishing all plagues which infest humanity, war, outrage, poverty, diseases, might fasten upon its inhabitants, praying the just gods to confound all Athenians, both young and old, high and low; so wishing, he went to the woods, where he said he should find the unkindest beast much kinder than mankind. He stripped himself naked, that he might retain no fashion of a man, and dug a cave to live in, and lived solitary in the manner of a beast, eating the wild roots, and drinking water, flying from the face of his kind, and choosing rather to herd with wild beasts, as more harmless and friendly than man.

What a change from Lord Timon the rich, Lord Timon the delight of mankind, to Timon the naked, Timon the man-hater! Where were his flatterers now? Where were his attendants and retinue? Would the bleak air, that boisterous servitor, be his chamberlain, to put his shirt on warm? Would those stiff trees that had outlived the eagle, turn young and airy pages to him, to skip on his errands when he bade them? Would the cool brook, when it was iced with winter, administer to him his warm broths and caudles when sick of an overnight's surfeit? Or would the creatures that lived in those wild woods come and lick his hand and flatter him?

Here on a day, when he was digging for roots, his poor sustenance, his spade struck against something heavy, which proved to be gold, a great heap which some miser had probably buried in a time of alarm, thinking to have come again, and taken it from its prison, but died before the opportunity had arrived, without making any man privy to the concealment; so it lay, doing neither good nor harm, in the bowels of the earth, its mother, as if it had never come from thence, till the accidental striking of Timon's spade against it once more brought it to light.

Here was a mass of treasure which, if Timon had retained his old mind, was enough to have purchased him friends and flatterers again; but Timon was sick of the false world, and the sight of gold was poisonous to his eyes; and he would have restored it to the earth, but that, thinking of the infinite calamities which by means of gold happen to mankind, how the lucre of it causes robberies, oppression, injustice, briberies, violence, and murder, among men, he had a pleasure in imagining (such a rooted hatred did he bear to his species) that out of this heap, which in digging he had discovered, might arise some mischief to plague mankind. And some soldiers passing through the woods near to his cave at that instant, which proved to be a part of the troops of the Athenian captain Alcibiades, who upon some disgust taken against the senators of Athens (the Athenians were ever noted to be a thankless and ungrateful people, giving disgust to their generals and best friends), was marching at the head of the same triumphant army which he had formerly headed in their defence, to war against them; Timon, who liked their business well, bestowed upon their captain the gold to pay his soldiers, requiring no other service from him, than that he should with his conquering army lay Athens level with the ground, and burn, slay, kill all her inhabitants; not sparing the old men for their white beards, for (he said) they were usurers, nor the young children for their seeming innocent smiles, for those (he said) would live, if they grew up, to be traitors; but to steel his eyes and ears against any sights or sounds that might awaken compassion; and not to let the cries of virgins, babes, or mothers, hinder him from making one universal massacre of the city, but to confound them all in his conquest; and when he had conquered, he prayed that the gods would confound him also, the conqueror: so thoroughly did Timon hate Athens, Athenians, and all mankind.

While he lived in this forlorn state, leading a life more brutal than human, he was suddenly surprised one day with the appearance of a man standing in an admiring posture at the door of his cave. It was Flavius, the honest steward, whom love and zealous affection to his master had led to seek him out at his wretched dwelling, and to offer his services; and the first sight of his master, the once noble Timon, in that abject condition, naked as he was born, living in the manner of a beast among beasts, looking like his own sad ruins and a monument of decay, so affected this good servant, that he stood speechless, wrapped up in horror, and confounded. And when he found utterance at last to his words, they were so choked with tears, that Timon had much ado to know him again, or to make out who it was that had come (so contrary to the experience he had had of mankind) to offer him service in extremity. And being in the form and shape of a man, he suspected him for a traitor, and his tears for false; but the good servant by so many tokens confirmed the truth of his fidelity, and made it clear that nothing but love and zealous duty to his once dear master had brought him there, that Timon was forced to confess that the world contained one honest man; yet, being in the shape and form of a man, he could not look upon his man's face without abhorrence, or hear words uttered from his man's lips without loathing; and this singly honest man was forced to depart, because he was a man, and because, with a heart more gentle and compassionate than is usual to man, he bore man's detested form and outward feature.

But greater visitants than a poor steward were about to interrupt the savage quiet of Timon's solitude. For now the day was come when the ungrateful lords of Athens sorely repented the injustice which they had done to the noble Timon. For Alcibiades, like an incensed wild boar, was raging at the walls of their city, and with his hot siege threatened to lay fair Athens in the dust. And now the memory of Lord Timon's former prowess and military conduct came fresh into their forgetful minds, for Timon had been their general in past times, and a valiant and expert soldier, who alone of all the Athenians was deemed able to cope with a besieging army such as then threatened them, or to drive back the furious approaches of Alcibiades.

A deputation of the senators was chosen in this emergency to wait upon Timon. To him they came in their extremity, to whom, when he was in extremity, they had shown but small regard; as if they presumed upon his gratitude whom they had disobliged, and had derived a claim to his courtesy from their own most discourteous and unpiteous treatment.

Now they earnestly beseech him, implore him with tears, to return and save that city, from which their ingratitude had so lately driven him; now they offer him riches, power, dignities, satisfaction for past injuries, and public honours, and the public love; their persons, lives, and fortunes, to be at his disposal, if he will but come back and save them. But Timon the naked, Timon the man-hater, was no longer Lord Timon, the lord of bounty, the flower of valour, their defence in war, their ornament in peace. If Alcibiades killed his countrymen, Timon cared not. If he sacked fair Athens, and slew her old men and her infants, Timon would rejoice. So he told them; and that there was not a knife in the unruly camp which he did not prize above the reverendest throat in Athens.

This was all the answer he vouchsafed to the weeping disappointed senators; only at parting he bade them commend him to his countrymen, and tell them, that to ease them of their griefs and anxieties, and to prevent the consequences of fierce Alcibiades' wrath, there was yet a way left, which he would teach them, for he had yet so much affection left for his dear countrymen as to be willing to do them a kindness before his death. These words a little revived the senators, who hoped that his kindness for their city was returning. Then Timon told them that he had a tree, which grew near his cave, which he should shortly have occasion to cut down, and he invited all his friends in Athens, high or low, of what degree soever, who wished to shun affliction, to come and take a taste of his tree before he cut it down; meaning, that they might come and hang themselves on it, and escape affliction that way.

And this was the last courtesy, of all his noble bounties, which Timon showed to mankind, and this the last sight of him which his countrymen had: for not many days after, a poor soldier, passing by the sea-beach, which was at a little distance from the woods which Timon frequented, found a tomb on the verge of the sea, with an inscription upon it, purporting that it was the grave of Timon the man-hater, who 'While he lived, did hate all living men, and dying wished a plague might consume all caitiffs left!'

Whether he finished his life by violence, or whether mere distaste of life and the loathing he had for mankind brought Timon to his conclusion, was not clear, yet all men admired the fitness of his epitaph, and the consistency of his end; dying, as he had lived, a hater of mankind: and some there were who fancied a conceit in the very choice which he had made of the sea-beach for his place of burial, where the vast sea might weep for ever upon his grave, as in contempt of the transient and shallow tears of hypocritical and deceitful mankind.

JULIUS CAESAR

◆◆◆◆◆◆◆◆◆

UPON a day in the spring of the year 44 B.C. a shouting, jostling crowd of labouring people filled a Roman street. Good-tempered though the commoners were this afternoon, they made so fierce an uproar that the tribunes Flavius and Marullus, enemies of the dictator Julius Caesar, came to ask why they had gathered in the street and why, as mechanics, they dared to walk abroad on a working day without wearing the signs of their profession. Flavius spoke to a man in the forefront of the crowd: 'What is your trade, fellow?' The man replied that he was a carpenter. Whereupon the second tribune Marullus flashed back at him, 'Where is your leather apron and your rule? Why are you wearing your best apparel?' Before the carpenter could reply, the tribune was looking elsewhere: 'And you – what trade do you follow?' 'I am a cobbler,' answered a little red-haired man while the crowd laughed. 'All that I live by is by the awl. I am, sir, a surgeon to old shoes: when they are in great danger I recover them.'

'But why are you not in your shop to-day?' put in Flavius. 'Why do you lead these men about the city?'

The cobbler chuckled. 'Truly, sir, to wear out their shoes to get myself more work.' Then, as he saw Marullus and Flavius gesture impatiently, he added, 'But indeed, sir, we make holiday to see great Caesar and to rejoice in his triumph.'

Wrathfully, Marullus rounded upon the man. What need was there to rejoice? What conquest had Caesar made? What prisoners had he brought to Rome? All he was celebrating was his triumph over the dead Pompey, the leader they used to acclaim, the man for whom once they had waited through a day to cheer. Now here they were in their best attire, making holiday, prepared to strew flowers before Pompey's conqueror. 'Be gone!' he cried. 'Run to your houses, fall upon your knees, pray that the gods forgive ingratitude.' The mob began guiltily to break up; and Flavius and Marullus moved away to disperse other crowds and to tear down the wreaths from the images of Caesar.

Not long afterwards, on the feast-day of the Lupercalia (so called from the cave of Lupercal in which the wolf kept alive the infants, Romulus and Remus, who founded Rome), Julius Caesar passed through the city in full state procession. Ailing though he was, he was absolute ruler in spite of the dangerous and rising wrath of the republicans. But to-day, as he moved along a crowded street, golden-wreathed and purple-robed, his wife Calpurnia at his side and the senators about him, a voice from the thickest multitude cried loudly to him, 'Caesar!'

'Ha!' said the dictator. 'Who calls?' In the ensuing hush Caesar spoke again: 'Who is it calls on me? Speak! Caesar is turned to hear.'

There stirred among the dense crowd an old and ragged man, his stick tapping on the ground as he attempted to come forward, his blind eyes fixed upon Caesar. He uttered only five words: 'Beware the Ides of March!'

'What man is that?' asked Caesar. 'Set him before me.'

'He is a soothsayer,' said Marcus Brutus. When the man stumbled forward and knelt, Caesar glanced down at him pityingly. 'What do you say to me now? Speak once more.' And the soothsayer repeated in his strange, ringing voice: 'Beware the Ides of March!'

'The man is a dreamer,' said Caesar. He waved his hand; and the procession moved on, the crowd surging after it and the soothsayer lost helplessly among the surge. Only two figures remained behind: patricians both, the noble Marcus Brutus, his face troubled and reflective, and the lean Caius Cassius, once Pompey's friend, a man – a thinker and a schemer – whose life was as stern as his countenance. Cassius detested Caesar's arrogance and ambition, and was opposed to his growing tyranny. On this early spring afternoon, with the dictator's power apparently at its zenith, Cassius had resolved that only one thing could be done to end the present rule in Rome. Marcus Brutus, loved by all and trusted by Caesar, must be persuaded to join the republican conspiracy, and Cassius began at once to sound him. Why had he been so aloof of late?

Brutus replied that he had been engaged with personal problems. Cassius, guessing what these were, took his chance; in terms veiled at first, he wished that Brutus would realise his power, for many 'of the best respect in Rome' looked to him as a leader.

A shout echoed in the distance. 'What does this mean?' said Brutus. 'I do fear the people choose Caesar for their king.'

'Then,' Cassius exclaimed, 'you would not have it so?'

'I would not,' said Brutus, 'though I love him well.' He faced Cassius. 'Come, what is it you would tell me? If it be anything towards the general good, believe me that I love the name of honour more than I fear death.'

Cassius did not pause. 'Honour is the subject of my story. I was born free as Caesar; so were you.' And he went on to describe a raw day by the Tiber; how Caesar dared him to leap into the angry flood and swim to a distant point; how, fully clothed, they had made the plunge; and how, after a while, when Caesar cried, 'Help me, Cassius, or I sink,' he had borne the tired man upon his shoulders from the torrential swirling flood. Now this same Caesar had become a god, one to whom Cassius must bow at any careless greeting.

Another great shout; another trumpet-call. 'They are cheering,' said Brutus, 'for some new honour to Caesar.'

'Why,' cried Cassius, 'Caesar bestrides the narrow world like a Colossus, and we are petty men that walk under his huge legs and find ourselves dishonourable graves. It should not be. Brutus and Caesar: what is in the name of Caesar? Why is it sounded more than yours? Write them together: speak them—yours is as fair. . . By all the gods, why has this Caesar grown so great? When has our Rome been servant to a single man?' He knew that Brutus was moved. 'What you have said, Cassius, I will consider. And hear this: I would rather be a villager than under dark oppression call myself a son of Rome.'

The procession was coming back. Cassius whispered quickly, 'As they go by, pluck Casca by the sleeve: he will tell us all.' Caesar and his train were now beside them. They saw that the dictator had an air of moody disappointment. Though he had longed for a crown, he knew it would be unwise to accept it, for the republicans of Rome were sharply opposed to any further widening of his power. By him all walked silently, as if they had been reproved, and Calpurnia's cheek was as pale as her robe. Caesar beckoned to him his friend Mark Antony, the patrician whom Cassius disdained as a masquerader and a reveller. 'Antony,' he said, 'Caius Cassius has a lean and hungry look. He thinks too much. Such men are dangerous.'

'Fear him not, Caesar,' said Antony. 'He's not dangerous.'

Caesar shook his head. 'If I could fear any man, it might be that lean Cassius. He is a great reader, Antony, a great observer. He loves no plays, he hears no music. When he smiles, it is to mock himself for smiling. Such men as Cassius can never be at ease if they behold a nobler than themselves.' The procession trailed along. Unobtrusively, Brutus twitched at a cloak, and its wearer, the plump, cynical Casca, halted. 'Ah, Brutus, would you speak with me?'

'Yes, Casca. What has happened that Caesar looks so sad?'

'Why,' said Casca bluntly, ' a crown was offered him. He waved it aside, and all the people shouted. No more than that.'

'They shouted thrice?'

'Ay, the crown – one of these coronets merely – was offered him thrice. Thrice he put it by, every time less willingly, while the crowd cheered and clapped so long that their breath must have choked him. He swooned and fell down, and, for my own part, Brutus, I dared not laugh for fear of opening my lips and receiving the bad air.'

'But, soft,' said Cassius, 'did our Caesar swoon?'

'Indeed he did,' replied Casca. 'He fell down in the market-place, foamed at the mouth, and was speechless. Before he fell, when he saw that the mob was glad he had refused the crown, he plucked open his robe and offered them his throat to cut. If I had been quick enough I might have taken him at his word. When he came to again, he said that if he had done or said anything amiss, it was because of his infirmity, and three or four women near me cried "Alas, good soul!" and forgave him with all their hearts. There's no heed to be taken of them. If Caesar had stabbed their mothers, they would have done no less.'

'So it was because of this that he came away so sad?'

Casca nodded. 'Yes. One thing more. For pulling scarves off Caesar's images, the tribunes Marullus and Flavius have been put to silence . . . Fare you well.'

'Will you sup with me to-night, Casca?' asked Cassius.

'No,' said Casca, 'I am promised forth.'

'Then will you dine with me to-morrow?'

'Ay, if I be alive, and your mind hold, and your dinner worth eating.' With a careless wave he moved, unhurrying, after the now distant procession.

'Casca has grown blunt,' said Brutus. 'He was quick mettle in his schooldays.'

'So is he now,' Cassius answered, 'in execution of any bold or noble enterprise.' Brutus did not speak. Then he roused himself: 'For the time I leave you. To-morrow we shall meet?'

'We shall do so,' said Cassius. 'Till then, think of the world.' He stood alone in contemplation. 'To-night I will throw in at Brutus' window, as if they came from several citizens, writings that speak of nothing but Rome's love for him and hint at Caesar's pride.

And after this, let Caesar seat him sure,
For we will shake him, or worse days endure.'

That night of March 14, eve of the Ides of March, was marked by terrifying signs and portents. A long storm of thunder and lightning raged and glittered above Rome. A lion was seen prowling by the Capitol. Fiery phantoms haunted the streets; and people remembered that on the previous noon an owl had hovered in the market-place, hooting and shrieking. On this grim night Casca, hurrying in fear through the streets, saw by a lightning flash the figure of Cassius with his robe opened, gazing towards the sky as if challenging it to strike. He called to Casca: 'I could show to you a man most like this dreadful night, and yet a man no greater than yourself or me.'

'It is Caesar that you mean?'

'Let it be who it is,' said Cassius. 'Woe the while! Our fathers' minds are dead. We are grown womanish.'

'Indeed,' Casca said, flinching at a prolonged thunder-roll, 'they say the senators tomorrow mean to establish Caesar as a king. He is to wear his crown by sea and land – in every place save here in Italy.'

Cassius responded in sharp and deadly anger. 'How weak is Rome, how base, when it submits to so vile a thing as Caesar! . . . But, Casca, do I say this before a willing bondman?'

Casca held out his hand: 'Know that in your enterprise I go as far as any.' As they stood under the heavy sky, torn suddenly by forked lightning, Cassius said in his quietest tone, 'There's a bargain made. Our friends await us – the noblest-minded Romans, Decius Brutus and Cinna, Trebonius, Metellus Cimber. We must yet see Brutus at his house. What is the hour?'

'Past midnight.'

'Then before dawn we will awake him and be sure of him.'

Between two and three o'clock the storm had lulled, though the sky above Rome seemed still to flash and flicker. Marcus Brutus had gone into his orchard where he walked to and fro beneath the trees in earnest meditation. Even though he had no personal feud with Caesar, he knew that for the general good the man must die. As Brutus, burdened by his thoughts, paced back and forth, his young servant Lucius ran out with a sealed paper he had found beneath a window. Brutus opened the paper and read it in the glow of the strange exhalations overhead. 'Brutus, thou sleep'st: awake and see thyself. Speak, strike, redress! . . .' There had been other such letters as these. 'Speak, strike, redress! . . .' He dropped the paper and gazed up at the troubled sky. 'O Rome, I make you promise. If the redress will follow, my sword is yours.'

There came a measured knocking at the orchard gate; and as Lucius hastened to undo the bolts, Brutus reflected, 'Since Cassius first did whet me against Caesar, I have had no other thought.' He heard the voice of Lucius: 'Sir, it is Cassius at the door. Others are with him, their faces hidden.' It was the conspirators, and like ghosts the men glided into the hushed garden and upon the marble terrace before the house.

Cassius gave their names to Brutus as they greeted him. 'This is Trebonius . . . this Decius Brutus . . . this Casca, this Cinna; and here Metellus Cimber.'

'Give me your hands over one by one,' said Brutus.

'And let us swear an oath.'

'No, Cassius,' Brutus exclaimed. 'Swear unto bad causes such creatures as men doubt; but do not stain this noble enterprise. We have made a promise; no one now will break it.'

They had questions to resolve. Should only Caesar die? Cassius wished to kill Mark Antony, whom Caesar loved, but Brutus warned him that the deed would seem too fierce: their task was sacrifice, not butchery, and Mark Antony could do no more than Caesar's arm when Caesar's head was off. Trebonius agreed. None could fear Antony; let him live and laugh at this thereafter.

Then to the deed itself. It was doubtful whether Caesar would go to the Capitol that day: he had become intensely superstitious, and the prodigies of the night, the unaccustomed terrors, and the persuasion of his priests, might keep him in the house. But Decius Brutus, who had studied Caesar's moods, was confident that he could overrule him and coax him to the Capitol.

Morning began to glimmer; and the conspirators withdrew after a final word from Brutus: 'Good gentlemen, go fresh and merrily. Let not our looks betray us.' Brutus summoned Lucius, but the boy was sleeping. While he hesitated, alone on the terrace above the city in a sudden chill after the sultry night, his wife Portia came quietly from the house. 'Portia,' he said, 'what mean you? You are sick. Is it right to expose yourself to this raw, cold morning?'

Unheeding, Portia begged him to tell her what was wrong, why he was up all night, why earlier he had been sighing and impatient. Brutus tried to say he was not well; but she rebuked him quietly. As his wife she ought to know his grief; and, sinking upon her knee, she entreated him, by all their vows of love, to tell the cause of his anxiety, and why men with faces hidden even from the darkness had come to him that night.

He sought to calm her: she was, he said, his true and honourable wife, dear to him as his life's blood. Portia answered proudly that if this were true, she then should know his secrets. Woman she might be, but was she not the woman Brutus took to wife, a woman well reputed, Cato's daughter? 'Tell me your counsels, I will not disclose them. As proof of my loyalty I have given myself a voluntary wound – here on the thigh.' She pointed to the blood upon her robe. 'Brutus, can I bear that with patience, and not my husband's secrets?'

Deeply moved, he embraced her: 'O ye gods, render me worthy of this noble wife! Portia, go in a while, and I will come to you. All that I know is yours.'

Far off, an occasional noise of thunder still ushered in the Ides of March; but a few hours later the skies were calm when Julius Caesar, in night attire, looked out on the grey morning. 'Nor heaven, nor earth, has been at peace to-night,' he muttered to himself. 'Thrice has Calpurnia in her sleep cried out, "Help ho! They murder Caesar!" . . . Who's within?' When a servant hurried in, sleepy-eyed, Caesar bade him tell the priests to offer a sacrifice and bring speedily their judgement of the day. The servant had hardly left before Calpurnia, distracted and dishevelled, was urging her husband not to stir from the house. There had been news of horrid portents. A lioness had given birth in the streets; graves had yielded up their dead; above Rome ghostly warriors battled in the sky and drizzled blood upon the Capitol. She had heard the sound of battle in the air, neighing horses, and the groans of dying men. 'O Caesar, these things are beyond all use, and I do fear them.'

He answered steadily, 'Yet Caesar shall go forth.'

'When beggars die there are no comets seen. The heavens themselves blaze forth the death of princes.'

Caesar was untouched: 'Cowards, Calpurnia, die many times before their death. The valiant never taste of death but once.' Then, to the returning servant: 'What say the priests?' The man flung himself down: 'They urge you not to leave the house.' But Caesar, gazing at him arrogantly, said, 'Danger knows that Caesar is more dangerous than he. We are two lions born in a single day, and I am the elder and more terrible.'

'Do not go, my lord,' wailed Calpurnia in despair. 'Say it is my fear that keeps you in the house. Or let Mark Antony say you are not well.'

Caesar sighed. 'Well, have it so. For your humour, Calpurnia, I will stay at home. Here is Decius Brutus; he shall bear the news.'

Decius Brutus guessed immediately what had happened; but he gave no sign. Smiling as usual, he bowed to Caesar and Calpurnia, and said in the smooth beguiling voice that the dictator had always admired, 'I am come to fetch you to the Senate House.'

'Then tell the senators,' ordered Caesar, 'that I will not come. Cannot is false; I dare not, falser. I will not come to-day: tell them so, Decius.' 'Say he is sick,' entreated Calpurnia, and Caesar tapped an angry foot. 'Sick! Shall I send a lie? Decius, go tell them Caesar will not come.'

When Decius pleaded to know some cause, lest he be laughed at, Caesar answered that, though publicly his will must be cause enough, privately it was because Calpurnia had dreamed a most curious dream. She had seen his statue running in blood like a fountain with a hundred spouts, and many Romans came and washed their hands in it. For her it was a warning of evils imminent: she had begged that he would stay at home that day. Hearing this with grave attention, Decius said that surely the dream was ill interpreted: it was a fair vision and a fortunate, and it meant only that from Caesar great Rome would suck reviving blood. That day the senators had decided to give to him a crown. If he sent them word he would not come, their minds might change. They might say mockingly, 'Break up the senate till another time when Caesar's wife shall have a better dream.'

'How foolish are your fears now, Calpurnia,' said Caesar. Hastily he robed, then emerged to greet the main body of the conspirators, Marcus Brutus, Metellus Cimber, Cinna, Trebonius: only Cassius was absent. A moment later Mark Antony came through the hall with his cheerful greeting. 'Good friends,' invited Caesar, 'come and drink some wine with me, and like friends we will straightway go together.'

It was shortly after nine o'clock when a man named Artemidorus, who suspected treachery, placed himself carefully on the line of the progress to the Capitol, reading to himself a letter he had written to warn Caesar. All the conspirators were named in it: 'Caesar, beware of Brutus; take heed of Cassius; come not near Casca; have an eye to Cinna; trust not Trebonius; mark well Metellus Cimber; Decius Brutus loves thee not; thou hast wronged Caius Ligarius. There is but one mind in all these men, and it is bent against Caesar. If thou beest not immortal, look about you; security gives way to conspiracy. The mighty gods defend thee. Thy lover, Artemidorus.' At the same time, and not far distant, the old soothsayer was ready to take his stand and to repeat his warning.

Now the cheering that accompanied Caesar as if it belonged to his retinue, ran along the wide street where the two men waited. Observing the soothsayer, Caesar halted: 'The Ides of March are come.' Brutus, a few paces behind him, started a little as he heard the words.

'Ay, Caesar,' returned the soothsayer, 'but not gone.' He could not speak further, for Artemidorus advanced in desperation with his parchment extended. 'Hail Caesar! read!' At once he was elbowed away roughly by Decius Brutus who thrust forward with another paper: 'Trebonius doth desire you to read over, at your best leisure, this his humble suit.' Artemidorus protested, 'Caesar, read mine first, for mine's a suit that touches Caesar nearer.' Unyielding, the dictator motioned him away: 'What touches us ourself shall be last served.' Cassius, who was now in Caesar's party, said with a frowning glance at the paper that Artemidorus was holding crumpled, 'What, do you bring your petitions in the street? Come to the Capitol.' And Artemidorus was tossed away in the mob that environed Caesar and his train as they reached the Senate House.

There, while the dictator was walking to the gilded chair of state, the conspirators talked nervously together. An old senator, Popilius Lena, had said with a smile to Cassius, 'I wish to-day your enterprise may thrive,' and it seemed for a second that the plot must be known. But Popilius Lena did no more; Trebonius, as instructed, drew Mark Antony out of the Senate House with a whispered suggestion; and Metellus Cimber prepared to kneel as a petitioner before Caesar's feet. Casca was warned that he must be the first to strike. All, when Caesar spoke, were frozen into anxious silence.

'Are we all ready? What is now amiss that Caesar and his senate must redress?'

At the words, Metellus Cimber, with humble protestations, knelt to ask pardon for his banished brother Publius. Aloofly, Caesar told him not to bend and pray: Publius Cimber by decree was banished, and fawning would not serve. Metellus Cimber swung round to the conspirators. They heard what Caesar said. Was there no voice more worthy? And at this Marcus Brutus knelt, desiring pardon for the banished Cimber. 'What, Brutus?' said Caesar in astonishment, for he loved the man and wondered at this insistence on a trivial cause. Then Cassius darted forward to kneel by Brutus in exaggerated subjection: 'As low as to thy foot does Cassius fall to beg enfranchisement for Publius Cimber.'

It was too much. Caesar rose in arrogant majesty. Just as the northern star held its unchanging place, only one man held on his course unassailable. 'That I am he, let me a little show it, even in this. I was constant Publius Cimber should be banished – and constant I remain to keep him so.'

Cinna had knelt: 'O Caesar!——'

'Hence, wilt thou lift up Olympus?'

Now Decius: 'Great Caesar!——'

'Doth not Brutus vainly kneel?'

The burly Casca had worked his way behind the chair of state Suddenly, with great force, he lunged round it, a bared dagger gleaming. 'Speak, hands, for me!' Caesar, stabbed in the neck, cried out, swaying. At once the other conspirators sprang to their feet, and as Caesar wavered from one to the other, drove home their swords or daggers. Mortally wounded, Caesar held out his arms to the one man in the semicircle before him who had not struck. As he looked into the eyes of Marcus Brutus, Brutus stabbed him deliberately to the heart. With a choked cry, '*Et tu, Brute?* Then fall, Caesar!' he hid his face in the folds of his purple toga, and there at the plinth of Pompey's statue fell dead.

A moment's silence was like an hour. Cinna, overwrought, shattered it with a wild 'Liberty! Freedom! Tyranny is dead!' Cassius called, 'On to the common pulpits, and cry out "Liberty, freedom, and enfranchisement!"' Only Brutus spoke quietly: 'People and senators, be not affrighted! Fly not; stand still; ambition's debt is paid.' Among an uproar, a medley of cheers and counter-cries, Trebonius entered: 'Antony is fled to his house amazed. Everywhere the people stare and run. Brutus, it might be doomsday.' In sudden bravado the conspirators bent round Caesar's body and dipped their daggers in his blood, while Cassius said, with a hysterical note in his voice, 'How many ages hence shall this our lofty scene be acted over – in states unborn and accents yet unknown?' He gazed at the stain upon his dagger. 'So often shall the group of us be called the men that gave their country liberty.'

Still unnerved by their action, they were preparing to walk to the market-place when a servant, pale of face, ran in and fell before Brutus as a messenger from Mark Antony. If Brutus, he said, would satisfy his master why Caesar had thus deserved death, Antony would love the slayer better than the slain.

'Your master,' said Brutus, 'is a wise and valiant Roman; I never thought him otherwise. If he comes to us now he shall be satisfied – and tell him, by my honour, that he shall depart unharmed.' Cassius muttered, 'Brutus, I have a mind that fears him much.' But almost immediately Mark Antony walked up the steps, and, without a glance at the conspirators, knelt beside the body of Caesar. 'Do you lie so low?' he whispered. 'Are all your conquests, glories, triumphs, spoils, shrunk to this little measure? Fare you well . . .'

Looking up at the set faces round him, he besought the murderers, if they would, to kill him there: no place, no death, so fitting as by Caesar's body and by their hands cut off – the voice had a bitter irony – 'the choice and master spirits of this age.' Brutus assured Antony that they had no grievance against him, and Cassius added insinuatingly, 'Your voice shall be as strong as any man's in the disposing of new dignities.'

Antony, smiling faintly, made no reply; but when Brutus told him that all would be explained as soon as they had appeased the frightened crowd, he said without apparent emotion, 'You are wise, I doubt not.' Moving round the circle, he grasped the bloodstained hands – those of Brutus and Cassius, of Decius Brutus and Metellus, of Cinna, 'my valiant Casca,' and last, Trebonius, who had beguiled him from the scene. Once more he glanced at the body. Would it not grieve Caesar to see this act of friendship? 'Here were you trapped, brave hart, here you did fall, and here your hunters stand.' Cassius interrupted him, 'Come, Antony, what is your purpose?' And Antony replied, 'I am friends with you all – if you can give me reasons why and wherein Caesar was dangerous.'

Brutus, the only man he could respect, said earnestly: 'Our reasons are so full of good import that, if you were Caesar's son, you would be satisfied.' When, upon this, Antony asked for permission to take the body to the market-place and to speak over it as became a friend, Brutus, in spite of a horrified interjection by Cassius, granted the request. One thing only: Brutus himself would enter the pulpit first and give his reasons for Caesar's death, and Antony, following, should not blame them in his funeral speech, but say simply that he came there by permission to praise Caesar in what way he could. On this understanding the conspirators left Antony alone to prepare the corpse while at last he released above it his rage and anguish: 'You are the ruins of the noblest man that ever lived in the tide of times. Woe to the hands that shed your costly blood!' He was still in revengeful contemplation when a servant of Caesar's nephew Octavius, who had not heard the news, ran in with a message and broke down at the sight of the corpse. Octavius, he said, was within seven leagues of Rome. Antony ordered the man to help him in preparing the body, and later to report to Octavius how the crowd had received his speech in the Forum. 'Listen,' he said, 'and watch. We shall discover from my oration how the people take this cruel deed.'

In the Forum an immense crowd, sombre and still at first, waited while Brutus ascended the marble pulpit. His speech was short and clear. 'If there be in this assembly,' he said, 'any dear friend of Caesar's, then I avow to him that my love for Caesar was no less than his. But if, then, that friend demand why I rose against Caesar, here is my answer to him: not that I loved Caesar less, but that I loved Rome more. Would you prefer Caesar to be living and yourselves to die enslaved, or Caesar to be dead and yourselves to live as freemen? As Caesar loved me, I weep for him; as he was fortunate, I rejoice at it; as he was valiant, I honour him; but as he was ambitious, I slew him. There is tears, for his love; joy, for his fortune; honour, for his valour . . . and death, for his ambition.' At once he conquered the crowd; and after he had ended with the promise, 'As I slew my best lover for the good of Rome, I have here the same dagger for myself when it shall please my country to need my death,' the mob thundered into a repeated roar of 'Live, Brutus, live, live!' and 'We'll bring him to his house with shouts and clamours!'

Brutus calmed them. Mark Antony, he said, had been allowed to make a speech on Caesar's glories, and he hoped that until this was over no one would leave the Forum. Descending, he walked slowly through the crowd that opened obsequiously to let him pass. When he had gone, Mark Antony, heavily cloaked in black, climbed to the pulpit, leaving Octavius' servant to stand below by the litter on which, its face hidden, the body lay beneath a torn and crumpled mantle.

The crowd was murmuring 'This Caesar was a tyrant' and 'Nay, that's certain.' Its hubbub strengthened and Antony's first words were inaudible. Twice he raised his hand until at length, in a momentary hush, his voice – full and strong as ever – carried across the Forum:

> 'Friends, Romans, countrymen, lend me your ears:
> I come to bury Caesar, not to praise him . . .'

Brutus had told them that Caesar was ambitious, and they all knew Brutus to be honourable. Yet Caesar had brought home many captives whose ransoms filled the general coffer of the state. Was this ambitious? He had wept when the poor had cried. Was this ambitious? Thrice he had been presented with a kingly crown which he had thrice refused. Did this in Caesar seem ambitious? Yet Brutus was an honourable man . . .

At the name of Brutus the crowd continued to cheer, and Antony said with haste, 'I speak not to disprove what Brutus spoke; but here I am to speak what I do know. You all loved Caesar once – not without cause. What cause then withholds you to mourn for him?'

With his questions and repetitions Antony was playing on the emotional instability of the mob. Those immediately beneath the pulpit were shaking their heads: 'If you consider rightly of the matter, Caesar has had great wrong'; 'He would not take the crown, therefore 'tis certain he was not ambitious'; 'There's not a nobler man in Rome than Antony.' When Antony began again to speak, the rabble listened to him, hushed, and he did not lose his chance. He said he would not stir their hearts and minds to mutiny and rage, for that would do Brutus wrong and Cassius wrong, and surely they were honourable men. Hearing mutters of dissent, he hastened to hold up a paper with the seal of Caesar. 'I found it in his closet, 'tis his will.'

The crowd was pressing forward now. Antony still held the parchment aloft, saying that he did not mean to read it, for if he did the people would kiss dead Caesar's wounds and beg a hair of him for memory.

Throughout the Forum the gusts of shouting swelled. 'We'll hear the will! Read it, Mark Antony!' Antony begged their patience. It was not right for them to know how Caesar loved them; it would inflame them, it would make them mad. They must not know that they were Caesar's heirs. And the shouting was trebled. 'The will! Read the will! We'll hear it, Antony!'

'But,' said Antony, 'I fear I wrong the honourable men whose daggers have stabbed Caesar.'

Back pealed the shout, 'They were traitors!' Leaving the pulpit, Antony asked for a ring to be formed around the corpse of Caesar. There, he said, was the purple mantle that Caesar put on one summer evening in his tent on the day he overcame the Nervii. Antony pointed to the spot where Cassius's dagger struck, to the rent that envious Casca made, and where the well-beloved Brutus stabbed before great Caesar fell. 'O, what a fall was there, my countrymen!'

Women in the crowd had begun to sob, and Antony with a sweeping gesture lifted and flung aside the mantle: 'Look you here, here is himself – marred as you see by traitors!'

At the sight of the body the crowd broke into lamentation, 'O piteous spectacle!', 'O traitors, villains!', ending with a terrible concerted cry, 'Seek! Burn! Kill! Slay! Let not a traitor live!'

'Stay, countrymen!' Antony appealed to them. 'Let me not stir you up to mutiny. They that have done this deed are honourable. I do not know their private griefs, the reasons they will give you. I am no orator as Brutus is. I am merely a plain, blunt man that loved my friend, and they knew that well when they allowed me public leave to speak of him.' He paused. 'I only speak right on; I tell you what you know yourselves, show you sweet Caesar's wounds, and bid them speak for me. But if I were Brutus, and Brutus were Antony – there were a man indeed to ruffle up your spirits, one to put a tongue in every wound of Caesar that should move these very stones of Rome to rise and mutiny.'

The crowd took up the final word. 'We'll mutiny!' And again, 'We'll burn the house of Brutus.' They were swarming already to the side of the market-place when Antony raised his voice, 'You have forgot the will I told you of!'

'The will! The will! Let's stay and hear the will!'

Antony held it up. 'Here is the will, and under Caesar's seal. To every Roman citizen he gives – to every several man – seventy-five drachmas.'

'Most noble Caesar! We'll revenge his death.'

'Hear me with patience. There is more. He has left you all his walks, his private arbours and his new-planted orchards on this side of the

Tiber. They are for you and for your heirs – for ever. Here was a Caesar. When comes such another?'

His listeners would hear no more. With a storm of 'Never, never, never! Come away, away!', they rushed from the Forum, vowing to burn Caesar's body in the holy place and to use the brands to fire the traitors' houses.

It was done. Antony stared after the frenzied rabble. 'Let it work,' he said to himself. 'Mischief, thou art afoot. Now take what course thou wilt!' A servant, who had been struggling to push through the crowd, stood before him: 'Sir, Octavius has already come to Rome. He and Lepidus are at Caesar's house.'

'Thither,' said Antony, 'I will go to visit him. Fortune in this mood may give us anything.'

The servant pointed to the south. 'Brutus and Cassius, men say, have ridden like madmen through the gates of Rome.' And Antony smiled: 'No doubt they heard how I had moved the people. Come, bring me to Octavius.'

The rest was slow retribution. Antony, with Octavius and Lepidus (a soldier Antony despised but found useful for his purpose), now took over the government, as triumvirs, and for a long period battled against the rebel forces raised by Brutus and Cassius outside Rome.

Ever quick to be offended, Cassius drove into a passionate quarrel with Brutus when they were encamped upon an autumn evening at Sardis in Asia Minor. When the quarrel had been resolved, Brutus admitted that he was sick of many griefs. Portia, his wife, was dead. Grieved by his absence and by the news that Octavius and Antony had made themselves so strong, she fell distracted and, when left alone, swallowed burning coals. That evening, at a council of war, Brutus urged that it would be wise to make the long journey to the north-west, and, upon the plains of Philippi in Thrace, give battle to Octavius and Mark Antony who had marched from Rome. 'There is,' he said, 'a tide in the affairs of men, which, taken at the flood, leads on to fortune. We must take the current when it serves, or lose our ventures.' A few hours later, when Brutus was reading in his tent at the dead of night, his taper burned low; in the darkness he saw the ghost of Julius Caesar advancing upon him.

'Speak to me,' said Brutus, 'what are you?' And the ghost answered, 'Your evil spirit, Brutus.'

'Why do you come?'

'To tell you that we shall meet at Philippi.'

'Then I shall see you again?'

'Ay, at Philippi.' As the phantom faded, Brutus cried out and brought to his side the guards who had seen nothing. It was time to march. 'Commend me,' said Brutus, 'to my brother Cassius. Bid him set on his powers, and we will follow.'

In due time the enemies met for parley upon the plains of Philippi. Brutus spoke first: 'Words before blows. Is it so, countrymen?' 'Not that we love words better, as you do,' said Octavius. So they taunted each other until Octavius drew his sword, exclaiming that he would not sheathe it until Caesar's three-and-thirty wounds were well avenged. When the parley was over, Cassius (whose birthday it was) spoke aside to his officer Messala, calling him to witness that against his will – as Pompey had been – he had to gamble all upon a single fight. The eagles that had accompanied them from Sardis had flown away, and above their army hovered only ravens, crows, and kites, 'a company most fatal'. Then he turned to Brutus and warned him that if they lost the battle it would be the last time they could speak together. Brutus stretched out his hand:

'This same day
Must end that work the Ides of March begun.
And whether we shall meet again, I know not:
Therefore our everlasting farewell take:
For ever, and for ever, farewell, Cassius!
If we do meet again, why, we shall smile;
If not, why then this parting was well made.'

Cassius repeated the last words. Soon battle was joined. During its full heat, in the early afternoon, Cassius sent his officer Titinius to make sure whether an approaching troop were friend or enemy. The Parthian Pindarus, his faithful bondsman, told him that horsemen had encircled Titinius and shouted for joy as he leapt down among them. And Cassius, calling himself a coward to have lived only to see his best friend taken before his face, ordered Pindarus to stab him. 'Caesar,' he gasped as he fell, 'you are revenged, even with the sword that killed you.'

It was a tragic error, for Titinius had been surrounded by friendly troops who sent him back to Cassius with a wreath of victory. Overcome on seeing the dead man, he took Cassius' sword, and with the words, 'This is a Roman's part,' killed himself and fell across his general. Brutus, against whom the battle had turned, found them lying together and exclaimed sadly, 'O Julius Caesar, you are mighty yet. Your spirit walks abroad; our swords are turned against ourselves.' Weeping, he covered the face of Cassius: 'The last of all the Romans, fare you well.'

By the thickening of the autumn dusk the army of the conspirators was broken. Only a few poor remnants gathered round Brutus who saw that all was over. On the previous night the ghost of Caesar had reappeared to him. 'I know,' he said, 'that my hour has come'; and he asked soldier after soldier to kill him. Every man refused until one of them, Strato, consented to hold the sword while Brutus ran upon it and sank, mortally wounded, with the words, 'Caesar, now be still; I killed you not with half so good a will.'

There, shortly afterwards, his victorious foes discovered the body. Mark Antony, generous in triumph, saluted the noblest Roman of them all. Influenced neither by envy nor base thoughts of gain, Brutus had raised his hand solely for the common good. In the October night, where torches gleamed through the murk upon the stricken field of Philippi, Antony spoke a last epitaph: 'His life was gentle, and the elements so mixed in him, that Nature might stand up and say to all the world, "This was a man!" '

MACBETH

◆◆◆◆◆◆◆◆◆◆◆◆◆◆◆◆◆◆◆◆◆◆◆◆◆◆◆◆◆◆◆◆◆◆◆

WHEN Duncan the Meek reigned King of Scotland, there lived a great thane, or lord, called Macbeth. This Macbeth was a near kinsman to the king, and in great esteem at court for his valour and conduct in the wars; an example of which he had lately given, in defeating a rebel army assisted by the troops of Norway in terrible numbers.

The two Scottish generals, Macbeth and Banquo, returning victorious from this great battle, their way lay over a blasted heath, where they were stopped by the strange appearance of three figures like women, except that they had beards, and their withered skins and wild attire made them look not like any earthly creatures. Macbeth first addressed them, when they, seemingly offended, laid each one her choppy finger upon her skinny lips, in token of silence; and the first of them saluted Macbeth with the title of thane of Glamis. The general was not a little startled to find himself known by such creatures; but how much more, when the second of them followed up that salute by giving him the title of thane of Cawdor, to which honour he had no pretensions; and again the third bid him 'All hail! king that shalt be hereafter!' Such a prophetic greeting might well amaze him, who knew that while the king's sons lived he could not hope to succeed to the throne. Then turning to Banquo, they pronounced him, in a sort of riddling terms, to be *lesser than Macbeth and greater! not so happy, but much happier!* and prophesied that though he should never reign, yet his sons after him should be kings in Scotland. They then turned into air, and vanished: by which the generals knew them to be the weird sisters, or witches.

While they stood pondering on the strangeness of this adventure, there arrived certain messengers from the king, who were empowered by him to confer upon Macbeth the dignity of thane of Cawdor: an event so miraculously corresponding with the prediction of the witches astonished Macbeth, and he stood wrapped in amazement, unable to make reply to the messengers; and in that point of time swelling hopes arose in his mind that the prediction of the third witch might in like manner have its accomplishment, and that he should one day reign king in Scotland.

Turning to Banquo, he said, 'Do you not hope that your children shall be kings, when what the witches promised to me has so wonderfully come to pass?' 'That hope,' answered the general, 'might enkindle you to aim at the throne; but oftentimes these ministers of darkness tell us truths in little things, to betray us into deeds of greatest consequence.'

But the wicked suggestions of the witches had sunk too deep into the mind of Macbeth to allow him to attend to the warnings of the good Banquo. From that time he bent all his thoughts how to compass the throne of Scotland.

Macbeth had a wife, to whom he communicated the strange prediction of the weird sisters, and its partial accomplishment. She was a bad, ambitious woman, and so as her husband and herself could arrive at greatness, she cared not much by what means. She spurred on the reluctant purpose of Macbeth, who felt compunction at the thoughts of blood, and did not cease to represent the murder of the king as a step absolutely necessary to the fulfilment of the flattering prophecy.

It happened at this time that the king, who out of his royal condescension would oftentimes visit his principal nobility upon gracious terms, came to Macbeth's house, attended by his two sons, Malcolm and Donalbain, and a numerous train of thanes and attendants, the more to honour Macbeth for the triumphal success of his wars.

The castle of Macbeth was pleasantly situated, and the air about it was sweet and wholesome, which appeared by the nests which the martlet, or swallow, had built under all the jutting friezes and buttresses of the building, wherever it found a place of advantage; for where those birds most breed and haunt, the air is observed to be delicate. The king entered well-pleased with the place and not less so with the attentions and respect of his honoured hostess, Lady Macbeth, who had the art of covering treacherous purposes with smiles; and could look like the innocent flower, while she was indeed the serpent under it.

The king being tired with his journey, went early to bed, and in his state-room two grooms of his chamber (as was the custom) slept beside him. He had been unusually pleased with his reception, and had made presents before he retired to his principal officers; and among the rest, had sent a rich diamond to Lady Macbeth, greeting her by the name of his most kind hostess.

Now was the middle of night, when over half the world nature seems dead, and wicked dreams abuse men's minds asleep, and none but the wolf and the murderer is abroad. This was the time when Lady Macbeth waked to plot the murder of the king. She would not have undertaken a deed so abhorrent to her sex, but that she feared her husband's nature, that it was too full of the milk of human kindness, to do a contrived murder. She knew him to be ambitious, but withal to be scrupulous, and not yet prepared for that height of crime which commonly in the end accompanies inordinate ambition. She had won him to consent to the murder, but she doubted his resolution; and she feared that the natural tenderness of his disposition (more humane than her own) would come between, and defeat the purpose. So with her own hands armed with a dagger, she approached the king's bed; having taken care to ply the grooms of his chamber so with wine, that they slept intoxicated, and careless of their charge. There lay Duncan in a sound sleep after the fatigues of his journey, and as she viewed him earnestly, there was something in his face, as he slept, which resembled her own father; and she had not the courage to proceed.

She returned to confer with her husband. His resolution had begun to stagger. He considered that there were strong reasons against the deed. In the first place, he was not only a subject, but a near kinsman to the king; and he had been his host and entertainer that day, whose duty, by the laws of hospitality, it was to shut the door against his murderers, not bear the knife himself. Then he considered how just and merciful a king this Duncan had been, how clear of offence to his subjects, how loving to his nobility, and in particular to him; that such kings are the peculiar care of Heaven, and their subjects doubly bound to revenge their deaths. Besides, by the favours of the king, Macbeth stood high in the opinion of all sorts of men, and how would those honours be stained by the reputation of so foul a murder!

In these conflicts of the mind Lady Macbeth found her husband inclining to the better part, and resolving to proceed no further. But she being a woman not easily shaken from her evil purpose, began to pour in at his ears words which infused a portion of her own spirit into his mind, assigning reason upon reason why he should not shrink from what he had undertaken; how easy the deed was; how soon it would be over; and how the action of one short night would give to all their nights and days to come sovereign sway and royalty! Then she threw contempt on his change of purpose, and accused him of fickleness and cowardice; and declared that she had given suck, and knew how tender it was to love the babe that milked her; but she would, while it was smiling in her face, have plucked it from her breast, and dashed its brains out, if she had so sworn to do it, as he had sworn to perform that murder. Then she added, how practicable it was to lay the guilt of the deed upon the drunken sleepy grooms. And with the valour of her tongue she so chastised his sluggish resolutions, that he once more summoned up courage to the bloody business.

So, taking the dagger in his hand, he softly stole in the dark to the room where Duncan lay; and as he went, he thought he saw another dagger in the air, with the handle towards him, and on the blade and at the point of it drops of blood; but when he tried to grasp at it, it was nothing but air, a mere phantasm proceeding from his own hot and oppressed brain and the business he had in hand.

Getting rid of this fear, he entered the king's room, whom he despatched with one stroke of his dagger. Just as he had done the murder, one of the grooms, who slept in the chamber, laughed in his sleep, and the other cried, 'Murder,' which woke them both; but they said a short prayer; one of them said, 'God bless us!' and the other answered 'Amen;' and addressed themselves to sleep again. Macbeth, who stood listening to them, tried to say, 'Amen,' when the fellow said, 'God bless us!' but, though he had most need of a blessing, the word stuck in his throat, and he could not pronounce it.

Again he thought he heard a voice which cried, 'Sleep no more: Macbeth doth murder sleep, the innocent sleep, that nourishes life.' Still it cried, 'Sleep no more,' to all the house. 'Glamis hath murdered sleep, and therefore Cawdor shall sleep no more, Macbeth shall sleep no more.'

With such horrible imaginations Macbeth returned to his listening wife, who began to think he had failed of his purpose, and that the deed was somehow frustrated. He came in so distracted a state, that she reproached him with his want of firmness, and sent him to wash his hands of the blood which stained them, while she took his dagger, with purpose to stain the cheeks of the grooms with blood, to make it seem their guilt.

Morning came, and with it the discovery of the murder, which could not be concealed; and though Macbeth and his lady made great show of grief, and the proofs against the grooms (the dagger being produced against them and their faces smeared with blood) were sufficiently strong, yet the entire suspicion fell upon Macbeth, whose inducements to such a deed were so much more forcible than such poor silly grooms could be supposed to have; and Duncan's two sons fled. Malcolm, the eldest, sought for refuge in the English court; and the youngest, Donalbain, made his escape to Ireland.

The king's sons, who should have succeeded him, having thus vacated the throne, Macbeth as next heir was crowned king, and thus the prediction of the weird sisters was literally accomplished.

Though placed so high, Macbeth and his queen could not forget the prophecy of the weird sisters, that, though Macbeth should be king, yet not his children, but the children of Banquo, should be kings after him. The thought of this, and that they had defiled their hands with blood, and done so great crimes, only to place the posterity of Banquo upon the throne, so rankled within them, that they determined to put to death both Banquo and his son, to make void the predictions of the weird sisters, which in their own case had been so remarkably brought to pass.

For this purpose they made a great supper, to which they invited all the chief thanes; and, among the rest, with marks of particular respect, Banquo and his son Fleance were invited. The way by which Banquo was to pass to the palace at night was beset by murderers appointed by Macbeth, who stabbed Banquo; but in the scuffle Fleance escaped. From that Fleance descended a race of monarchs who afterwards filled the Scottish throne, ending with James the Sixth of Scotland and the First of England, under whom the two crowns of England and Scotland were united.

At supper, the queen, whose manners were in the highest degree affable and royal, played the hostess with a gracefulness and attention which conciliated every one present, and Macbeth discoursed freely with his thanes and nobles, saying, that all that was honourable in the country was under his roof, if he had but his good friend Banquo present, whom yet he hoped he should rather have to chide for neglect, than to lament for any mischance. Just at these words the ghost of Banquo, whom he had caused to be murdered, entered the room and placed himself on the chair which Macbeth was about to occupy. Though Macbeth was a bold man, and one that could have faced the devil without trembling, at this horrible sight his cheeks turned white with fear, and he stood quite unmanned with his eyes fixed upon the ghost. His queen and all the nobles, who saw nothing, but perceived him gazing (as they thought) upon an empty chair, took it for a fit of distraction; and she reproached him, whispering that it was but the same fancy which made him see the dagger in the air, when he was about to kill Duncan. But Macbeth continued to see the ghost, and gave no heed to all they could say, while he addressed it with distracted words, yet so significant, that his queen, fearing the dreadful secret would be disclosed, in great haste dismissed the guests, excusing the infirmity of Macbeth as a disorder he was often troubled with.

To such dreadful fancies Macbeth was subject. His queen and he had their sleeps afflicted with terrible dreams, and the blood of Banquo troubled them not more than the escape of Fleance, whom now they looked upon as father to a line of kings who should keep their posterity out of the throne. With these miserable thoughts they found no peace, and Macbeth determined once more to seek out the weird sisters, and know from them the worst.

He sought them in a cave upon the heath, where they, who knew by foresight of his coming, were engaged in preparing their dreadful charms, by which they conjured up infernal spirits to reveal to them futurity. Their horrid ingredients were toads, bats, and serpents, the eye of a newt, and the tongue of a dog, the leg of a lizard, and the wing of the night-owl, the scale of a dragon, the tooth of a wolf, the maw of the ravenous salt-sea shark, the mummy of a witch, the root of the poisonous hemlock (this to have effect must be digged in the dark), the gall of a goat, and the liver of a Jew, with slips of the yew tree that roots itself in graves, and the finger of a dead child: all these were set on to boil in a great kettle, or cauldron, which, as fast as it grew too hot, was cooled with a baboon's blood: to these they poured in the blood of a sow that had eaten her young, and they threw into the flame the grease that had sweaten from a murderer's gibbet. By these charms they bound the infernal spirits to answer their questions.

It was demanded of Macbeth, whether he would have his doubts resolved by them, or by their masters, the spirits. He, nothing daunted by the dreadful ceremonies which he saw, boldly answered, 'Where are they? let me see them.' And they called the spirits, which were three. And the first arose in the likeness of an armed head, and he called Macbeth by name, and bid him beware of the thane of Fife; for which caution Macbeth thanked him; for Macbeth had entertained a jealousy of Macduff, the thane of Fife.

And the second spirit arose in the likeness of a bloody child, and he called Macbeth by name, and bid him have no fear, but laugh to scorn the power of man, for none of woman born should have power to hurt him; and he advised him to be bloody, bold, and resolute. 'Then live, Macduff!' cried the king; 'what need I fear of thee? but yet I will make assurance doubly sure. Thou shalt not live; that I may tell pale-hearted Fear it lies, and sleep in spite of thunder.'

That spirit being dismissed, a third arose in the form of a child crowned, with a tree in his hand. He called Macbeth by name, and comforted him against conspiracies, saying, that he should never be vanquished, until the wood of Birnam to Dunsinane Hill should come against him. 'Sweet bodements! good!' cried Macbeth; 'who can unfix the forest, and move it from its earth-bound roots? I see I shall live the usual period of man's life, and not be cut off by a violent death. But my heart throbs to know one thing. Tell me, if your art can tell so much, if Banquo's issue shall ever reign in this kingdom?' Here the cauldron sank into the ground, and a noise of music was heard, and eight shadows, like kings, passed by Macbeth, and Banquo last, who bore a glass which showed the figures of many more, and Banquo all bloody smiled upon Macbeth, and pointed to them; by which Macbeth knew that these were the posterity of Banquo, who should reign after him in Scotland; and the witches, with a sound of soft music, and with dancing, making a show of duty and welcome to Macbeth, vanished. And from this time the thoughts of Macbeth were all bloody and dreadful.

The first thing he heard when he got out of the witches' cave, was that Macduff, thane of Fife, had fled to England, to join the army which was forming against him under Malcolm, the eldest son of the late king, with intent to displace Macbeth, and set Malcolm, the right heir, upon the throne. Macbeth, stung with rage, set upon the castle of Macduff, and put his wife and children, whom the thane had left behind, to the sword, and extended the slaughter to all who claimed the least relationship to Macduff.

These and such-like deeds alienated the minds of all his chief nobility from him. Such as could, fled to join with Malcolm and Macduff, who were now approaching with a powerful army, which they had raised in England; and the rest secretly wished success to their arms, though for fear of Macbeth they could take no active part. His recruits went on slowly. Everybody hated the tyrant; nobody loved or honoured him; but all suspected him, and he began to envy the condition of Duncan, whom he had murdered, who slept soundly in his grave, against whom treason had done its worst: steel nor poison, domestic malice nor foreign levies, could hurt him any longer.

While these things were acting, the queen, who had been the sole partner in his wickedness, in whose bosom he could sometimes seek a momentary repose from those terrible dreams which afflicted them both nightly, died, it is supposed, by her own hands, unable to bear the remorse of guilt, and public hate; by which event he was left alone, without a soul to love or care for him, or a friend to whom he could confide his wicked purposes.

He grew careless of life, and wished for death; but the near approach of Malcolm's army roused in him what remained of his ancient courage, and he determined to die (as he expressed it) 'with armour on his back.' Besides this, the hollow promises of the witches had filled him with a false confidence, and he remembered the sayings of the spirits, that none of woman born was to hurt him, and that he was never to be vanquished till Birnam wood should come to Dunsinane, which he thought could never be. So he shut himself up in his castle, whose impregnable strength was such as defied a siege: here he sullenly waited the approach of Malcolm. When, upon a day, there came a messenger to him, pale and shaking with fear, almost unable to report that which he had seen; for he averred, that as he stood upon his watch on the hill, he looked towards Birnam, and to his thinking the wood began to move! 'Liar and slave!' cried Macbeth; 'if thou speakest false, thou shalt hang alive upon the next tree, till famine end thee. If thy tale be true, I care not if thou dost as much by me:' for Macbeth now began to faint in resolution, and to doubt the equivocal speeches of the spirits. He was not to fear till Birnam wood should come to Dunsinane; and now a wood did move! 'However,' said he, 'if this which he avouches be true, let us arm and out. There is no flying hence, nor staying here. I begin to be weary of the sun, and wish my life at an end.' With these desperate speeches he sallied forth upon the besiegers, who had now come up to the castle.

The strange appearance which had given the messenger an idea of a wood moving is easily solved. When the besieging army marched through the wood of Birnam, Malcolm, like a skilful general, instructed his soldiers to hew down every one a bough and bear it before him, by way of concealing the true numbers of his host. This marching of the soldiers with boughs had at a distance the appearance which had frightened the messenger. Thus were the words of the spirit brought to pass, in a sense different from that in which Macbeth had understood them, and one great hold of his confidence was gone.

And now a severe skirmishing took place, in which Macbeth, though feebly supported by those who called themselves his friends, but in reality hated the tyrant and inclined to the party of Malcolm and Macduff, yet fought with the extreme of rage and valour, cutting to pieces all who were opposed to him, till he came to where Macduff was fighting. Seeing Macduff, and remembering the caution of the spirit who had counselled him to avoid Macduff, above all men, he would have turned, but Macduff, who had been seeking him through the whole fight, opposed his turning, and a fierce contest ensued; Macduff giving him many foul reproaches for the murder of his wife and children. Macbeth, whose soul was charged enough with blood of that family already, would still have declined the combat; but Macduff still urged him to it, calling him tyrant, murderer, hell-hound, and villain.

Then Macbeth remembered the words of the spirit, how none of woman born should hurt him; and smiling confidently he said to Macduff, 'Thou losest thy labour, Macduff. As easily thou mayest impress the air with thy sword, as make me vulnerable. I bear a charmed life, which must not yield to one of woman born.'

'Despair thy charm,' said Macduff, 'and let that lying spirit whom thou hast served, tell thee, that Macduff was never born of woman, never as the ordinary manner of men is to be born, but was untimely taken from his mother.'

'Accursed be the tongue which tells me so,' said the trembling Macbeth, who felt his last hold of confidence give way; 'and let never man in future believe the lying equivocations of witches and juggling spirits, who deceive us in words which have double senses, and while they keep their promise literally, disappoint our hopes with a different meaning. I will not fight with thee.'

'Then live!' said the scornful Macduff; 'we will have a show of thee, as men show monsters, and a painted board, on which shall be written, "Here men may see the tyrant!"'

'Never,' said Macbeth, whose courage returned with despair; 'I will not live to kiss the ground before young Malcolm's feet, and to be baited with the curses of the rabble. Though Birnam wood be come to Dunsinane, and thou opposed to me, who wast never born of woman, yet will I try the last.' With these frantic words he threw himself upon Macduff, who, after a severe struggle, in the end overcame him, and cutting off his head, made a present of it to the young and lawful king, Malcolm; who took upon him the government which, by the machinations of the usurper, he had so long been deprived of, and ascended the throne of Duncan the Meek, amid the acclamations of the nobles and the people.

HAMLET
PRINCE OF DENMARK

◆◆◆◆◆◆◆◆◆◆◆◆◆◆◆◆◆◆◆◆◆◆◆◆◆◆◆◆◆◆◆◆◆◆◆◆◆

GERTRUDE, Queen of Denmark, becoming a widow by the sudden death of King Hamlet, in less than two months after his death married his brother Claudius, which was noted by all people at the time for a strange act of indiscretion, or unfeelingness, or worse: for this Claudius did no ways resemble her late husband in the qualities of his person or his mind, but was as contemptible in outward appearance, as he was base and unworthy in disposition; and suspicions did not fail to arise in the minds of some, that he had privately made away with his brother, the late king, with the view of marrying his widow, and ascending the throne of Denmark, to the exclusion of young Hamlet, the son of the buried king, and lawful successor to the throne.

But upon no one did this unadvised action of the queen make such impression as upon this young prince, who loved and venerated the memory of his dead father almost to idolatry, and being of a nice sense of honour, and a most exquisite practiser of propriety himself, did sorely take to heart this unworthy conduct of his mother Gertrude: insomuch that, between grief for his father's death and shame for his mother's marriage, this young prince was overclouded with a deep melancholy, and lost all his mirth and all his good looks; all his customary pleasure in books forsook him, his princely exercises and sports, proper to his youth, were no longer acceptable; he grew weary of the world, which seemed to him an unweeded garden, where all the wholesome flowers were choked up, and nothing but weeds could thrive. Not that the prospect of exclusion from the throne, his lawful inheritance, weighed so much upon his spirits, though that to a young and high-minded prince was a bitter wound and a sore indignity; but what so galled him, and took away all his cheerful spirits, was, that his mother had shown herself so forgetful to his father's memory: and such a father! who had been to her so loving and so gentle a husband! and then she always appeared as loving and obedient a wife to him, and would hang upon him as if her affection grew to him: and now within two months, or as it seemed to young Hamlet, less than two months, she had married again, married his uncle, her dear husband's brother, in itself a highly improper and unlawful marriage, from the nearness of relationship, but made much more so by the indecent haste with which it was concluded, and the unkingly character of the man whom she had chosen to be the partner of her throne and bed. This it was, which more than the loss of ten kingdoms, dashed the spirits and brought a cloud over the mind of this honourable young prince.

In vain was all that his mother Gertrude or the king could do to contrive to divert him; he still appeared in court in a suit of deep black, as mourning for the king his father's death, which mode of dress he had never laid aside, not even in compliment to his mother upon the day she was married, nor could he be brought to join in any of the festivities or rejoicings of that (as appeared to him) disgraceful day.

What mostly troubled him was an uncertainty about the manner of his father's death. It was given out by Claudius that a serpent had stung him; but young Hamlet had shrewd suspicions that Claudius himself was the serpent; in plain English, that he had murdered him for his crown, and that the serpent who stung his father did now sit on the throne.

How far he was right in this conjecture, and what he ought to think of his mother, how far she was privy to this murder, and whether by her consent or knowledge, or without, it came to pass, were the doubts which continually harassed and distracted him.

A rumour had reached the ear of young Hamlet, that an apparition, exactly resembling the dead king his father, had been seen by the soldiers upon watch, on the platform before the palace at midnight, for two or three nights successively. The figure came constantly clad in the same suit of armour, from head to foot, which the dead king was known to have worn: and they who saw it (Hamlet's bosom friend Horatio was one) agreed in their testimony as to the time and manner of its appearance: that it came just as the clock struck twelve; that it looked pale, with a face more of sorrow than of anger; that its beard was grisly, and the colour a *sable silvered*, as they had seen it in his life-time: that it made no answer when they spoke to it; yet once they thought it lifted up its head, and addressed itself to motion, as if it were about to speak; but in that moment the morning cock crew, and it shrunk in haste away, and vanished out of their sight.

The young prince, strangely amazed at their relation, which was too consistent and agreeing with itself to disbelieve, concluded that it was his father's ghost which they had seen, and determined to take his watch with the soldiers that night, that he might have a chance of seeing it; for he reasoned with himself, that such an appearance did not come for nothing, but that the ghost had something to impart, and though it had been silent hitherto, yet it would speak to him. And he waited with impatience for the coming of night.

When night came he took his stand with Horatio, and Marcellus, one of the guard, upon the platform, where this apparition was accustomed to walk: and it being a cold night, and the air unusually raw and nipping, Hamlet and Horatio and their companion fell into some talk about the coldness of the night, which was suddenly broken off by Horatio announcing that the ghost was coming.

At the sight of his father's spirit, Hamlet was struck with a sudden surprise and fear. He at first called upon the angels and heavenly ministers to defend them, for he knew not whether it were a good spirit or bad; whether it came for good or evil: but he gradually assumed more courage; and his father (as it seemed to him) looked upon him so piteously, and as it were desiring to have conversation with him, and did in all respects appear so like himself as he was when he lived, that Hamlet could not help addressing him: he called him by his name, Hamlet, King, Father! and conjured him that he would tell the reason why he had left his grave, where they had seen him quietly bestowed, to come again and visit the earth and the moonlight: and besought him that he would let them know if there was anything which they could do to give peace to his spirit. And the ghost beckoned to Hamlet, that he should go with him to some more removed place, where they might be alone; and Horatio and Marcellus would have dissuaded the young prince from following it, for they feared lest it should be some evil spirit, who would tempt him to the neighbouring sea, or to the top of some dreadful cliff, and there put on some horrible shape which might deprive the prince of his reason. But their counsels and entreaties could not alter Hamlet's determination, who cared too little about life to fear the losing of it; and as to his soul, he said, what could the spirit do to that, being a thing immortal as itself? And he felt as hardy as a lion, and bursting from them, who did all they could to hold him, he followed whithersoever the spirit led him.

And when they were alone together, the spirit broke silence, and told him that he was the ghost of Hamlet, his father, who had been cruelly murdered, and he told the manner of it; that it was done by his own brother Claudius, Hamlet's uncle, as Hamlet had already but too much suspected, for the hope of succeeding to his bed and crown. That as he was sleeping in his garden, his custom always in the afternoon, his treasonous brother stole upon him in his sleep, and poured the juice of poisonous henbane into his ears, which has such an antipathy to the life of man, that swift as quicksilver it courses through all the veins of the body, baking up the blood, and spreading a crustlike leprosy all over the skin: thus sleeping, by a brother's hand he was cut off at once from his crown, his queen, and his life: and he adjured Hamlet, if he did ever his dear father love, that he would revenge his foul murder. And the ghost lamented to his son, that his mother should so fall off from virtue, as to prove false to the wedded love of her first husband, and to marry his murderer; but he cautioned Hamlet, howsoever he proceeded in his revenge against his wicked uncle, by no means to act any violence against the person of his mother, but to leave her to heaven, and to the stings and thorns of conscience. And Hamlet promised to observe the ghost's direction in all things, and the ghost vanished.

And when Hamlet was left alone, he took up a solemn resolution, that all he had in his memory, all that he had ever learned by books or observation, should be instantly forgotten by him, and nothing live in his brain but the memory of what the ghost had told him, and enjoined him to do. And Hamlet related the particulars of the conversation which had passed to none but his dear friend Horatio; and he enjoined both to him and Marcellus the strictest secrecy as to what they had seen that night.

The terror which the sight of the ghost had left upon the senses of

Hamlet, he being weak and dispirited before, almost unhinged his mind, and drove him beside his reason. And he, fearing that it would continue to have this effect, which might subject him to observation, and set his uncle upon his guard, if he suspected that he was meditating anything against him, or that Hamlet really knew more of his father's death than he professed, took up a strange resolution, from that time to counterfeit as if he were really and truly mad; thinking that he would be less an object of suspicion when his uncle should believe him incapable of any serious project, and that his real perturbation of mind would be best covered and pass concealed under a disguise of pretended lunacy.

From this time Hamlet affected a certain wildness and strangeness in his apparel, his speech, and behaviour, and did so excellently counterfeit the madman, that the king and queen were both deceived, and not thinking his grief for his father's death a sufficient cause to produce such a distemper, for they knew not of the appearance of the ghost, they concluded that his malady was love, and they thought they had found out the object.

Before Hamlet fell into the melancholy way which has been related, he had dearly loved a fair maid called Ophelia, the daughter of Polonius, the king's chief counsellor in affairs of state. He had sent her letters and rings, and made many tenders of his affection to her, and importuned her with love in honourable fashion: and she had given belief to his vows and importunities. But the melancholy which he fell into latterly had made him neglect her, and from the time he conceived the project of counterfeiting madness, he affected to treat her with unkindness, and a sort of rudeness: but she, good lady, rather than reproach him with being false to her, persuaded herself that it was nothing but the disease in his mind, and no settled unkindness, which had made him less observant of her than formerly; and she compared the faculties of his once noble mind and excellent understanding, impaired as they were with the deep melancholy that oppressed him, to sweet bells which in themselves are capable of most exquisite music, but when jangled out of tune, or rudely handled, produce only a harsh and unpleasing sound.

Though the rough business which Hamlet had in hand, the revenging of his father's death upon his murderer, did not suit with the playful state of courtship, or admit of the society of so idle a passion as love now seemed to him, yet it could not hinder but that soft thoughts of his Ophelia would come between, and in one of these moments, when he thought that his treatment of this gentle lady had been unreasonably harsh, he wrote her a letter full of wild starts of passion, and in extravagant terms, such as agreed with his supposed madness, but mixed with some gentle touches of affection, which could not but show to this honoured lady that a deep love for her yet lay at the bottom of his heart. He bade her to doubt the stars were fire, and to doubt that the sun did move, to doubt truth to be a liar, but never to doubt that he loved; with more of such extravagant phrases. This letter Ophelia dutifully showed to her father, and the old man thought himself bound to communicate it to the king and queen, who from that time supposed that the true cause of Hamlet's madness was love. And the queen wished that the good beauties of Ophelia might be the happy cause of his wildness, for so she hoped that her virtues might happily restore him to his accustomed way again, to both their honours.

But Hamlet's malady lay deeper than she supposed, or than could be so cured. His father's ghost, which he had seen, still haunted his imagination, and the sacred injunction to revenge his murder gave him no rest till it was accomplished. Every hour of delay seemed to him a sin, and a violation of his father's commands. Yet how to compass the death of the king, surrounded as he constantly was with his guards, was no easy matter. Or if it had been, the presence of the queen, Hamlet's mother, who was generally with the king, was a restraint upon his purpose, which he could not break through. Besides, the very circumstance that the usurper was his mother's husband filled him with some remorse, and still blunted the edge of his purpose. The mere act of putting a fellow-creature to death was in itself odious and terrible to a disposition naturally so gentle as Hamlet's was. His very melancholy, and the dejection of spirits he had so long been in, produced an irresoluteness and wavering of purpose, which kept him from proceeding to extremities. Moreover, he could not help having some scruples upon his mind, whether the spirit which he had seen was indeed his father, or whether it might not be the devil, who he had heard has power to take any form he pleases, and who might have assumed his father's shape only to take advantage of his weakness and his melancholy, to drive him to the doing of so desperate an act as murder. And he determined that he would have more certain grounds to go upon than a vision, or apparition, which might be a delusion.

While he was in this irresolute mind there came to the court certain players, in whom Hamlet formerly used to take delight, and particularly to hear one of them speak a tragical speech, describing the death of old Priam, King of Troy, with the grief of Hecuba his queen. Hamlet welcomed his old friends, the players, and remembering how that speech had formerly given him pleasure, requested the player to repeat it; which he did in so lively a manner, setting forth the cruel murder of the feeble old king, with the destruction of his people and city by fire, and the mad grief of the old queen, running barefoot up and down the palace, with a poor clout upon that head where a crown had been, and with nothing but a blanket upon her loins, snatched up in haste, where she had worn a royal robe; that not only it drew tears from all that stood by, who thought they saw the real scene, so lively was it represented, but even the player himself delivered it with a broken voice and real tears. This put Hamlet upon thinking, if that player could so work himself up to passion by a mere fictitious speech, to weep for one that he had never seen, for Hecuba, that had been dead so many hundred years, how dull was he, who having a real motive and cue for passion, a real king and a dear father murdered, was yet so little moved, that his revenge all this while had seemed to have slept in dull and muddy forgetfulness! and while he meditated on actors and acting, and the powerful effects which a good play, represented to the life, has upon the spectator, he remembered the instance of some murderer, who seeing a murder on the stage, was by the mere force of the scene and resemblance of circumstances so affected, that on the spot he confessed the crime which he had committed. And he determined that these players should play something like the murder of his father before his uncle, and he would watch narrowly what effect it might have upon him, and from his looks he would be able to gather with more certainty if he were the murderer or not. To this effect he ordered a play to be prepared, to the representation of which he invited the king and queen.

The story of the play was of a murder done in Vienna upon a duke. The duke's name was Gonzago, his wife Baptista. The play showed how one Lucianus, a near relation to the duke, poisoned him in his garden for his estate, and how the murderer in a short time after got the love of Gonzago's wife.

At the representation of this play, the king, who did not know the trap which was laid for him, was present, with his queen and the whole court: Hamlet sitting attentively near him to observe his looks. The play began with a conversation between Gonzago and his wife, in which the lady made many protestations of love, and of never marrying a second husband, if she should outlive Gonzago; wishing she might be accursed if she ever took a second husband, and adding that no woman did so, but those wicked women who kill their first husbands. Hamlet observed the king his uncle change colour at this expression, and that it was as bad as wormwood both to him and to the queen. But when Lucianus, according to the story, came to poison Gonzago sleeping in the garden, the strong resemblance which it bore to his own wicked act upon the late king, his brother, whom he had poisoned in his garden, so struck upon the conscience of this usurper, that he was unable to sit out the rest of the play, but on a sudden calling for lights to his chamber, and affecting or partly feeling a sudden sickness, he abruptly left the theatre. The king being departed, the play was given over. Now Hamlet had seen enough to be satisfied that the words of the ghost were true, and no illusion; and in a fit of gaiety, like that which comes over a man who suddenly has some great doubt or scruple resolved, he swore to Horatio, that he would take the ghost's word for a thousand pounds. But before he could make up his resolution as to what measures of revenge he should take, now he was certainly informed that his uncle was his father's murderer, he was sent for by the queen his mother, to a private conference in her closet.

It was by desire of the king that the queen sent for Hamlet, that she might signify to her son how much his late behaviour had displeased them both, and the king, wishing to know all that passed at that conference, and thinking that the too partial report of a mother might let slip some part of Hamlet's words, which it might much import the king to know, Polonius, the old counsellor of state, was ordered to plant himself behind the hangings in the queen's closet, where he might unseen hear all that passed. This artifice was particularly adapted to the disposition of Polonius, who was a man grown old in crooked maxims and policies of state, and delighted to get at the knowledge of matters in an indirect and cunning way.

Hamlet being come to his mother, she began to tax him in the roundest way with his actions and behaviour, and she told him that he had given great offence to *his father*, meaning the king, his uncle, whom, because he had married her, she called Hamlet's father. Hamlet, sorely indignant that she should give so dear and honoured a name as father seemed to him, to a wretch who was indeed no better than the murderer of his true father, with some sharpness replied, 'Mother, *you* have much offended *my father*.' The queen said that was but an idle answer. 'As good as the question deserved,' said Hamlet. The queen asked him if he had forgotten who it was he was speaking to? 'Alas!' replied Hamlet, 'I wish I could forget. You are the queen, your husband's brother's wife; and you are my mother: I wish you were not what you are.' 'Nay, then,' said the queen, 'if you show me so little respect, I will set those to you that can speak,' and was going to send the king or Polonius to him. But Hamlet would not let her go, now he had her alone, till he had tried if his words could not bring her to some sense of her wicked life; and, taking her by the wrist, he held her fast, and made her sit down. She, affrighted at his earnest manner, and fearful lest in his lunacy he should do her a mischief, cried out; and a voice was heard from behind the hangings, 'Help, help, the queen!' which Hamlet hearing, and verily thinking that it was the king himself there concealed, he drew his sword and stabbed at the place where the voice came from, as he would have stabbed a rat that ran there, till the voice ceasing, he concluded the person to be dead. But when he dragged forth the body, it was not the king, but Polonius, the old officious counsellor, that had planted himself as a spy behind the hangings. 'Oh me!' exclaimed the queen, 'what rash and bloody deed have you done!' 'A bloody deed, mother,' replied Hamlet, 'but not so bad as yours, who killed a king, and married his brother.' Hamlet had gone too far to leave off here. He was now in the humour to speak plainly to his mother, and he pursued it. And though the faults of parents are to be tenderly treated by their children, yet in the case of great crimes the son may have leave to speak even to his own mother with some harshness, so as that harshness is meant for her good, and to turn her from her wicked ways, and not done for the purpose of upbraiding. And now this virtuous prince did in moving terms represent to the queen the heinousness of her offence, in being so forgetful of the dead king, his father, as in so short a space of time to marry with his brother and reputed murderer: such an act as, after the vows which she had sworn to her first husband, was enough to make all vows of women suspected, and all virtue to be accounted hypocrisy, wedding contracts to be less than gamesters' oaths, and religion to be a mockery and a mere form of words. He said she had done such a deed, that the heavens blushed at it, and the earth was sick of her because of it. And he showed her two pictures, the one of the late king, her first husband, and the other of the present king, her second husband, and he bade her mark the difference; what a grace was on the brow of his father, how like a god he looked! the curls of Apollo, the forehead of Jupiter, the eye of Mars, and a posture like to Mercury newly alighted on some heaven-kissing hill! this man, he said, *had been* her husband. And then he showed her whom she had got in his stead: how like a blight or a mildew he looked, for so he had blasted his wholesome brother. And the queen was sore ashamed that he should so turn her eyes inward upon her soul, which she now saw so black and deformed. And he asked her how she could continue to live with this man, and be a wife to him, who had murdered her first husband, and got the crown by as false means as a thief———and just as he spoke, the ghost of his father, such as he was in his lifetime, and such as he had lately seen it, entered the room, and Hamlet, in great terror, asked what it would have; and the ghost said that it came to remind him of the revenge he had promised, which Hamlet seemed to have forgot; and the ghost bade him speak to his mother, for the grief and terror she was in would else kill her. It then vanished, and was seen by none but Hamlet, neither could he by pointing to where it stood, or by any description, make his mother perceive it; who was terribly frightened all this while to hear him conversing, as it seemed to her, with nothing; and she imputed it to the disorder of his mind. But Hamlet begged her not to flatter her wicked soul in such a manner as to think that it was his madness, and not her own offences, which had brought his father's spirit again on the earth. And he bade her feel his pulse, how temperately it beat, not like a madman's. And he begged of her with tears, to confess herself to heaven for what was past, and for the future to avoid the company of the king, and be no more as a wife to him: and when she should show herself a mother to him, by respecting his father's memory, he would ask a blessing of her as a son. And she promising to observe his directions, the conference ended.

And now Hamlet was at leisure to consider who it was that in his unfortunate rashness he had killed: and when he came to see that it was Polonius, the father of the Lady Ophelia, whom he so dearly loved, he drew apart the dead body, and, his spirits being now a little quieter, he wept for what he had done.

The unfortunate death of Polonius gave the king a pretence for sending Hamlet out of the kingdom. He would willingly have put him to death, fearing him as dangerous; but he dreaded the people, who loved Hamlet, and the queen, who, with all her faults, doted upon the prince, her son. So this subtle king, under pretence of providing for Hamlet's safety, that he might not be called to account for Polonius' death, caused him to be conveyed on board a ship bound for England, under the care of two courtiers, by whom he despatched letters to the English court, which in that time was in subjection and paid tribute to Denmark, requiring for special reasons there pretended, that Hamlet should be put to death as soon as he landed on English ground. Hamlet, suspecting some treachery, in the night-time secretly got at the letters, and skilfully erasing his own name, he in the stead of it put in the names of those two courtiers, who had the charge of him, to be put to death: then sealing up the letters, he put them into their place again. Soon after the ship was attacked by pirates, and a sea-fight commenced; in the course of which Hamlet, desirous to show his valour, with sword in hand singly boarded the enemy's vessel; while his own ship, in a cowardly manner, bore away, and leaving him to his fate, the two courtiers made the best of their way to England, charged with those letters the sense of which Hamlet had altered to their own deserved destruction.

The pirates, who had the prince in their power, showed themselves gentle enemies; and knowing whom they had got prisoner, in the hope that the prince might do them a good turn at court in recompense for any favour they might show him, they set Hamlet on shore at the nearest port in Denmark. From that place Hamlet wrote to the king, acquainting him with the strange chance which had brought him back to his own country, and saying that on the next day he should present himself before his majesty. When he got home, a sad spectacle offered itself the first thing to his eyes.

This was the funeral of the young and beautiful Ophelia, his once dear mistress. The wits of this young lady had begun to turn ever since her poor father's death. That he should die a violent death, and by the hands of the prince whom she loved, so affected this tender young maid, that in a little time she grew perfectly distracted, and would go about giving flowers away to the ladies of the court, and saying that they were for her father's burial, singing songs about love and about death, and sometimes such as had no meaning at all, as if she had no memory of what happened to her. There was a willow which grew slanting over a brook, and reflected its leaves on the stream. To this brook she came one day when she was unwatched, with garlands she had been making, mixed up of daisies and nettles, flowers and weeds together, and clambering up to hang her garland upon the boughs of the willow, a bough broke, and precipitated this fair young maid, garland, and all that she had gathered, into the water, where her clothes bore her up for a while, during which she chanted scraps of old tunes, like one insensible to her own distress, or as if she were a creature natural to that element: but long it was not before her garments, heavy with the wet, pulled her in from her melodious singing to a muddy and miserable death. It was the funeral of this fair maid which her brother Laertes was celebrating, the king and queen and whole court being present, when Hamlet arrived. He knew not what all this show imported, but stood on one side, not inclining to interrupt the ceremony. He saw the flowers strewed upon her grave, as the custom was in maiden burials, which the queen herself threw in; and as she threw them she said, 'Sweets to the sweet! I thought to have decked thy bride-bed, sweet maid, not to have strewed thy grave. Thou shouldst have been my

Hamlet's wife.' And he heard her brother wish that violets might spring from her grave: and he saw him leap into the grave all frantic with grief, and bid the attendants pile mountains of earth upon him, that he might be buried with her. And Hamlet's love for this fair maid came back to him, and he could not bear that a brother should show so much transport of grief, for he thought that he loved Ophelia better than forty thousand brothers. Then discovering himself, he leaped into the grave where Laertes was, all as frantic or more frantic than he, and Laertes knowing him to be Hamlet, who had been the cause of his father's and his sister's death, grappled him by the throat as an enemy, till the attendants parted them: and Hamlet, after the funeral, excused his hasty act in throwing himself into the grave as if to brave Laertes; but he said he could not bear that any one should seem to outgo him in grief for the death of the fair Ophelia. And for the time these two noble youths seemed reconciled.

But out of the grief and anger of Laertes for the death of his father and Ophelia, the king, Hamlet's wicked uncle, contrived destruction for Hamlet. He set on Laertes, under cover of peace and reconciliation, to challenge Hamlet to a friendly trial of skill at fencing, which Hamlet accepting, a day was appointed to try the match. At this match all the court was present, and Laertes, by direction of the king, prepared a poisoned weapon. Upon this match great wagers were laid by the courtiers, as both Hamlet and Laertes were known to excel at this sword play; and Hamlet taking up the foils chose one, not at all suspecting the treachery of Laertes, or being careful to examine Laertes' weapon, who, instead of a foil or blunted sword, which the laws of fencing require, made use of one with a point, and poisoned. At first Laertes did but play with Hamlet, and suffered him to gain some advantages, which the dissembling king magnified and extolled beyond measure, drinking to Hamlet's success, and wagering rich bets upon the issue: but after a few pauses, Laertes growing warm made a deadly thrust at Hamlet with his poisoned weapon, and gave him a mortal blow. Hamlet incensed, but not knowing the whole of the treachery, in the scuffle exchanged his own innocent weapon for Laertes' deadly one, and with a thrust of Laertes' own sword repaid Laertes home, who was thus justly caught in his own treachery. In this instant the queen shrieked out that she was poisoned. She had inadvertently drunk out of a bowl which the king had prepared for Hamlet, in case, that being warm in fencing, he should call for drink: into this the treacherous king had infused a deadly poison, to make sure of Hamlet, if Laertes had failed. He had forgotten to warn the queen of the bowl, which she drank of, and immediately died, exclaiming with her last breath that she was poisoned. Hamlet, suspecting some treachery, ordered the doors to be shut, while he sought it out. Laertes told him to seek no farther, for he was the traitor; and feeling his life go away with the wound which Hamlet had given him, he made confession of the treachery he had used, and how he had fallen a victim to it: and he told Hamlet of the envenomed point, and said that Hamlet had not half an hour to live, for no medicine could cure him; and begging forgiveness of Hamlet, he died, with his last words accusing the king of being the contriver of the mischief. When Hamlet saw his end draw near, there being yet some venom left upon the sword, he suddenly turned upon his false uncle, and thrust the point of it to his heart, fulfilling the promise which he had made to his father's spirit, whose injunction was now accomplished, and his foul murder revenged upon the murderer. Then Hamlet, feeling his breath fail and life departing, turned to his dear friend Horatio, who had been spectator of this fatal tragedy; and with his dying breath requested him that he would live to tell his story to the world (for Horatio had made a motion as if he would slay himself to accompany the prince in death), and Horatio promised that he would make a true report, as one that was privy to all the circumstances. And, thus satisfied, the noble heart of Hamlet cracked; and Horatio and the bystanders with many tears commended the spirit of this sweet prince to the guardianship of angels. For Hamlet was a loving and a gentle prince, and greatly beloved for his many noble and princelike qualities; and if he had lived, would no doubt have proved a most royal and complete king to Denmark.

KING LEAR

◆◆◆◆◆◆◆◆◆◆◆◆◆◆◆◆◆◆◆◆◆◆◆◆◆◆◆◆◆◆◆◆◆◆◆◆

LEAR, King of Britain, had three daughters; Goneril, wife to the Duke of Albany; Regan, wife to the Duke of Cornwall; and Cordelia, a young maid, for whose love the King of France and Duke of Burgundy were joint suitors, and were at this time making stay for that purpose in the court of Lear.

The old king, worn out with age and the fatigues of government, he being more than fourscore years old, determined to take no further part in state affairs, but to leave the management to younger strengths, that he might have time to prepare for death, which must at no long period ensue. With this intent he called his three daughters to him, to know from their own lips which of them loved him best, that he might part his kingdom among them in such proportions as their affection for him should seem to deserve.

Goneril, the eldest, declared that she loved her father more than words could give out, that he was dearer to her than the light of her own eyes, dearer than life and liberty, with a deal of such professing stuff, which is easy to counterfeit where there is no real love, only a few fine words delivered with confidence being wanted in that case. The king, delighted to hear from her own mouth this assurance of her love, and thinking truly that her heart went with it, in a fit of fatherly fondness bestowed upon her and her husband one third of his ample kingdom.

Then calling to him his second daughter, he demanded what she had to say. Regan, who was made of the same hollow metal as her sister, was not a whit behind in her professions, but rather declared that what her sister had spoken came short of the love which she professed to bear for his highness; insomuch that she found all other joys dead, in comparison with the pleasure which she took in the love of her dear king and father.

Lear blessed himself in having such loving children, as he thought; and could do no less, after the handsome assurances which Regan had made, than bestow a third of his kingdom upon her and her husband, equal in size to that which he had already given away to Goneril.

Then turning to his youngest daughter Cordelia, whom he called his joy, he asked what she had to say, thinking no doubt that she would glad his ears with the same loving speeches which her sisters had uttered, or rather that her expressions would be so much stronger than theirs, as she had always been his darling, and favoured by him above either of them. But Cordelia, disgusted with the flattery of her sisters, whose hearts she knew were far from their lips, and seeing that all their coaxing speeches were only intended to wheedle the old king out of his dominions, that they and their husbands might reign in his lifetime, made no other reply but this, – that she loved his majesty according to her duty, neither more nor less.

The king, shocked with this appearance of ingratitude in his favourite child, desired her to consider her words, and to mend her speech, lest it should mar her fortunes.

Cordelia then told her father, that he was her father, that he had given her breeding, and loved her; that she returned those duties back as was most fit, and did obey him, love him, and most honour him. But that she could not frame her mouth to such large speeches as her sisters had done, or promise to love nothing else in the world. Why had her sisters husbands, if (as they said) they had no love for anything but their father? If she should ever wed, she was sure the lord to whom she gave her hand would want half her love, half of her care and duty; she should never marry like her sisters, to love her father all.

Cordelia, who in earnest loved her old father even almost as extravagantly as her sisters pretended to do, would have plainly told him so at any other time, in more daughter-like and loving terms, and without these qualifications, which did indeed sound a little ungracious; but after the crafty flattering speeches of her sisters, which she had seen draw such extravagant rewards, she thought the handsomest thing she could do was to love and be silent. This put her affection out of suspicion of mercenary ends, and showed that she loved, but not for gain; and that her professions, the less ostentatious they were, had so much the more truth and sincerity than her sisters'.

This plainness of speech, which Lear called pride, so enraged the old monarch – who in his best of times always showed much of spleen and rashness, and in whom the dotage incident to old age had so clouded over his reason, that he could not discern truth from flattery, nor a gay painted speech from words that came from the heart – that in a fury of resentment he retracted the third part of his kingdom which yet remained, and which he had reserved for Cordelia, and gave it away from her, sharing it equally between her two sisters and their husbands, the Dukes of Albany and Cornwall; whom he now called to him, and in presence of all his courtiers bestowing a coronet between them, invested them jointly with all the power, revenue, and execution of government, only retaining to himself the name of king; all the rest of royalty he resigned; with this reservation, that himself, with a hundred knights for his attendants, was to be maintained by monthly course in each of his daughters' palaces in turn.

So preposterous a disposal of his kingdom, so little guided by reason, and so much by passion, filled all his courtiers with astonishment and sorrow; but none of them had the courage to interpose between this incensed king and his wrath, except the Earl of Kent, who was beginning to speak a good word for Cordelia, when the passionate Lear on pain of death commanded him to desist; but the good Kent was not so to be repelled. He had been ever loyal to Lear, whom he had honoured as a king, loved as a father, followed as a master; and he had never esteemed his life further than as a pawn to wage against his royal master's enemies, nor feared to lose it when Lear's safety was the motive; nor now that Lear was most his own enemy, did this faithful servant of the king forget his old principles, but manfully opposed Lear, to do Lear good; and was unmannerly only because Lear was mad. He had been a most faithful counsellor in times past to the king, and he besought him now, that he would see with his eyes (as he had done in many weighty matters), and go by his advice still; and in his best consideration recall this hideous rashness: for he would answer with his life, his judgment that Lear's youngest daughter did not love him least, nor were those empty-hearted whose low sound gave no token of hollowness. When power bowed to flattery, honour was bound to plainness. For Lear's threats, what could he do to him, whose life was already at his service? That should not hinder duty from speaking.

The honest freedom of this good Earl of Kent only stirred up the king's wrath the more, and like a frantic patient who kills his physician, and loves his mortal disease, he banished this true servant, and allotted him but five days to make his preparations for departure; but if on the sixth his hated person was found within the realm of Britain, that moment was to be his death. And Kent bade farewell to the king, and said, that since he chose to show himself in such fashion, it was but banishment to stay there; and before he went, he recommended Cordelia to the protection of the gods, the maid who had so rightly thought, and so discreetly spoken; and only wished that her sisters' large speeches might be answered with deeds of love; and then he went, as he said, to shape his old course to a new country.

The King of France and Duke of Burgundy were now called in to hear the determination of Lear about his youngest daughter, and to know whether they would persist in their courtship to Cordelia, now that she was under her father's displeasure, and had no fortune but her own person to recommend her: and the Duke of Burgundy declined the match, and would not take her to wife upon such conditions; but the King of France, understanding what the nature of the fault had been which had lost her the love of her father, that it was only a tardiness of speech, and the not being able to frame her tongue to flattery like her sisters, took this young maid by the hand, and saying that her virtues were a dowry above a kingdom, bade Cordelia to take farewell of her sisters and of her father, though he had been unkind, and she should go with him, and be queen of him and of fair France, and reign over fairer possessions than her sisters: and he called the Duke of Burgundy in contempt a waterish duke, because his love for this young maid had in a moment run all away like water.

Then Cordelia with weeping eyes took leave of her sisters, and besought them to love their father well, and make good their professions: and they sullenly told her not to prescribe to them, for they knew their duty; but to strive to content her husband, who had taken her (as they tauntingly expressed it) as Fortune's alms. And Cordelia with a heavy heart departed, for she knew the cunning of her sisters, and she wished her father in better hands than she was about to leave him in.

Cordelia was no sooner gone, than the devilish dispositions of her sisters began to show themselves in their true colours. Even before the expiration of the first month, which Lear was to spend by agreement with his eldest daughter Goneril, the old king began to find out the difference between promises and performances. This wretch having got from her father all that he had to bestow, even to the giving away of the crown from off his head, began to grudge even those small remnants of royalty which the old man had reserved to himself, to please his fancy with the idea of being still a king. She could not bear to see him and his hundred knights. Every time she met her father, she put on a frowning countenance; and when the old man wanted to speak with her, she would feign sickness, or anything to get rid of the sight of him; for it was plain that she esteemed his old age a useless burden, and his attendants an unnecessary expense: not only she herself slackened in her expressions of duty to the king, but by her example, and (it is to be feared) not without her private instructions, her very servants affected to treat him with neglect, and would either refuse to obey his orders, or still more contemptuously pretend not to hear them. Lear could not but perceive this alteration in the behaviour of his daughter, but he shut his eyes against it as long as he could, as people commonly are unwilling to believe the unpleasant consequences which their own mistakes and obstinacy have brought upon them.

True love and fidelity are no more to be estranged by *ill*, than falsehood and hollow-heartedness can be conciliated by *good*, *usage*. This eminently appears in the instance of the good Earl of Kent, who, though banished by Lear, and his life made forfeit if he were found in Britain, chose to stay and abide all consequences, as long as there was a chance of his being useful to the king his master. See to what mean shifts and disguises poor loyalty is forced to submit sometimes; yet it counts nothing base or unworthy, so as it can but do service where it owes an obligation!

In the disguise of a serving man, all his greatness and pomp laid aside, this good earl proffered his services to the king, who, not knowing him to be Kent in that disguise, but pleased with a certain plainness, or rather bluntness in his answers, which the earl put on (so different from that smooth oily flattery which he had so much reason to be sick of, having found the effects not answerable in his daughter), a bargain was quickly struck, and Lear took Kent into his service by the name of Caius, as he called himself, never suspecting him to be his once great favourite, the high and mighty Earl of Kent.

This Caius quickly found means to show his fidelity and love to his royal master: for Goneril's steward that same day behaving in a disrespectful manner to Lear, and giving him saucy looks and language, as no doubt he was secretly encouraged to do by his mistress, Caius, not enduring to hear so open an affront put upon his majesty, made no more ado but presently tripped up his heels, and laid the unmannerly slave in the kennel; for which friendly service Lear became more and more attached to him.

Nor was Kent the only friend Lear had. In his degree, and as far as so insignificant a personage could show his love, the poor fool, or jester, that had been of his palace while Lear had a palace, as it was the custom of kings and great personages at that time to keep a fool (as he was called) to make them sport after serious business: this poor fool clung to Lear after he had given away his crown, and by his witty sayings would keep up his good humour, though he could not refrain sometimes from jeering at his master for his imprudence in uncrowning himself, and giving all away to his daughters; at which time, as he rhymingly expressed it, these daughters

For sudden joy did weep
And he for sorrow sung,
That such a king should play bo-peep
And go the fools among.

And in such wild sayings, and scraps of songs, of which he had plenty, this pleasant fool poured out his heart even in the presence of Goneril herself, in many a bitter taunt and jest which cut to the quick: such as comparing the king to the hedge-sparrow, who feeds the young of the cuckoo till they grow old enough, and then has its head bit off for its pains; and saying, that an ass may know when the cart draws the horse (meaning that Lear's daughters, that ought to go behind, now ranked before their father); and that Lear was no longer Lear, but the shadow of Lear: for which free speeches he was once or twice threatened to be whipped.

The coolness and falling off of respect which Lear had begun to perceive, were not all which this foolish fond father was to suffer from his unworthy daughter: she now plainly told him that his staying in her palace was inconvenient so long as he insisted upon keeping up an establishment of a hundred knights; that this establishment was useless and expensive, and only served to fill her court with riot and feasting; and she prayed him that he would lessen their number, and keep none but old men about him, such as himself, and fitting his age.

Lear at first could not believe his eyes or ears, nor that it was his daughter who spoke so unkindly. He could not believe that she who had received a crown from him could seek to cut off his train, and grudge him the respect due to his old age. But she, persisting in her undutiful demand, the old man's rage was so excited, that he called her a detested kite, and said that she spoke an untruth; and so indeed she did, for the hundred knights were all men of choice behaviour and sobriety of manners, skilled in all particulars of duty, and not given to rioting or feasting, as she said. And he bid his horses to be prepared, for he would go to his other daughter, Regan, he and his hundred knights; and he spoke of ingratitude, and said it was a marble-hearted devil, and showed more hideous in a child than the sea-monster. And he cursed his eldest daughter Goneril so as was terrible to hear; praying that she might never have a child, or if she had, that it might live to return that scorn and contempt upon her which she had shown to him: that she might feel how sharper than a serpent's tooth it was to have a thankless child. And Goneril's husband, the Duke of Albany, beginning to excuse himself for any share which Lear might suppose he had in the unkindness, Lear would not hear him out, but in a rage ordered his horses to be saddled, and set out with his followers for the abode of Regan, his other daughter. And Lear thought to himself how small the fault of Cordelia (if it was a fault) now appeared, in comparison with her sister's, and he wept; and then he was ashamed that such a creature as Goneril should have so much power over his manhood as to make him weep.

Regan and her husband were keeping their court in great pomp and state at their palace; and Lear despatched his servant Caius with letters to his daughter, that she might be prepared for his reception, while he and his train followed after. But it seems that Goneril had been beforehand with him, sending letters also to Regan, accusing her father of waywardness and ill humours, and advising her not to receive so great a train as he was bringing with him. This messenger arrived at the same time with Caius, and Caius and he met: and who should it be but Caius's old enemy the steward, whom he had formerly tripped up by the heels for his saucy behaviour to Lear. Caius not liking the fellow's look, and suspecting what he came for, began to revile him, and challenged him to fight, which the fellow refusing, Caius, in a fit of honest passion, beat him soundly, as such a mischief-maker and carrier of wicked messages deserved; which coming to the ears of Regan and her husband, they ordered Caius to be put in stocks, though he was a messenger from the king her father, and in that character demanded the highest respect: so that the first thing the king saw when he entered the castle, was his faithful servant Caius sitting in that disgraceful situation.

This was but a bad omen of the reception which he was to expect; but a worse followed, when, upon inquiry for his daughter and her husband, he was told they were weary with travelling all night, and could not see him; and when lastly, upon his insisting in a positive and angry manner to see them, they came to greet him, whom should he see in their company but the hated Goneril, who had come to tell her own story, and set her sister against the king her father!

This sight much moved the old man, and still more to see Regan take her by the hand; and he asked Goneril if she was not ashamed to look upon his old white beard. And Regan advised him to go home again with Goneril, and live with her peaceably, dismissing half of his attendants, and to ask her forgiveness; for he was old and wanted discretion, and must be ruled and led by persons that had more discretion than himself. And Lear showed how preposterous that would sound, if he were to go down on his knees, and beg of his own daughter for food and raiment, and he argued against such an unnatural dependence, declaring his resolution never to return with her, but to stay where he was with Regan, he and his hundred knights; for he said that she had not forgot the half of the kingdom which he had endowed her with, and that her eyes were not fierce like Goneril's, but mild and kind. And he said that rather than return to Goneril, with half his train cut off, he would go over to France, and beg a wretched pension of the king there, who had married his youngest daughter without a portion.

But he was mistaken in expecting kinder treatment of Regan than he had experienced from her sister Goneril. As if willing to outdo her sister in unfilial behaviour, she declared that she thought fifty knights too many to wait upon him: that five-and-twenty were enough. Then Lear, nigh heart-broken, turned to Goneril and said that he would go back with her, for her fifty doubled five-and-twenty, and so her love was twice as much as Regan's. But Goneril excused herself, and said, what need of so many as five-and-twenty? or even ten? or five? when he might be waited upon by her servants, or her sister's servants? So these two wicked daughters, as if they strove to exceed each other in cruelty to their old father, who had been so good to them, by little and little would have abated him of all his train, all respect (little enough for him that once commanded a kingdom), which was left him to show that he had once been a king! Not that a splendid train is essential to happiness, but from a king to a beggar is a hard change, from commanding millions to be without one attendant; and it was the ingratitude in his daughters' denying it, more than what he would suffer by the want of it, which pierced this poor king to the heart; insomuch, that with this double ill-usage, and vexation for having so foolishly given away a kingdom, his wits began to be unsettled, and while he said he knew not what, he vowed revenge against those unnatural hags, and to make examples of them that should be a terror to the earth!

While he was thus idly threatening what his weak arm could never execute, night came on, and a loud storm of thunder and lightning with rain; and his daughters still persisting in their resolution not to admit his followers, he called for his horses, and chose rather to encounter the utmost fury of the storm abroad, than stay under the same roof with these ungrateful daughters: and they, saying that the injuries which wilful men procure to themselves are their just punishment, suffered him to go in that condition and shut their doors upon him.

The winds were high, and the rain and storm increased, when the old man sallied forth to combat with the elements, less sharp than his daughters' unkindness. For many miles about there was scarce a bush; and there upon a heath, exposed to the fury of the storm in a dark night, did King Lear wander out, and defy the winds and the thunder; and he bid the winds to blow the earth into the sea, or swell the waves of the sea till they drowned the earth, that no token might remain of any such ungrateful animal as man. The old king was now left with no other companion than the poor fool, who still abided with him, with his merry conceits striving to outjest misfortune, saying it was but a naughty night to swim in, and truly the king had better go in and ask his daughters' blessing:

> But he that has a little tiny wit,
> With heigh ho, the wind and the rain!
> Must make content with his fortunes fit,
> Though the rain it raineth every day:

and swearing it was a brave night to cool a lady's pride.

Thus poorly accompanied, this once great monarch was found by his ever-faithful servant the good Earl of Kent, now transformed to Caius, who ever followed close at his side, though the king did not know him to be the earl; and he said, 'Alas! sir, are you here? creatures that love night, love not such nights as these. This dreadful storm has driven the beasts to their hiding places. Man's nature cannot endure the affliction or the fear.' And Lear rebuked him and said, these lesser evils were not felt, where a greater malady was fixed. When the mind is at ease, the body has leisure to be delicate, but the tempest in his mind did take all feeling else from his senses, but of that which beat at his heart. And he spoke of filial ingratitude, and said it was all one as if the mouth should tear the hand for lifting food to it; for parents were hands and food and everything to children.

But the good Caius still persisting in his entreaties that the king would not stay out in the open air, at last persuaded him to enter a little wretched hovel which stood upon the heath, where the fool first entering, suddenly ran back terrified, saying that he had seen a spirit. But upon examination this spirit proved to be nothing more than a poor Bedlam beggar, who had crept into this deserted hovel for shelter, and with his talk about devils frighted the fool, one of those poor lunatics who are either mad, or feign to be so, the better to extort charity from the compassionate country people, who go about the country, calling themselves poor Tom and poor Turlygood, saying, 'Who gives anything to poor Tom?' sticking pins and nails and sprigs of rosemary into their arms to make them bleed; and with such horrible actions, partly by prayers, and partly with lunatic curses, they move or terrify the ignorant countryfolks into giving them alms. This poor fellow was such a one; and the king seeing him in so wretched a plight, with nothing but a blanket about his loins to cover his nakedness, could not be persuaded but that the fellow was some father who had given all away to his daughters, and brought himself to that pass: for nothing he thought could bring a man to such wretchedness but the having unkind daughters.

And from this and many such wild speeches which he uttered, the good Caius plainly perceived that he was not in his perfect mind, but that his daughters' ill usage had really made him go mad. And now the loyalty of this worthy Earl of Kent showed itself in more essential services than he had hitherto found opportunity to perform. For with the assistance of some of the king's attendants who remained loyal, he had the person of his royal master removed at daybreak to the castle of Dover, where his own friends and influence, as Earl of Kent, chiefly lay; and himself embarking for France, hastened to the court of Cordelia, and did there in such moving terms represent the pitiful condition of her royal father, and set out in such lively colours the inhumanity of her sisters, that this good and loving child with many tears besought the king her husband that he would give her leave to embark for England, with a sufficient power to subdue these cruel daughters and their husbands, and restore the old king her father to his throne; which being granted, she set forth, and with a royal army landed at Dover.

Lear having by some chance escaped from the guardians which the good Earl of Kent had put over him to take care of him in his lunacy, was found by some of Cordelia's train, wandering about the fields near Dover, in a pitiable condition, stark mad, and singing aloud to himself, with a crown upon his head which he had made of straw, and nettles, and other wild weeds that he had picked up in the cornfields. By the advice of the physicians, Cordelia, though earnestly desirous of seeing her father, was prevailed upon to put off the meeting, till by sleep and the operation of herbs which they gave him, he should be restored to greater composure. By the aid of these skilful physicians, to whom Cordelia promised all her gold and jewels for the recovery of the old king, Lear was soon in a condition to see his daughter.

A tender sight it was to see the meeting between this father and daughter; to see the struggles between the joy of this poor old king at beholding again his once darling child, and the shame at receiving such filial kindness from her whom he had cast off for so small a fault in his displeasure; both these passions struggling with the remains of his malady, which in his half-crazed brain sometimes made him that he scarce remembered where he was, or who it was that so kindly kissed him and spoke to him: and then he would beg the standers-by not to laugh at him, if he were mistaken in thinking this lady to be his daughter Cordelia! And then to see him fall on his knees to beg pardon of his child; and she, good lady, kneeling all the while to ask a blessing of him, and telling him that it did not become him to kneel, but it was her duty, for she was his child, his true and very child Cordelia! and she kissed him (as she said) to kiss away all her sisters' unkindness, and said that they might be ashamed of themselves, to turn their old kind father with his white beard out into the cold air, when her enemy's dog, though it had bit her (as she prettily expressed it), should have stayed by her fire such a night as that, and warmed himself. And she told her father how she had come from France with purpose to bring him assistance; and he said that she must forget and forgive, for he was old and foolish, and did not know what he did; but that to be sure she had great cause not to love him, but her sisters had none. And Cordelia said that she had no cause, no more than they had.

So we will leave this old king in the protection of his dutiful and loving child, where, by the help of sleep and medicine, she and her physicians at length succeeded in winding up the untuned and jarring senses which the cruelty of his daughters had so violently shaken. Let us return to say a word or two about those cruel daughters.

These monsters of ingratitude, who had been so false to their old father, could not be expected to prove more faithful to their own husbands. They soon grew tired of paying even the appearance of duty and affection, and in an open way showed they had fixed their loves upon another. It happened that the object of their guilty loves was the same. It was Edmund, a natural son of the late Earl of Gloucester, who by his treacheries had succeeded in disinheriting his brother Edgar, the lawful heir, from his earldom, and by his wicked practices was now earl himself; a wicked man, and a fit object for the love of such wicked creatures as Goneril and Regan. It falling out about this time that the Duke of Cornwall, Regan's husband, died, Regan immediately declared her intention of wedding this Earl of Gloucester, which rousing the jealousy of her sister, to whom as well as to Regan this wicked earl had at sundry times professed love, Goneril found means to make away with her sister by poison; but being detected in her practices, and imprisoned by her husband, the Duke of Albany, for this deed, and for her guilty passion for the earl which had come to his ears, she, in a fit of disappointed love and rage, shortly put an end to her own life. Thus the justice of Heaven at last overtook these wicked daughters.

While the eyes of all men were upon this event, admiring the justice displayed in their deserved deaths, the same eyes were suddenly taken off from the sight to admire at the mysterious ways of the same power in the melancholy fate of the young and virtuous daughter, the Lady Cordelia, whose good deeds did seem to deserve a more fortunate conclusion: but it is an awful truth, that innocence and piety are not always successful in this world. The forces which Goneril and Regan had sent out under the command of the bad Earl of Gloucester were victorious, and Cordelia, by the practices of this wicked earl, who did not like that any should stand between him and the throne, ended her life in prison. Thus, Heaven took this innocent lady to itself in her young years, after showing her to the world an illustrious example of filial duty. Lear did not long survive this kind child.

Before he died, the good Earl of Kent, who had still attended his old master's steps from the first of his daughters' ill usage to this sad period of his decay, tried to make him understand that it was he who had followed him under the name of Caius; but Lear's care-crazed brain at that time could not comprehend how that could be, or how Kent and Caius could be the same person: so Kent thought it needless to trouble him with explanations at such a time; and Lear soon after expiring, this faithful servant to the king, between age and grief for his old master's vexations, soon followed him to the grave.

How the judgment of Heaven overtook the bad Earl of Gloucester, whose treasons were discovered, and himself slain in single combat with his brother, the lawful earl; and how Goneril's husband, the Duke of Albany, who was innocent of the death of Cordelia, and had never encouraged his lady in her wicked proceedings against her father, ascended the throne of Britain after the death of Lear, is needless here to narrate; Lear and his Three Daughters being dead, whose adventures alone concern our story.

OTHELLO
THE MOOR OF VENICE

◆◆◆◆◆◆◆◆◆◆◆◆◆◆◆◆◆◆◆◆◆◆◆◆◆◆◆◆◆◆◆◆◆◆◆◆

BRABANTIO, the rich senator of Venice, had a fair daughter, the gentle Desdemona. She was sought to by divers suitors, both on account of her many virtuous qualities, and for her rich expectations. But among the suitors of her own clime and complexion, she saw none whom she could affect: for this noble lady, who regarded the mind more than the features of men, with a singularity rather to be admired than imitated, had chosen for the object of her affections, a Moor, a black, whom her father loved, and often invited to his house.

Neither is Desdemona to be altogether condemned for the unsuitableness of the person whom she selected for her lover. Bating that Othello was black, the noble Moor wanted nothing which might recommend him to the affections of the greatest lady. He was a soldier, and a brave one; and by his conduct in bloody wars against the Turks, had risen to the rank of general in the Venetian service, and was esteemed and trusted by the state.

He had been a traveller, and Desdemona (as is the manner of ladies) loved to hear him tell the story of his adventures, which he would run through from his earliest recollection; the battles, sieges, and encounters, which he had passed through; the perils he had been exposed to by land and by water; his hair-breadth escapes, when he had entered a breach, or marched up to the mouth of a cannon; and how he had been taken prisoner by the insolent enemy, and sold to slavery; how he demeaned himself in that state, and how he escaped: all these accounts, added to the narration of the strange things he had seen in foreign countries, the vast wilderness and romantic caverns, the quarries, the rocks and mountains, whose heads are in the clouds; of the savage nations, the cannibals who are man-eaters, and a race of people in Africa whose heads do grow beneath their shoulders: these travellers' stories would so enchain the attention of Desdemona, that if she were called off at any time by household affairs, she would despatch with all haste that business, and return, and with a greedy ear devour Othello's discourse. And once he took advantage of a pliant hour, and drew from her a prayer, that he would tell her the whole story of his life at large, of which she had heard so much, but only by parts: to which he consented, and beguiled her of many a tear, when he spoke of some distressful stroke which his youth had suffered.

His story being done, she gave him for his pains a world of sighs: she swore a pretty oath, that it was all passing strange, and pitiful, wondrous pitiful: she wished (she said) she had not heard it, yet she wished that heaven had made her such a man; and then she thanked him, and told him, if he had a friend who loved her, he had only to teach him how to tell his story, and that would woo her. Upon this hint, delivered not with more frankness than modesty, accompanied with certain bewitching prettiness, and blushes, which Othello could not but understand, he spoke more openly of his love, and in this golden opportunity gained the consent of the generous Lady Desdemona privately to marry him.

Neither Othello's colour nor his fortune were such that it could be hoped Brabantio would accept him for a son-in-law. He had left his daughter free; but he did expect that, as the manner of noble Venetian ladies was, she would choose ere long a husband of senatorial rank or expectations; but in this he was deceived; Desdemona loved the Moor, though he was black, and devoted her heart and fortunes to his valiant parts and qualities; so was her heart subdued to an implicit devotion to the man she had selected for a husband, that his very colour, which to all but this discerning lady would have proved an insurmountable objection, was by her esteemed above all the white skins and clear complexions of the young Venetian nobility, her suitors.

Their marriage, which, though privately carried out, could not long be kept a secret, came to the ears of the old man, Brabantio, who appeared in a solemn council of the senate, as an accuser of the Moor Othello, who by spells and witchcraft (he maintained) had seduced the affections of the fair Desdemona to marry him, without the consent of her father, and against the obligations of hospitality.

At this juncture of time it happened that the state of Venice had immediate need of the services of Othello, news having arrived that the

Turks with mighty preparation had fitted out a fleet, which was bending its course to the island of Cyprus, with intent to regain that strong post from the Venetians, who then held it; in this emergency the state turned its eyes upon Othello, who alone was deemed adequate to conduct the defence of Cyprus against the Turks. So that Othello, now summoned before the senate, stood in their presence at once as a candidate for a great state employment, and as a culprit, charged with offences which by the laws of Venice were made capital.

The age and senatorial character of old Brabantio, commanded a most patient hearing from that grave assembly; but the incensed father conducted his accusation with so much intemperance, producing likelihoods and allegations for proofs, that, when Othello was called upon for his defence, he had only to relate a plain tale of the course of his love; which he did with such an artless eloquence, recounting the whole story of his wooing, as we have related it above, and delivered his speech with so noble a plainness (the evidence of truth), that the duke, who sat as chief judge, could not help confessing that a tale so told would have won his daughter too: and the spells and conjurations which Othello had used in his courtship, plainly appeared to have been no more than the honest arts of men in love; and the only witchcraft which he had used, the faculty of telling a soft tale to win a lady's ear.

This statement of Othello was confirmed by the testimony of the Lady Desdemona herself, who appeared in court, and professing a duty to her father for life and education, challenged leave of him to profess a yet higher duty to her lord and husband, even so much as her mother had shown in preferring him (Brabantio) above *her* father.

The old senator, unable to maintain his plea, called the Moor to him with many expressions of sorrow, and, as an act of necessity, bestowed upon him his daughter, whom, if he had been free to withhold her (he told him), he would with all his heart have kept from him; adding, that he was glad at soul that he had no other child, for this behaviour of Desdemona would have taught him to be a tyrant, and hang clogs on them for her desertion.

This difficulty being got over, Othello, to whom custom had rendered the hardships of a military life as natural as food and rest are to other men, readily undertook the management of the wars in Cyprus: and

Desdemona, preferring the honour of her lord (though with danger) before the indulgence of those idle delights in which new-married people usually waste their time, cheerfully consented to his going.

No sooner were Othello and his lady landed in Cyprus, than news arrived, that a desperate tempest had dispersed the Turkish fleet, and thus the island was secure from any immediate apprehension of an attack. But the war, which Othello was to suffer, was now beginning; and the enemies, which malice stirred up against his innocent lady, proved in their nature more deadly than strangers or infidels.

Among all the general's friends no one possessed the confidence of Othello more entirely than Cassio. Michael Cassio was a young soldier, a Florentine, gay, amorous, and of pleasing address, favourite qualities with women; he was handsome and eloquent, and exactly such a person as might alarm the jealousy of a man advanced in years (as Othello in some measure was), who had married a young and beautiful wife; but Othello was as free from jealousy as he was noble, and as incapable of suspecting as of doing a base action. He had employed this Cassio in his love affair with Desdemona, and Cassio had been a sort of go-between in his suit: for Othello, fearing that himself had not those soft parts of conversation which please ladies, and finding these qualities in his friend, would often depute Cassio to go (as he phrased it) a-courting for him: such innocent simplicity being rather an honour than a blemish to the character of the valiant Moor. So that no wonder, if next to Othello himself (but at far distance, as beseems a virtuous wife) the gentle Desdemona loved and trusted Cassio. Nor had the marriage of this couple made any difference in their behaviour to Michael Cassio. He frequented their house, and his free and rattling talk was no unpleasing variety to Othello, who was himself of a more serious temper: for such tempers are observed often to delight in their contraries, as a relief from the oppressive excess of their own: and Desdemona and Cassio would talk and laugh together, as in the days when he went a-courting for his friend.

Othello had lately promoted Cassio to be the lieutenant, a place of trust, and nearest to the general's person. This promotion gave great offence to Iago, an older officer who thought he had a better claim than Cassio, and would often ridicule Cassio as a fellow fit only for the company of ladies, and one that knew no more of the art of war or how to set an army in array for battle, than a girl. Iago hated Cassio, and he hated Othello, as well for favouring Cassio, as for an unjust suspicion, which he had lightly taken up against Othello, that the Moor was too fond of Iago's wife Emilia. From these imaginary provocations, the plotting mind of Iago conceived a horrid scheme of revenge, which should involve both Cassio, the Moor, and Desdemona, in one common ruin.

Iago was artful, and had studied human nature deeply, and he knew that of all the torments which afflict the mind of man (and far beyond bodily torture), the pains of jealousy were the most intolerable, and had the sorest sting. If he could succeed in making Othello jealous of Cassio, he thought it would be an exquisite plot of revenge, and might end in the death of Cassio or Othello, or both; he cared not.

The arrival of the general and his lady, in Cyprus, meeting with the news of the dispersion of the enemy's fleet, made a sort of holiday in the island. Everybody gave themselves up to feasting and making merry. Wine flowed in abundance, and cups went round to the health of the black Othello, and his lady the fair Desdemona.

Cassio had the direction of the guard that night, with a charge from Othello to keep the soldiers from excess in drinking, that no brawl might arise, to fright the inhabitants, or disgust them with the new-landed forces. That night Iago began his deep-laid plans of mischief: under colour of loyalty and love to the general, he enticed Cassio to make rather too free with the bottle (a great fault in an officer upon guard). Cassio for a time resisted, but he could not long hold out against the honest freedom which Iago knew how to put on, but kept swallowing glass after glass (as Iago still plied him with drink and encouraging songs), and Cassio's tongue ran over in praise of the Lady Desdemona, whom he again and again toasted, affirming that she was a most exquisite lady: until at last the enemy which he put into his mouth stole away his brains; and upon some provocation given him by a fellow whom Iago had set on, swords were drawn, and Montano, a worthy officer, who interfered to appease the dispute, was wounded in the scuffle. The riot now began to be general, and Iago, who had set on foot the mischief, was foremost in spreading the alarm, causing the castle-bell to be rung (as if some dangerous mutiny instead of a slight drunken quarrel had arisen): the alarm-bell ringing awakened Othello, who, dressing in a hurry, and coming to the scene of action, questioned Cassio of the cause. Cassio was now come to himself, the effect of the wine having a little gone off, but was too much ashamed to reply; and Iago, pretending a great reluctance to accuse Cassio, but, as it were, forced into it by Othello, who insisted to know the truth, gave an account of the whole matter (leaving out his own share in it, which Cassio was too far gone to remember) in such a manner, as while he seemed to make Cassio's offence less, did indeed make it appear greater than it was. The result was, that Othello, who was a strict observer of discipline, was compelled to take away Cassio's place of lieutenant from him.

Thus did Iago's first artifice succeed completely; he had now undermined his hated rival, and thrust him out of his place: but a further use was hereafter to be made of the adventure of this disastrous night.

Cassio, whom this misfortune had entirely sobered, now lamented to his seeming friend Iago that he should have been such a fool as to transform himself into a beast. He was undone, for how could he ask the general for his place again? he would tell him he was a drunkard. He despised himself. Iago, affecting to make light of it, said, that he, or any man living, might be drunk upon occasion; it remained now to make the best of a bad bargain; the general's wife was now the general, and could do anything with Othello; that he were best to apply to the Lady Desdemona to mediate for him with her lord; that she was of a frank, obliging disposition, and would readily undertake a good office of this sort, and set Cassio right again in the general's favour; and then this crack in their love would be made stronger than ever. A good advice of Iago, if it had not been given for wicked purposes, which will after appear.

Cassio did as Iago advised him, and made application to the Lady Desdemona, who was easy to be won over in any honest suit; and she promised Cassio that she should be his solicitor with her lord, and rather die than give up his cause. This she immediately set about in so earnest and pretty a manner, that Othello, who was mortally offended with Cassio, could not put her off. When he pleaded delay, and that it was too soon to pardon such an offender, she would not be beat back, but insisted that it should be the next night, or the morning after, or the next morning to that at farthest. Then she showed how penitent and humbled poor Cassio was, and that his offence did not deserve so sharp a check. And when Othello still hung back, 'What! my lord,' said she, 'that I should have so much to do to plead for Cassio, Michael Cassio, that came a-courting for you, and oftentimes, when I have spoken in dispraise of you, has taken your part! I count this but a little thing to ask of you. When I mean to try your love indeed, I shall ask a weighty matter.' Othello could deny nothing to such a pleader, and only requesting that Desdemona would leave the time to him, promised to receive Michael Cassio again in favour.

It happened that Othello and Iago had entered into the room where Desdemona was, just as Cassio, who had been imploring her intercession, was departing at the opposite door: and Iago, who was full of art, said in a low voice, as if to himself, 'I like not that.' Othello took no great notice of what he said; indeed, the conference which immediately took place with his lady put it out of his head; but he remembered it afterwards. For when Desdemona was gone, Iago, as if for mere satisfaction of his thought, questioned Othello whether Michael Cassio, when Othello was courting his lady, knew of his love. To this the general answering in the affirmative, and adding, that he had gone between them very often during the courtship, Iago knitted his brow, as if he had got fresh light on some terrible matter, and cried, 'Indeed!' This brought into Othello's mind the words which Iago had let fall upon entering the room, and seeing Cassio with Desdemona; and he began to think there was some meaning in all this; for he deemed Iago to be a just man, and full of love and honesty, and what in a false knave would be tricks, in him seemed to be the natural workings of an honest mind, big with something too great for utterance: and Othello prayed Iago to speak what he knew, and to give his worst thoughts words. 'And what,' said Iago, 'if some thoughts very vile should have intruded into my breast, as where is the palace into which foul things do not enter?' Then Iago went on to say, what a pity it were, if any trouble should arise to Othello out of his imperfect observations; that it would not be for Othello's peace to know his thoughts; that people's good names were not to be taken away for slight suspicions; and when Othello's curiosity was raised almost to distraction with these hints and scattered words,

Iago, as if in earnest care for Othello's peace of mind, besought him to beware of jealousy: with such art did this villain raise suspicions in the unguarded Othello, by the very caution which he pretended to give him against suspicion. 'I know,' said Othello, 'that my wife is fair, loves company and feasting, is free of speech, sings, plays, and dances well: but where virtue is, these qualities are virtuous. I must have proof before I think her dishonest.' Then Iago, as if glad that Othello was slow to believe ill of his lady, frankly declared that he had no proof, but begged Othello to observe her behaviour well, when Cassio was by; not to be jealous nor too secure neither, for that he (Iago) knew the dispositions of the Italian ladies, his countrywomen, better than Othello could do; and that in Venice the wives let heaven see many pranks they dared not show their husbands. Then he artfully insinuated that Desdemona deceived her father in marrying with Othello, and carried it so closely, that the poor old man thought that witchcraft had been used. Othello was much moved with this argument, which brought the matter home to him, for if she had deceived her father, why might she not deceive her husband?

Iago begged pardon for having moved him; but Othello, assuming an indifference, while he was really shaken with inward grief at Iago's words, begged him to go on, which Iago did with many apologies, as if unwilling to produce anything against Cassio, whom he called his friend: he then came strongly to the point, and reminded Othello how Desdemona had refused many suitable matches of her own clime and complexion, and had married him, a Moor, which showed unnatural in her, and proved her to have a headstrong will: and when her better judgment returned, how probable it was she should fall upon comparing Othello with the fine forms and clear white complexions of the young Italians her countrymen. He concluded with advising Othello to put off his reconcilement with Cassio a little longer, and in the meanwhile to note with what earnestness Desdemona should intercede in his behalf; for that much would be seen in that. So mischievously did this artful villain lay his plots to turn the gentle qualities of this innocent lady into her destruction, and make a net for her out of her own goodness to entrap her: first setting Cassio on to entreat her mediation, and then out of that very mediation contriving stratagems for her ruin.

The conference ended with Iago's begging Othello to account his wife innocent, until he had more decisive proof; and Othello promised to be patient; but from that moment the deceived Othello never tasted content of mind. Poppy, nor the juice of mandragora, nor all the sleeping potions in the world, could ever again restore to him that sweet rest, which he had enjoyed but yesterday. His occupation sickened upon him. He no longer took delight in arms. His heart, that used to be roused at the sight of troops, and banners, and battle-array, and would stir and leap at the sound of a drum, or a trumpet, or a neighing war-horse, seemed to have lost all that pride and ambition which are a soldier's virtue; and his military ardour and all his old joys forsook him. Sometimes he thought his wife honest, and at times he thought her not so; sometimes he thought Iago just, and at times he thought him not so; then he would wish that he had never known of it; he was not the worse for her loving Cassio, so long as he knew it not: torn to pieces with these distracting thoughts, he once laid hold on Iago's throat, and demanded proof of Desdemona's guilt, or threatened instant death for his having belied her. Iago, feigning indignation that his honesty should be taken for a vice, asked Othello, if he had not sometimes seen a handkerchief spotted with strawberries in his wife's hand. Othello answered, that he had given her such a one, and that it was his first gift. 'That same handkerchief,' said Iago, 'did I see Michael Cassio this day wipe his face with.' 'If it be as you say,' said Othello, 'I will not rest till a wide revenge swallow them up: and first, for a token of your fidelity, I expect that Cassio shall be put to death within three days; and for that fair devil (meaning his lady), I will withdraw and devise some swift means of death for her.'

Trifles light as air are to the jealous proofs as strong as holy writ. A handkerchief of his wife's seen in Cassio's hand, was motive enough to the deluded Othello to pass sentence of death upon them both, without once inquiring how Cassio came by it. Desdemona had never given such a present to Cassio, nor would this constant lady have wronged her lord with doing so naughty a thing as giving his presents to another man; both Cassio and Desdemona were innocent of any offence against Othello: but the wicked Iago, whose spirits never slept in contrivance of villainy, had made his wife (a good, but a weak woman) steal this handkerchief from Desdemona, under pretence of getting the work copied, but in reality to drop it in Cassio's way, where he might find it, and give a handle to Iago's suggestion that it was Desdemona's present.

Othello, soon after meeting his wife, pretended that he had a head-ache (as he might indeed with truth), and desired her to lend him her handkerchief to hold to his temples. She did so. 'Not this,' said Othello, 'but that handkerchief I gave you.' Desdemona had it not about her (for indeed it was stolen, as we have related). 'How?' said Othello, 'this is a fault indeed. That handkerchief an Egyptian woman gave to my mother; the woman was a witch and could read people's thoughts: she told my mother, while she kept it, it would make her amiable, and my father would love her; but, if she lost it, or gave it away, my father's fancy would turn, and he would loathe her as much as he had loved her. She dying gave it to me, and bade me, if I ever married, to give it to my wife. I did so; take heed of it. Make it a darling as precious as your eye.' 'Is it possible?' said the frighted lady. ''Tis true,' continued Othello; 'it is a magical handkerchief; a sibyl that had lived in the world two hundred years, in a fit of prophetic fury worked it; the silkworms that furnished the silk were hallowed, and it was dyed in a mummy of maidens' hearts conserved.' Desdemona, hearing the wondrous virtues of the handkerchief, was ready to die with fear, for she plainly perceived she had lost it, and with it, she feared, the affections of her husband. Then Othello started, and looked as if he were going to do some rash thing, and still he demanded the handkerchief, which when she could not produce, she tried to divert her husband from too serious thoughts, and cheerfully told him she saw all his talk about the handkerchief was only to put her off from her suit about Michael Cassio, whom she went on to praise (as Iago had foretold), till Othello in perfect distraction burst out of the room, and then Desdemona, though unwillingly, began to suspect that her lord was jealous.

What cause she could have ministered to him she knew not, and then she accused herself for accusing the noble Othello, and thought to be sure that some untoward news from Venice, or some state troubles had puddled his spirits, and made his temper not so sweet as formerly. And she said, 'Men are not gods, and we must not look for that observance from them when they are married, which they show us on the bridal day.' And she beshrewed herself for so unkindly judging of his unkindness.

Again Othello and Desdemona met, and he accused her more plainly of being unfaithful, and of loving another man, but he did not name whom: and Othello wept, and Desdemona said, 'Alas! the heavy day! why do you weep?' And Othello told her, he could have borne all sorts of evils with fortitude – poverty, and disease, and disgrace; but her infidelity had broken his heart: and he called her a weed, that looked so fair, and smelled so sweet, that the sense ached at it; and wished she had never been born. And when he had left her, this innocent lady was so stupefied with wonder at her lord's untrue suspicion of her, that a weight-like sleep came over her, and she only desired her attendant to make her bed, and to lay her wedding-sheets upon it, saying, that when people teach their babes, they do it by gentle means and easy tasks, and Othello might have chid her so; for in good faith she was but a child when she was chidden. And this was all the complaint which this gentle lady made.

Desdemona being retired to bed expecting her lord would follow her, soon fell into a slumber, the effect of her troubled spirits, when Othello entered the chamber, full of the black purpose which he had meditated of putting his lady to death. But when he saw her asleep, he thought he would not shed her blood, nor scar that white skin of hers, more white than alabaster. But he was resolved she should die; else (as he said) she would live to betray more men, as she had done him. Then he kissed her for the last time (as he said), and that kiss was so sweet, that he must needs kiss her again: and he wept, but he said they were cruel tears.

Desdemona was awakened with his kisses, and she looked upon Othello, and she saw him gnaw his under lip, and roll his eyes, and she knew he was always fatal when he looked so: and he bade her prepare for death, and to say her prayers, for he would not kill her soul. And this innocent wife, as she lay at his mercy, begged for compassion, and to know her fault, and then he named Cassio, and the handkerchief which (he said) she had given him; and as the guiltless lady was proceeding to clear herself he suddenly would hear no more, but covering her up in the bed-clothes, stifled her till she died.

In this instant of time was brought into the house Cassio, wounded and bleeding, whom Iago had set one of his creatures on to assassinate; but the fellow not succeeding in his attempt to kill Cassio (whom he wounded, but not mortally), and being himself killed by Iago to prevent discovery, in his pockets were found certain letters, which made the guilt of Iago, and the innocence of Cassio, clear beyond all doubt; and Cassio now came to beg pardon of Othello, and to ask wherein he had offended him, that he had employed Iago to murder him.

This discovery was as a thunderstroke to Othello, who now plainly saw that he was no better than a murderer, and that his wife (poor innocent lady) had been ever faithful to him; the extreme anguish of which discovery making life insupportable, he fell upon his sword, and throwing himself upon the body of his dear injured lady, expired.

These rash acts raised much passion of horror and amazement in the bystanders, for Othello had borne a fair reputation, and till he was wrought upon by the arts of a villain, which his own noble nature never gave him leave to suspect, he was a loving and doting husband. He had loved not wisely, but too well; and his manly eyes (when he learned his mistake), though not used to weep on every small occasion, dropped tears as fast as the Arabian trees their gum. And when he was dead all his former merits and his valiant acts were remembered. Nothing now remained for his successor but to put the utmost censure of the law in force against Iago, who was executed with strict tortures; and to send word to the state of Venice of the lamentable death of their renowned general.

ANTONY AND CLEOPATRA

◆◆

IN the year 42 B.C., Mark Antony, then with Octavius Caesar and Lepidus one of the three rulers or triumvirs of the Roman Empire, stayed in the city of Alexandria, infatuated by the surpassingly beautiful young Queen of Egypt. Though Antony had been a noble soldier, his friends were troubled now by his obvious weakening, his surrender to Cleopatra's every whim. On a summer night in the royal palace where two of his officers awaited him, one of them, a trusted veteran, said sadly, 'This dotage of our general's is beyond belief. Look where they come – the triple pillar of the world transformed into a woman's fool.'

There, between her palm fans and attended by her court, Cleopatra, a glittering vision beneath her diadem, leant upon Antony as they walked down the steps. 'If it be love indeed,' she was saying in her languid way, 'tell me how much.' And Antony replied to her, 'Then you must find out new heaven, new earth.'

A court chamberlain prostrated himself: 'News, my good lord, from Rome,' and Antony said to him imperatively, 'Be brief!' Cleopatra looked on with a mocking smile: 'Nay, hear it, Antony. Perhaps Fulvia your wife is angry, or maybe young Caesar has sent some powerful message to you: "Do this, or this. Take in this kingdom, or else set free that." Why, as I am Egypt's Queen, you are blushing, Antony.' Sharply she called, 'Bring in the messengers!'

Antony embraced her. 'My queen, let Rome in Tiber melt, and the wide arch of the ranged Empire fall . . . Here is my place. Have we no sport to-night?'

'Receive the ambassadors!' urged Cleopatra; but Antony shook his head. 'Fie, wrangling queen! To-night, alone, we'll wander through the streets, listening and watching, hidden in our cloaks. So come with me! Last night you did desire it.'

Wearily he waved off the messengers who had entered to stand bowing and astonished before him: 'Nay, speak not to us.' In a minute the royal party had vanished up the steps, leaving only the discomfited men with Antony's officers.

When at last he consented to hear the news, he found that it was grievous. One messenger told him that a Parthian leader was making unchecked conquests in Asia. From another he learned that Fulvia, his neglected wife, was dead. Antony, for a moment, was remorseful: 'There's a great spirit gone.' Knowing it was time to break from Cleopatra, and to take up again the sorely neglected duties of his office, he summoned Domitius Enobarbus, his chief lieutenant, long experienced in the wars, and told him that they must hasten from Alexandria. 'Would I had never seen Cleopatra!' he cried, to which Enobarbus – who knew his master's mind – said shortly, 'O, sir, you had then left unseen a wonderful piece of work.'

Antony looked at him with cold reproach: 'Fulvia my wife is dead.'

'If there were no other women,' said Enobarbus after a pause, 'you were indeed to be pitied.'

'Cease your light answers.' said Antony. 'I shall tell Cleopatra that we must part. Other letters, Enobarbus, call us home. Pompey's son Sextus Pompeius has challenged Caesar and commands the empire of the sea . . . We must go from hence, and quickly.'

When he reached Cleopatra to tell her so, the capricious beauty was with her waiting-maids Charmian and Iras. 'I am sick and sullen,' she exclaimed as Antony approached her. 'Help me away, dear Charmian, or I shall fall.' Antony spoke gently to her: 'Now my dearest queen—,' but Cleopatra told him, with a shrug, to stand further from her. Did Fulvia say that Antony must go back? Would she had never given him leave to come to Egypt. He was not to say that Cleopatra kept him there. As Antony strove to reason with her, the queen stormed on: 'At the first I knew you would be treacherous. Seek no excuses. Bid farewell, and go. When you wished to stay, you could find all the words you needed. Eternity, you said then, was in my lips and eyes, bliss in even the bending of my brows—.'

'Hear me, queen,' Antony protested. 'Though I have to go, my heart remains your own. There is civil war in Italy; Sextus Pompeius threatens the Roman gates. But over this – and surely news to move you most – my wife is dead.'

Cleopatra smiled in disbelief: 'Can Fulvia die?' Looking at Antony, she knew it to be true, but she went on without mercy: 'Most false love. No tears! . . . I see in Fulvia's death how you would answer mine.'

Antony bade her quarrel no more with him, and to cease her mirth, for he would go or stay at her pleasure. When he grew angry and prepared to leave, Cleopatra at last abandoned her teasing and held him back, asking his forgiveness and saying that his honour called him thence. 'Be deaf to my unpitied folly, and all the gods go with you. Upon your sword sit laurelled victory.' She motioned him away; and within the hour he was bound from Alexandria towards Rome.

At this very time, in Rome itself, Octavius Caesar was reading to his fellow-triumvir Lepidus the news from Egypt; how Antony, his nights wasted in revel, his duty forgotten, had become the book of all faults. Though Lepidus tried indulgently to excuse him, the austere Caesar would have none of it. While they talked a messenger arrived to report yet more terror on the sea that was ruled by Pompey and his fellow-pirates. Sadly, Caesar remembered the days of Antony's great and unsparing soldiership, and wished that his shame might drive him quickly back to Rome. It was time that Rome showed itself in full strength, for while it was idle Pompey must thrive unchecked.

Soon Caesar's hopes were to be realised, for already Mark Antony hurried back. Behind him, in the palace of Alexandria, Cleopatra, whom he had named 'the serpent of old Nile', lay disconsolate, mourning the absence of the lover she called the very crest of men. Her steward brought back to her Antony's last gift of an orient pearl, and Cleopatra, who had been sending out messenger after messenger, cried once more for ink and paper: 'Every day Antony shall hear from me, or I'll unpeople Egypt.'

At length, in Caesar's house in Rome, the triumvirs – together for the first time in many months – met for their embarrassing conference. Caesar was marble-cold, and Antony fatigued by his long journey from the East. Lepidus attempted with good-natured fussiness to compose all differences: 'What is amiss, may it be gently heard.'

Early in the conference, though Antony endeavoured to make what atonement he could, Caesar would not be pacified. Yet, he agreed grudgingly, if he knew what might hold them together, he would pursue it to the very end of the world. Then, very briefly, his shrewd counsellor Agrippa spoke. Caesar had a sister, the admired Octavia; Mark Antony was now a widower. To join their hearts and houses with an unslipping knot, let Antony take Octavia for his wife.

Without pause and without question, the careless Antony agreed. Caesar, touched sincerely, said, 'There is my hand. A sister I bequeath to you whom no brother did love so dearly. Let her live, Antony, to unite our kingdoms and our hearts.'

Friends once more, the triumvirs left the chamber, while Agrippa and Maecenas, of Caesar's party, welcomed Enobarbus. What had it been like in Egypt? Had they not heard of eight wild boars roasted at a breakfast for but twelve persons? This Cleopatra – was she the triumphant lady of report? And Enobarbus, his memories rising, sat on the edge of a table and told them how Antony had first met the queen as she sailed upon the river of Cydnus. Her barge, like a burnished throne, had burned upon the water; its poop was of beaten gold; its perfumed sails were purple, and to the tune of flutes the silver oars kept stroke. Cleopatra rested on deck in a pavilion of cloth-of-gold of tissue; on each side were boys like smiling Cupids, with many-coloured fans. Her gentlewomen, habited as mermaids, moved about her with a sinuous grace; and at the helm another silver mermaid steered. All hurried to the banks to see the vessel; and Mark Antony, enthroned in the market-place, sat alone, whistling to the air which had gone itself to gaze on Cleopatra and left a gap in nature. When the queen landed he sent messengers inviting her to supper; she replied that he must be her guest, and there for her welcome he had paid his heart as Cleopatra's thrall.

'Royal wench!' exclaimed Agrippa. 'But now,' said Maecenas, 'he must leave her utterly.'

Enobarbus laughed. 'Never! He will not. Age cannot wither her, nor custom stale her infinite variety.'

'Still,' said Maecenas, 'if beauty, wisdom, modesty, can settle Antony's heart, he will find them in Octavia.'

Enobarbus, smiling incredulously, shook his head. He knew that

Antony was too deeply in love with Cleopatra to let her go. Indeed, while he was thinking of this in Rome, Cleopatra in her Alexandrian palace was crying in despair after the vanished Antony, remembering how she had laughed him into patience and out of patience, and how once she had drunk him to his bed and put her own attire upon him while she wore his great sword Philippan.

As the weeks passed, and Cleopatra still languished, a messenger from Rome travelled in haste to Alexandria. Fearfully he entered the presence of the queen, for he had heavy news to bring. Yes, Antony was well; yes, he was friends with Caesar; but – and now the messenger cowered beneath the queen's angry gaze – he was married to Octavia. In uncontrolled fury Cleopatra struck the man to the floor. As he tried to rise, she struck him again and dragged him up and down by the hair while he pleaded pitifully, 'Gracious madam, I that do bring the news made not the match.' When he contrived at last to escape, Charmian said with reproach in her voice, 'Good madam, the man is innocent.' Cleopatra's rage had dulled a little. 'Call him back,' she said. 'It is ignoble to strike one meaner than myself.'

But when the man came back he could do no more than repeat, cringing, that his news was true. Cleopatra, in helpless grief, dismissed him. All was lost; but as she told Charmian and Iras to lead her to her bed, one hope glimmered yet. The messenger must tell her what Octavia looked like, her years and manners, the colour of her hair, even how tall she was. Then Cleopatra drooped upon the shoulders of her maids while Charmian and Iras exchanged glances above her head. 'Pity me, Charmian, but do not speak to me.'

Far off, near Misenum, the Roman triumvirs had met Pompey and his allies during a truce. Very quickly they made their agreement. Pompey, having accepted Sicily and Sardinia and promised to rid the sea of pirates, invited all to feast on board his galley. Before this wild and drunken orgy, Pompey's lieutenant Menas learned from Enobarbus what might befall. Octavia was cold and quiet. Soon, surely, Mark Antony would seek Cleopatra again; his desertion would kindle the wrath of Caesar, and desperate war must ensue.

Menas agreed gruffly, 'Thus it may be.' And thus it was.

Shortly after the meeting with Pompey, when all treaties were concluded, Antony travelled with Octavia from Rome to Athens, his new seat of government. In Alexandria Cleopatra had learned from the messenger, tactful and readily untruthful, unwilling now to risk himself again, that Octavia was short and low-voiced, a widow of about thirty, slow in gait and with a round face. This delighted the jealous queen ('The man has seen some majesty, and should know'), and she would have been more delighted than ever to realise that in Athens Antony had found a new grievance against Caesar. In his absence Caesar and Lepidus had themselves made war on Pompey; Pompey was slain; Caesar had turned suddenly on Lepidus and imprisoned him; and the triumvirate had ended.

Clearly Caesar was resolved to gain the supreme power of the Roman world. When Octavia begged Antony to let her go back to Rome and mediate with her brother, he agreed without warmth; it was plain to him, if not at once to her, that this must be the end of their marriage. She hastened to Rome, and, once she was gone, he went direct to Alexandria. There in the market-place he and Cleopatra, who wore the habiliments of the goddess Isis, were enthroned publicly in chairs of gold. To the queen he gave not only Egypt but also the absolute rule of Lower Syria, Cyprus, and Lydia. His sons he proclaimed the kings of kings: Alexander received Media, Parthia, and Armenia, and three other nations were assigned to Ptolemy.

To Caesar in Rome Antony sent fierce accusation, claiming that he had not received his share of the spoils taken from Pompey and demanding to know why Lepidus had been deposed. Caesar had barely replied to this before Octavia arrived from Athens. Her appearance added to his wrath, for she had come without ceremony, not as his sister or as Antony's wife, but almost as 'a market-maid to Rome'. She told him that she had begged her husband's leave to arbitrate between them; and Caesar, with what gentleness he could, replied that Antony had yielded again to the wiles of Cleopatra, that he had left Athens, given away his empire, and levied the Eastern kings to war upon his side.

Nothing could prevent a mortal conflict. Both Caesar and Antony knew that this must be a fight to the last, with the world as prize. While Antony established himself in camp near Actium, Cleopatra with him, the Roman fleet sailed rapidly towards Egypt.

Caesar dared Antony to fight at sea, but Enobarbus urged his leader to avoid this, for where Caesar's fleet was manned by tested sailors, Antony must depend upon reapers and muleteers, crews pressed swiftly into service. Caesar's ships were easy to manoeuvre. Antony's were heavy. It would be wiser to refuse a fight at sea, being well prepared by land.

'By sea, by sea!' repeated the obstinate Antony, while yet again Enobarbus impressed upon him that if he did this he wasted his army, ignored his own renowned experience, left the certain way, and gave himself to hazard. Antony still insisted on a sea battle; Cleopatra supported him, crying that she had sixty ships, none better. At once Antony gave orders; while his general Canidius would keep together a land army, he and others would take to the ships. A veteran soldier who had been listening to this pleaded with him not to fight by sea, not trust to rotten planks. But Antony laughed carelessly: 'Well, well, away!'

Octavius Caesar, meantime, ordered his own general not to provoke a land battle until the fighting at sea had ended. This, as it proved, was soon over. Before either side could claim any advantage, the sixty Egyptian ships hoisted sail and fled; and Cleopatra being gone, Antony hastened to follow her, leaving the battle at its height. 'I never saw an action of such shame,' said one of his officers. 'Experience, manhood, honour, were never so violated.' Canidius, general of the army, had no scruples: 'To Caesar will I render my legions and my horse. Six kings already show me the way to yield.'

Tired and humiliated after his flight, Mark Antony rested in the palace of Alexandria. There he told his friends to take a ship laden with gold, to divide it, and to make their peace with Caesar. He had lost his authority. When Cleopatra came to him he greeted her at first as a man distracted, asking why she had led him into this toil. The queen begged his forgiveness, saying that she did not know he would have followed her, and he answered sadly that his heart was tied to hers; whither she went he must go. Now he had to send to Caesar his humble entreaties; he who played at will with half the Roman world, making and marring fortunes, must beg for mercy. As Cleopatra, weeping, implored his pardon, he ceased suddenly to cry out. 'Weep not,' he said, 'for a single tear is worth all that is won and lost. Kiss me, my queen . . . Even this repays me. When fortune offers blows, 'tis then we scorn her most.'

He had sent to Caesar's camp his schoolmaster, the elderly Euphronius, a poor envoy from one who had had superfluous kings as messengers. Sadly the old man told Caesar that Antony, saluting him now as lord of his fortune, asked to live in Egypt, or, if this were denied, to stay as a private man in Athens. Cleopatra would acknowledge Caesar's greatness and submit.

Coldly, Caesar refused Antony's request. But he told Euphronius that Cleopatra should not beg unheard if she were either to drive Antony from Egypt or take his life there. When Euphronius was gone Caesar summoned the young and subtle Thyreus, ordering him to make good use of his eloquence, and by promising all that she asked and more, to win Cleopatra from Antony.

Antony himself was driven to desperation; he could think of nothing but a challenge to Caesar for single combat, sword against sword, and Enobarbus, who was listening, cynically said to himself, 'Caesar, you have subdued his judgement also.' It was then, with Antony for a moment out of the way, that the flatterer Thyreus arrived. Shrewdly he played on Cleopatra. Caesar well understood that she had feared Antony, not loved him; let her now use Caesar as her friend. The queen listened eagerly. Thyreus, she replied, must say that she kissed Caesar's conquering hand, that she was prompt to lay her crown at his feet and there to kneel before him. Triumphant, Thyreus asked for permission to kiss her hand, and he was doing so when Antony, whom Enobarbus had told of this, strode into the hall. 'I am Antony yet,' he cried. 'Take hence this boy and whip him. When he is whipped, bring him again.' Passionately he turned upon Cleopatra, abusing her for her intemperance, her deeds with other men. Now she would permit a mere menial to kiss her hand, that kingly seal, that plighter of hearts . . .

While he was raging at her, Thyreus was brought in again, whipped and faint. 'Get you back to Caesar,' said Antony. 'Say he has made me angry with him – angry that in disdainful pride he harps on what I am, not what I was. Hence with your lashes!'

Cleopatra, who had been watching, terrified, assured him of her constancy, whereupon he quietened and found hope returning. 'Call to me all my sad captains. Fill our bowls once more. We'll mock the midnight bell.' He rose in something of his old grandeur. 'The next time I do fight I'll make death love me.' They moved off together down the great lotus-columned hall; but Enobarbus went the other way, musing to himself that Antony's reason and his valour no longer matched each other; it was time to leave him.

In the enemy camp Caesar derided Antony's challenge to personal combat and prepared to make the following day the decisive battle in the war. That night, before the palace of Alexandria, soldiers on guard in the intense quiet heard a sound of music in the air or under the earth – where they knew not. 'What should this mean?' whispered one, and his fellow said, 'It is the god Hercules whom Antony loved, now leaves him.'

Certainly Mark Antony's hopes were small; but in the first glimmer of daybreak he stirred himself gallantly for what might be his last battle. Cleopatra herself helped to buckle his armour; trumpets spoke their summons to the day; and Antony cried, 'This morning's like the spirit of a youth that means to be of note.' It was not long before he suffered unexpected grief: the news that his most loyal comrade Enobarbus had deserted to the camp of Caesar. Receiving the news bravely, he said, 'Go, send his possessions after him. Write gently – I will sign it – saying that I hope he will never more find cause to change a master.' When Enobarbus, in Caesar's camp, heard this reply, he repented bitterly and resolved to take his own life.

All day the battle lasted. At night, with Antony still ruler of the field, Caesar retired to make ready for the next morning's attack. Not far away, under the walls of Alexandria, Cleopatra advanced in state to meet her 'lord of lords' while drums and trumpets sounded a martial welcome and Antony's men came cheering back into the city. As they caroused that night, Enobarbus, among the tents of Caesar, died upon his own sword with a last anguished cry, 'Be witness to me, O blessed moon, that Enobarbus repented his base revolt. Forgive me, Antony – nobler than I am infamous – but let the world think of me only as a traitor and a fugitive.'

Next morning Caesar the tactician sent out his forces both by sea and land, knowing that by this he would confuse Antony, whose best men must go to man the ships. For the second time Cleopatra's cowardly Egyptian sailors betrayed Antony. As he watched from land, he saw to his helpless dismay that the fleet had yielded to Caesar. Now he had but a single thought, to be revenged upon Cleopatra, the false soul of Egypt that had beguiled him to the very heart of loss. She hastened to him, asking why he was enraged; and when he shouted at her and she fled affrighted, he said slowly, 'The witch shall die. She has sold me to Caesar.'

For a time he scarcely knew what he did or said. Cleopatra, in terror, hurried to the great monument, or mausoleum, that had been built for her, and there locked herself and her maids within the walls, sending to Antony tidings that she had killed herself and that his name was the last word she spoke. When her servant brought this false message to him, Antony listened in grief-stricken silence. Then he spoke dully to his officer: 'Unarm, Eros, the long day's task is done, and we must sleep. Pluck off my armour.' Left alone, he said softly, 'I will die with you, Cleopatra, and weep for my pardon... Stay for me. All the ghosts shall gaze upon us as we come among them hand in hand. Even Dido and her Aeneas shall want troops, and all the haunt be ours.'

Summoning Eros again, he said, 'Kill me. The time is come.' Eros, dismayed, stepped back; but when his master insisted, he begged that Antony should at least turn away his face. Antony did so, and Eros said farewell, and, very quietly, 'Shall I strike now?' At once he struck himself to his own heart, gasping as he fell, 'Why, there: thus do I escape the sorrow of Antony's death.'

'Thrice nobler than myself!' cried Antony. 'You teach me what I should do, and you could not.' So saying, he ran upon his own sword; but the wound was not mortal, and in agony he summoned the guards and begged them to despatch him. Though the soldiers beheld him in sorrow, saying 'The star is fallen!', they would not end the work. Presently one of Cleopatra's attendants came to him, astonished at finding him there sorely wounded. 'Most absolute lord, my mistress sent me to you. She is locked in her monument, but I am here, I dread, too late.'

Once more Antony called his guards and ordered them now to bear him to Cleopatra's monument. With extreme gentleness they carried him to its base upon a litter; and Cleopatra, gazing down in tears, prepared with Charmian and Iras to draw him up to her. His voice was heard, low and broken: 'I am dying, Egypt, dying.' Slowly they hoisted him aloft to the ledge where Cleopatra stood. His life ebbed fast. 'Remember my former fortunes wherein I lived the greatest prince of the world. I do not basely die . . . A Roman by a Roman valiantly vanquished. Now my spirit is going. I can no more.' His head fell back, and Cleopatra lifted her voice in a great ecstasy of sorrow:

> 'The crown o' the earth doth melt. My lord?
> O, wither'd is the garland of the war,
> The soldier's pole is fallen: young boys and girls
> Are level now with men. The odds is gone,
> And there is nothing left remarkable
> Beneath the visiting moon.

She fainted. When she came to herself, she seemed at first to be a woman resolved: 'We'll bury him; and then, what's brave, what's noble, let's do it after the high Roman fashion, and make death proud to take us.'

Octavius Caesar, now absolute master of the Roman world, was told of Mark Antony's death. Even his cold nature was moved; but he had yet work to do. Cleopatra lived. Though she must follow his chariot as a prisoner at his Roman triumph, she must be wooed subtly, told that no shame would come to her. He sent to her therefore an envoy who promised nothing but kindness. While the envoy and Cleopatra were speaking together, other men of Caesar's army entered the monument from behind, and the queen found herself a prisoner. Distracted, she cried that she would die rather than be borne in Caesar's triumph through the shouting streets of Rome.

Still assuring her that she would be treated well, the envoy left her with another of Caesar's men. This Dolabella, touched by her anguish and her beauty, warned her that, whatever Caesar might say, she would be led in his Roman triumph; there could be no reprieve. Within a minute she faced Octavius Caesar himself, kneeling to him humbly as a slave before her master. 'I beg you, rise,' he said. 'Rise, Egypt.' And Cleopatra answered, 'Sir, the gods will have it thus. My master and my lord, I must obey.'

She had another humiliation yet. To Caesar she handed a document, calling it the full record of her wealth, nothing reserved. But her treasurer, fearful for his own life, refused to confirm the words, saying at once that she had kept back money for herself. Graciously ignoring the deception and her angry shame, Caesar said that he approved her wisdom, and he left her with all vows of friendship, alone with the faithful maids.

Iras, who spoke little but who saw much, knew that this must be the end of the journey. 'Finish, good lady, the bright day is done, and we are for the dark.' Dolabella hastened back, telling Cleopatra that after three days she and her children would be sent on the long journey to Rome and the inevitable progress through the streets; and Cleopatra raised her head and prepared for immediate death.

There could be no further delay. Already she had made certain preparations. First she told Charmian to dress her in her regal robe, as if she were once more to meet Mark Antony upon the river Cydnus. While Charmian prepared the robe, there entered quietly an old Egyptian peasant whom Cleopatra had ordered to bring, hidden in a basket of figs, some of the deadly vipers, or asps, found upon the bank of Nile. She took the basket from him. When he had gone Iras and Charmian invested her in royal splendour. 'Give me my robe. Put on my crown. I have immortal longings in me . . . Husband, I come. I am fire and air; my other elements I give to baser life.'

She stooped to kiss her maids. Iras, stricken by sorrow, fell in death. Charmian knelt, weeping, while Cleopatra, applying the asp to her breast, said gently, 'Poor venomous fool, be angry and despatch!'

'O eastern star!' cried Charmian. But Cleopatra reproved her. 'Peace, peace! Do you not see my baby at my breast, that sucks the nurse asleep.' She placed another asp upon her arm. Soon the poison worked. 'What, should I stay—' she began; but her voice faded into silence and her eyes closed in death while Charmian made a last obeisance:

'So fare thee well.
Now boast thee, death, in thy possession lies
A lass unparalleled. Downy windows, close,
And golden Phoebus never be beheld
Of eyes again so royal!'

Charmian raised her hand to straighten the royal diadem of Egypt, then took an asp to her own arm. As a horrified guard ran in, exclaiming 'Charmian, is this well done?', she said with her final breath, 'It is well done, and fitting for a princess descended of so many royal kings.'

There Octavius Caesar found them: the queen enthroned in death, her maids beside her. Wonderingly, he said, 'She looks like sleep, as she would catch another Antony in her strong toil of grace.' Raising his voice, he gave order: 'Take up her bed, and bear her women from the monument. She shall be buried by her Antony. No grave upon the earth shall hold in it a pair so famous.' Slowly, while the watchers bowed to her for the last time, Cleopatra was borne to meet her lover where souls couched on flowers and every ghost would gaze.

PERICLES
PRINCE OF TYRE

◆◆◆◆◆◆◆◆◆

PERICLES, Prince of Tyre, became a voluntary exile from his dominions, to avert the dreadful calamities which Antiochus, the wicked emperor of Greece, threatened to bring upon his subjects and city of Tyre, in revenge for a discovery which the prince had made of a shocking deed which the emperor had done in secret; as commonly it proves dangerous to pry into the hidden crimes of great ones. Leaving the government of his people in the hands of his able and honest minister, Helicanus, Pericles set sail from Tyre, thinking to absent himself till the wrath of Antiochus, who was mighty, should be appeased.

The first place which the prince directed his course to was Tarsus, and hearing that the city of Tarsus was at that time suffering under a severe famine, he took with him store of provisions for its relief. On his arrival he found the city reduced to the utmost distress; and, he coming like a messenger from heaven with his unhoped-for succour, Cleon, the governor of Tarsus, welcomed him with boundless thanks. Pericles had not been here many days, before letters came from his faithful minister, warning him that it was not safe for him to stay at Tarsus, for Antiochus knew of his abode, and by secret emissaries despatched for that purpose sought his life. Upon receipt of these letters Pericles put out to sea again, amidst the blessings and prayers of a whole people who had been fed by his bounty.

He had not sailed far, when his ship was overtaken by a dreadful storm, and every man on board perished except Pericles, who was cast by the sea-waves naked on an unknown shore, where he had not wandered long before he met with some poor fishermen, who invited him to their homes, giving him clothes and provisions. The fishermen told Pericles the name of their country was Pentapolis, and that their king was Simonides, commonly called the good Simonides, because of his peaceable reign and good government. From them he also learned that King Simonides had a fair young daughter, and that the following day was her birthday, when a grand tournament was to be held at court, many princes and knights being come from all parts to try their skill in arms for the love of Thaisa, this fair princess. While the prince was listening to this account, and secretly lamenting the loss of his good armour, which disabled him from making one among these valiant knights, another fisherman brought in a complete suit of armour that he had taken out of the sea with his fishing-net, which proved to be the very armour he had lost. When Pericles beheld his own armour, he said, 'Thanks, Fortune; after all my crosses you give me somewhat to repair myself. This armour was bequeathed to me by my dead father, for whose dear sake I have so loved it, that whithersoever I went, I still have kept it by me, and the rough sea that parted it from me, having now become calm, hath given it back again, for which I thank it, for, since I have my father's gift again, I think my shipwreck no misfortune.'

The next day Pericles, clad in his brave father's armour, repaired to the royal court of Simonides, where he performed wonders at the tournament, vanquishing with ease all the brave knights and valiant princes who contended with him in arms for the honour of Thaisa's love. When brave warriors contended at court tournaments for the love of kings' daughters, if one proved sole victor over all the rest, it was usual for the great lady for whose sake these deeds of valour were undertaken, to bestow all her respect upon the conqueror, and Thaisa did not depart from this custom, for she presently dismissed all the princes and knights whom Pericles had vanquished, and distinguished him by her especial favour and regard, crowning him with the wreath of victory, as king of that day's happiness; and Pericles became a most passionate lover of this beauteous princess from the first moment he beheld her.

The good Simonides so well approved of the valour and noble qualities of Pericles, who was indeed a most accomplished gentleman, and well learned in all excellent arts, that though he knew not the rank of this royal stranger (for Pericles for fear of Antiochus gave out that he was a private gentleman of Tyre), yet did not Simonides disdain to accept of the valiant unknown for a son-in-law, when he perceived his daughter's affections were firmly fixed upon him.

Pericles had not been many months married to Thaisa, before he received intelligence that his enemy Antiochus was dead; and that his subjects of Tyre, impatient of his long absence, threatened to revolt, and talked of placing Helicanus upon his vacant throne. This news came from Helicanus himself, who, being a loyal subject to his royal master, would not accept of the high dignity offered him, but sent to let Pericles know their intentions, that he might return home and resume his lawful right. It was matter of great surprise and joy to Simonides, to find that his son-in-law (the obscure knight) was the renowned Prince of Tyre; yet again he regretted that he was not the private gentleman he supposed him to be, seeing that he must now part both with his admired son-in-law and his beloved daughter, whom he feared to trust to the perils of the sea, because Thaisa was with child; and Pericles himself wished her to remain with her father till after her confinement, but the poor lady so earnestly desired to go with her husband, that at last they consented, hoping she would reach Tyre before she was brought to bed.

The sea was no friendly element to unhappy Pericles, for long before they reached Tyre another dreadful tempest arose, which so terrified Thaisa that she was taken ill, and in a short space of time her nurse Lychorida came to Pericles with a little child in her arms, to tell the prince the sad tidings that his wife died the moment her little babe was born. She held the babe towards its father, saying, 'Here is a thing too young for such a place. This is the child of your dead queen.' No tongue can tell the dreadful sufferings of Pericles when he heard his wife was dead. As soon as he could speak, he said, 'O you gods, why do you make us love your goodly gifts, and then snatch those gifts away?' 'Patience, good sir,' said Lychorida, 'here is all that is left alive of our dead queen, a little daughter, and for your child's sake be more manly. Patience, good sir, even for the sake of this precious charge.' Pericles took the new-born infant in his arms, and he said to the little babe, 'Now may your life be mild, for a more blusterous birth had never babe! May your condition be mild and gentle, for you have had the rudest welcome that ever prince's child did meet with! May that which follows be happy, for you have had as chiding a nativity as fire, air, water, earth, and heaven could make to herald you from the womb! Even at the first, your loss,' meaning in the death of her mother, 'is more than all joys, which you shall find upon this earth to which you are come a new visitor, shall be able to recompense.'

The storm still continuing to rage furiously, and the sailors having a superstition that while a dead body remained in the ship the storm would never cease, they came to Pericles to demand that his queen should be thrown overboard; and they said, 'What courage, sir? God save you!' 'Courage enough,' said the sorrowing prince: 'I do not fear the storm; it has done to me its worst; yet for the love of this poor infant, this fresh new seafarer, I wish the storm was over.' 'Sir,' said the sailors, 'your queen must overboard. The sea works high, the wind is loud, and the storm will not abate till the ship be cleared of the dead.' Though Pericles knew how weak and unfounded this superstition was, yet he patiently submitted, saying, 'As you think meet. Then she must overboard, most wretched queen!' And now this unhappy prince went to take a last view of his dear wife, and as he looked on his Thaisa, he said, 'A terrible childbed hast thou had, my dear; no light, no fire; the unfriendly elements forget thee utterly, nor have I time to bring thee hallowed to thy grave, but must cast thee scarcely coffined into the sea, where for a monument upon thy bones the humming waters must overwhelm thy corpse, lying with simple shells. O Lychorida, bid Nestor bring me spices, ink, and paper, my casket and my jewels, and bid Nicander bring me the satin coffin. Lay the babe upon the pillow, and go about this suddenly, Lychorida, while I say a priestly farewell to my Thaisa.'

They brought Pericles a large chest, in which (wrapped in a satin shroud) he placed his queen, and sweet-smelling spices he strewed over her, and beside her he placed rich jewels, and a written paper, telling who she was, and praying if haply any one should find the chest which contained the body of his wife, they would give her burial: and then with his own hands he cast the chest into the sea. When the storm was over, Pericles ordered the sailors to make for Tarsus. 'For,' said Pericles, 'the babe cannot hold out till we come to Tyre. At Tarsus I will leave it at careful nursing.'

After that tempestuous night when Thaisa was thrown into the sea, and while it was yet early morning, as Cerimon a worthy gentleman of Ephesus, and a most skilful physician, was standing by the sea-side, his servants brought to him a chest, which they said the sea-waves had thrown on the land. 'I never saw,' said one of them, 'so huge a billow as cast it on our shore.' Cerimon ordered the chest to be conveyed to his own house, and when it was opened he beheld with wonder the body of a young and lovely lady; and the sweet-smelling spices and rich casket of jewels made him conclude it was some great person who was thus strangely entombed: searching farther, he discovered a paper, from which he learned that the corpse which lay as dead before him had been a queen, and wife to Pericles, Prince of Tyre; and much admiring at the strangeness of that accident, and more pitying the husband who lost this sweet lady, he said, 'If you are living, Pericles, you have a heart that even cracks with woe.' Then observing attentively Thaisa's face, he saw how fresh and unlike death her looks were, and he said, 'They were too hasty that threw you into the sea:' for he did not believe her to be dead. He ordered a fire to be made, and proper cordials to be brought, and soft music to be played, which might help to calm her amazed spirits if she should revive; and he said to those who crowded round her, wondering at what they saw, 'I pray you, gentlemen, give her air; the queen will live; she has not been entranced above five hours; and see, she begins to blow into life again; she is alive; behold, her eyelids move; this fair creature will live to make us weep to hear her fate.' Thaisa had never died, but after the birth of her little baby had fallen into a deep swoon, which made all that saw her conclude her to be dead; and now by the care of this kind gentleman she once more revived to light and life; and opening her eyes, she said, 'Where am I? Where is my lord? What world is this?' By gentle degrees Cerimon let her understand what had befallen her; and when he thought she was enough recovered to bear the sight, he showed her the paper written by her husband, and the jewels; and she looked on the paper, and said, 'It is my lord's writing. That I was shipped at sea, I well remember, but whether there delivered of my babe, by the holy gods I cannot rightly say; but since my wedded lord I never shall see again, I will put on a vestal livery, and never more have joy.' 'Madam,' said Cerimon, 'if you purpose as you speak, the temple of Diana is not far distant from hence; there you may abide as a vestal. Moreover, if you please, a niece of mine shall there attend you.' This proposal was accepted with thanks by Thaisa; and when she was perfectly recovered, Cerimon placed her in the Temple of Diana, where she became a vestal or priestess of that goddess, and passed her days in sorrowing for her husband's supposed loss, and in the most devout exercises of those times.

Pericles carried his young daughter (whom he named Marina, because she was born at sea) to Tarsus, intending to leave her with Cleon, the governor of that city, and his wife Dionysia, thinking, for the good he had done to them at the time of their famine, they would be kind to his little motherless daughter. When Cleon saw Prince Pericles, and heard of the great loss which had befallen him, he said, 'O your sweet queen, that it had pleased Heaven you could have brought her hither to have blessed my eyes with the sight of her!' Pericles replied, 'We must obey the powers above us. Should I rage and roar as the sea does in which my Thaisa lies, yet the end must be as it is. My gentle babe, Marina here, I must charge your charity with her. I leave her the infant of your care, beseeching you to give her princely training.' And then turning to Cleon's wife, Dionysia, he said, 'Good madam, make me blessed in your care in bringing up my child:' and she answered, 'I have a child myself who shall not be more dear to my respect than yours, my lord;' and Cleon made the like promise, saying, 'Your noble services, Prince Pericles, in feeding my whole people with your corn (for which in their prayers they daily remember you) must in your child be thought on. If I should neglect your child my whole people that were by you relieved would force me to my duty; but if to that I need a spur, the gods revenge it on me and mine to the end of generation.' Pericles, being thus assured that his child would be carefully attended to, left her to the protection of Cleon and his wife Dionysia, and with her he left the nurse Lychorida. When he went away, the little Marina knew not her loss, but Lychorida wept sadly at parting with her royal master. 'O, no tears, Lychorida,' said Pericles: 'no tears; look to your little mistress, on whose grace you may depend hereafter.'

Pericles arrived in safety at Tyre, and was once more settled in the quiet possession of his throne, while his woeful queen, whom he thought dead, remained at Ephesus. Her little babe Marina, whom this hapless mother had never seen, was brought up by Cleon in a manner suitable to her high birth. He gave her the most careful education, so that by the time Marina attained the age of fourteen years, the most deeply-learned men were not more studied in the learning of those times than was Marina. She sang like one immortal, and danced as goddess-like, and with her needle she was so skilful that she seemed to compose nature's own shapes, in birds, fruits, or flowers, the natural roses being scarcely more like to each other than they were to Marina's silken flowers. But when she had gained from education all these graces, which made her the general wonder, Dionysia, the wife of Cleon, became her mortal enemy from jealousy, by reason that her own daughter, from the slowness of her mind, was not able to attain to that perfection wherein Marina excelled: and finding that all praise was bestowed on Marina, whilst her daughter, who was of the same age, and had been educated with the same care as Marina, though not with the same success, was in comparison disregarded, she formed a project to remove Marina out of the way, vainly imagining that her untoward daughter would be more respected when Marina was no more seen. To encompass this she employed a man to murder Marina, and she well timed her wicked design, when Lychorida, the faithful nurse, had just died. Dionysia was discoursing with the man she had commanded to commit this murder, when the young Marina was weeping over the dead Lychorida. Leonine, the man she employed to do this bad deed, though he was a very wicked man, could hardly be persuaded to undertake it, so had Marina won all hearts to love her. He said, 'She is a goodly creature!' 'The fitter then the gods should have her,' replied her merciless enemy: 'here she comes weeping for the death of her nurse Lychorida: are you resolved to obey me?' Leonine, fearing to disobey her, replied, 'I am resolved.' And so, in that one short sentence, was the matchless Marina doomed to an untimely death. She now approached, with a basket of flowers in her hand, which she said she would daily strew over the grave of good Lychorida. The purple violet and the marigold should as a carpet hang upon her grave, while summer days did last. 'Alas, for me!' she said, 'poor unhappy maid, born in a tempest, when my mother died. This world to me is like a lasting storm, hurrying me from my friends.' 'How now, Marina,' said the dissembling Dionysia, 'do you weep alone? How does it chance my daughter is not with you?

Do not sorrow for Lychorida, you have a nurse in me. Your beauty is quite changed with this unprofitable woe. Come, give me your flowers, the sea-air will spoil them; and walk with Leonine: the air is fine, and will enliven you. Come, Leonine, take her by the arm, and walk with her.' 'No, madam,' said Marina, 'I pray you let me not deprive you of your servant:' for Leonine was one of Dionysia's attendants. 'Come, come,' said this artful woman, who wished for a pretence to leave her alone with Leonine, 'I love the prince, your father, and I love you. We every day expect your father here; and when he comes, and finds you so changed by grief from the paragon of beauty we reported you, he will think we have taken no care of you. Go, I pray you, walk, and be cheerful once again. Be careful of that excellent complexion, which stole the hearts of old and young.' Marina, being thus importuned, said, 'Well, I will go, but yet I have no desire to it.' As Dionysia walked away, she said to Leonine, '*Remember what I have said!*' – shocking words, for their meaning was that he should remember to kill Marina.

Marina looked towards the sea, her birthplace, and said, 'Is the wind westerly that blows?' 'South-west,' replied Leonine. 'When I was born the wind was north,' said she: and then the storm and tempest, and all her father's sorrows, and her mother's death, came full into her mind; and she said, 'My father, as Lychorida told me, did never fear, but cried, *Courage, good seamen*, to the sailors, galling his princely hands with the ropes, and clasping to the masts, he endured a sea that almost split the deck.' 'When was this?' said Leonine. 'When I was born,' replied Marina: 'never were wind and waves more violent;' and then she described the storm, the action of the sailors, the boatswain's whistle, and the loud call of the master, 'which,' said she, 'trebled the confusion of the ship.' Lychorida had so often recounted to Marina the story of her hapless birth that these things seemed ever present to her imagination. But here Leonine interrupted her with desiring her to say her prayers. 'What mean you?' said Marina, who began to fear, she knew not why. 'If you require a little space for prayer, I grant it,' said Leonine; 'but be not tedious, the gods are quick of ear, and I am sworn to do my work in haste.' 'Will you kill me?' said Marina: 'alas! why?' 'To satisfy my lady,' replied Leonine. 'Why would she have me killed?'

said Marina: 'now, as I can remember, I never hurt her in all my life. I never spake bad word, nor did any ill turn to any living creature. Believe me now, I never killed a mouse, nor hurt a fly. I trod upon a worm once against my will, but I wept for it. How have I offended?' The murderer replied, 'My commission is not to reason on the deed, but to do it.' And he was just going to kill her, when certain pirates happened to land at that very moment, who seeing Marina, bore her off as a prize to their ship.

The pirate who had made Marina his prize carried her to Mitylene, and sold her for a slave, where, though in that humble condition, Marina soon became known throughout the whole city of Mitylene for her beauty and her virtues; and the person to whom she was sold became rich by the money she earned for him. She taught music, dancing, and fine needleworks, and the money she got by her scholars she gave to her master and mistress; and the fame of her learning and her great industry came to the knowledge of Lysimachus, a young nobleman who was governor of Mitylene, and Lysimachus went himself to the house where Marina dwelt, to see this paragon of excellence, whom all the city praised so highly. Her conversation delighted Lysimachus beyond measure, for though he had heard much of this admired maiden, he did not expect to find her so sensible a lady, so virtuous, and so good, as he perceived Marina to be; and he left her, saying, he hoped she would persevere in her industrious and virtuous course, and that if ever she heard from him again it should be for her good. Lysimachus thought Marina such a miracle for sense, fine breeding, and excellent qualities, as well as for beauty and all outward graces, that he wished to marry her, and notwithstanding her humble situation, he hoped to find that her birth was noble; but ever when they asked her parentage she would sit still and weep.

Meantime, at Tarsus, Leonine, fearing the anger of Dionysia, told her he had killed Marina; and that wicked woman gave out that she was dead, and made a pretended funeral for her, and erected a stately monument; and shortly after Pericles, accompanied by his loyal minister Helicanus, made a voyage from Tyre to Tarsus, on purpose to see his daughter, intending to take her home with him: and he never having beheld her since he left her an infant in the care of Cleon and his wife, how did this good prince rejoice at the thought of seeing this dear child of his buried queen! but when they told him Marina was dead, and showed the monument they had erected for her, great was the misery this most wretched father endured, and not being able to bear the sight of that country where his last hope and only memory of his dear Thaisa was entombed, he took ship, and hastily departed from Tarsus. From the day he entered the ship a dull and heavy melancholy seized him. He never spoke, and seemed totally insensible to everything around him.

Sailing from Tarsus to Tyre, the ship in its course passed by Mitylene, where Marina dwelt; the governor of which place, Lysimachus, observing this royal vessel from the shore, and desirous of knowing who was on board, went in a barge to the side of the ship, to satisfy his curiosity. Helicanus received him very courteously and told him that the ship came from Tyre, and that they were conducting thither Pericles, their prince; 'A man, sir,' said Helicanus, 'who has not spoken to any one these three months, nor taken any sustenance, but just to prolong his grief; it would be tedious to repeat the whole ground of his distemper, but the main springs from the loss of a beloved daughter and a wife.' Lysimachus begged to see this afflicted prince, and when he beheld Pericles, he saw he had been once a goodly person, and he said to him, 'Sir king, all hail, the gods preserve you, hail, royal sir!' But in vain Lysimachus spoke to him; Pericles made no answer, nor did he appear to perceive any stranger approached. And then Lysimachus bethought him of the peerless maid Marina, that haply with her sweet tongue she might win some answer from the silent prince: and with the consent of Helicanus he sent for Marina, and when she entered the ship in which her own father sat motionless with grief, they welcomed her on board as if they had known she was their princess; and they cried, 'She is a gallant lady.' Lysimachus was well pleased to hear their commendations, and he said, 'She is such a one, that were I well assured she came of noble birth, I would wish no better choice, and think me rarely blessed in a wife.' And then he addressed her in courtly terms, as if the lowly-seeming maid had been the high-born lady he wished to find her, calling her *Fair and beautiful Marina*, telling her a great prince on board that ship had fallen into a sad and mournful silence; and, as if Marina had the power of conferring health and felicity, he begged she would undertake to cure the royal stranger of his melancholy. 'Sir,' said Marina, 'I will use my utmost skill in his recovery, provided none but I and my maid be suffered to come near him.'

She, who at Mitylene had so carefully concealed her birth, ashamed to tell that one of royal ancestry was now a slave, first began to speak to Pericles of the wayward changes in her own fate, telling him from what a high estate herself had fallen. As if she had known it was her royal father she stood before, all the words she spoke were of her own sorrows; but her reason for so doing was, that she knew nothing more wins the attention of the unfortunate than the recital of some sad calamity to match their own. The sound of her sweet voice aroused the drooping prince; he lifted up his eyes, which had been so long fixed and motionless; and Marina, who was the perfect image of her mother, presented to his amazed sight the features of his dead queen. The long-silent prince was once more heard to speak. 'My dearest wife,' said the awakened Pericles, 'was like this maid, and such a one might my daughter have been. My queen's square brows, her stature to an inch, as wand-like straight, as silver-voiced, her eyes as jewel-like. Where do you live, young maid? Report your parentage. I think you said you had been tossed from wrong to injury, and that you thought your griefs would equal mine, if both were opened.' 'Some such thing I said,' replied Marina, 'and said no more than what my thoughts did warrant me as likely.' 'Tell me your story,' answered Pericles; 'if I find you have known the thousandth part of my endurance, you have borne your sorrows like a man, and I have suffered like a girl; yet you do look like Patience gazing on kings' graves, and smiling extremity out of act. How lost you your name, my most kind virgin? Recount your story I beseech you. Come, sit by me.' How was Pericles surprised when she said her name was *Marina*, for he knew it was no usual name, but had been invented by himself for his own child to signify *seaborn:* 'O, I am mocked,' said he, 'and you are sent hither by some incensed god to make the world laugh at me.' 'Patience, good sir,' said Marina, 'or I must cease here.' 'Nay,' said Pericles, 'I will be patient; you little know how you do startle me, to call yourself Marina.' 'The name,' she replied, 'was given me by one that had some power, my father, and a king.' 'How, a king's daughter!' said Pericles, 'and called Marina! But are you flesh and blood? Are you no fairy? Speak on; where were you born? and wherefore called Marina?' She replied, 'I was called Marina, because I was born at sea. My mother was the daughter of a king; she died the minute I was born, as my good nurse Lychorida has often told me weeping. The king, my father, left me at Tarsus, till the cruel wife of Cleon sought to murder me. A crew of pirates came and rescued me, and brought me here to Mitylene. But, good sir, why do you weep? It may be, you think me an impostor. But, indeed, sir, I am the daughter to King Pericles, if good King Pericles be living.' Then Pericles, terrified as he seemed at his own sudden joy, and doubtful if this could be real, loudly called for his attendants, who rejoiced at the sound of their beloved king's voice; and he said to Helicanus, 'O Helicanus, strike me, give me a gash, put me to present pain, lest this great sea of joys rushing upon me, overbear the shores of my mortality. O come hither, thou that wast born at sea, buried at Tarsus, and found at sea again. O Helicanus, down on your knees, thank the holy gods! This is Marina. Now blessings on thee, my child! Give me fresh garments, mine own Helicanus! She is not dead at Tarsus as she should have been by the savage Dionysia. She shall tell you all, when you shall kneel to her and call her your very princess. Who is this?' (observing Lysimachus for the first time). 'Sir,' said Helicanus, 'it is the governor of Mitylene, who, hearing of your melancholy, came to see you.' 'I embrace you, sir,' said Pericles. 'Give me my robes! I am well with beholding——O heaven bless my girl! But hark, what music is that?' – for now, either sent by some kind god, or by his own delighted fancy deceived, he seemed to hear soft music. 'My lord, I hear none,' replied Helicanus. 'None?' said Pericles; 'why, it is the music of the spheres.' As there was no music to be heard, Lysimachus concluded that the sudden joy had unsettled the prince's understanding; and he said, 'It is not good to cross him: let him have his way:' and then they told him they heard the music; and he now complaining of a drowsy slumber coming over him, Lysimachus persuaded him to rest on a couch, and placing a pillow under his head, he, quite overpowered with excess of joy, sank into a sound sleep, and Marina watched in silence by the couch of her sleeping parent.

While he slept, Pericles dreamed a dream which made him resolve to go to Ephesus. His dream was, that Diana, the goddess of the Ephesians, appeared to him, and commanded him to go to her temple at Ephesus, and there before her altar to declare the story of his life and misfortunes; and by her silver bow she swore, that if he performed her injunction, he should meet with some rare felicity. When he awoke, being miraculously refreshed, he told his dream, and that his resolution was to obey the bidding of the goddess.

Then Lysimachus invited Pericles to come on shore, and refresh himself with such entertainment as he should find at Mitylene, which courteous offer Pericles accepting, agreed to tarry with him for the space of a day or two. During which time we may well suppose what feastings, what rejoicings, what costly shows and entertainments the governor made in Mitylene, to greet the royal father of his dear Marina, whom in her obscure fortunes he had so respected. Nor did Pericles frown upon Lysimachus's suit, when he understood how he had honoured his child in the days of her low estate, and that Marina showed herself not averse to his proposals; only he made it a condition, before he gave his consent, that they should visit with him the shrine of the Ephesian Diana: to whose temple they shortly after all three undertook a voyage; and, the goddess herself filling their sails with prosperous winds, after a few weeks they arrived in safety at Ephesus.

There was standing near the altar of the goddess, when Pericles with his train entered the temple, the good Cerimon (now grown very aged) who had restored Thaisa, the wife of Pericles, to life; and Thaisa, now a priestess of the temple, was standing before the altar; and though the many years he had passed in sorrow for her loss had much altered Pericles, Thaisa thought she knew her husband's features, and when he approached the altar and began to speak, she remembered his voice, and listened to his words with wonder and a joyful amazement. And these were the words that Pericles spoke before the altar: 'Hail, Diana! to perform thy just commands, I here confess myself the Prince of Tyre, who, frighted from my country, at Pentapolis wedded the fair Thaisa: she died at sea in childbed, but brought forth a maid-child called Marina. She at Tarsus was nursed with Dionysia, who at fourteen years thought to kill her, but her better stars brought her to

Mitylene, by whose shores as I sailed, her good fortunes brought this maid on board, where by her most clear remembrance she made herself known to be my daughter.'

Thaisa, unable to bear the transports which his words had raised in her, cried out, 'You are, you are, O royal Pericles'——and fainted. 'What means this woman?' said Pericles: 'she dies! gentlemen, help.' – 'Sir,' said Cerimon, 'if you have told Diana's altar true, this is your wife.' 'Reverend gentleman, no,' said Pericles: 'I threw her overboard with these very arms.' Cerimon then recounted how, early one tempestuous morning, this lady was thrown upon the Ephesian shore; how, opening the coffin, he found therein rich jewels, and a paper; how, happily, he recovered her, and placed her here in Diana's temple. And now, Thaisa being restored from her swoon said, 'O my lord, are you not Pericles? Like him you speak, like him you are. Did you not name a tempest, a birth, and death?' He astonished said, 'The voice of dead Thaisa!' 'That Thaisa am I,' she replied, 'supposed dead and drowned.' 'O true Diana!' exclaimed Pericles, in a passion of devout astonishment. 'And now,' said Thaisa, 'I know you better. Such a ring as I see on your finger did the king my father give you, when we with tears parted from him at Pentapolis.' 'Enough, you gods!' cried Pericles, 'your present kindness makes my past miseries sport. O come, Thaisa, be buried a second time within these arms.'

And Marina said, 'My heart leaps to be gone into my mother's bosom.' Then did Pericles show his daughter to her mother, saying, 'Look who kneels here, flesh of thy flesh, thy burthen at sea, and called Marina, because she was yielded there.' 'Blessed and my own!' said Thaisa: and while she hung in rapturous joy over her child, Pericles knelt before the altar, saying, 'Pure Diana, bless thee for thy vision. For this, I will offer oblations nightly to thee.' And then and there did Pericles, with the consent of Thaisa, solemnly affiance their daughter, the virtuous Marina, to the well-deserving Lysimachus in marriage.

Thus have we seen in Pericles, his queen, and daughter, a famous example of virtue assailed by calamity (through the sufferance of Heaven, to teach patience and constancy to men), under the same guidance becoming finally successful, and triumphing over chance and change. In Helicanus we have beheld a notable pattern of truth, of faith, and loyalty, who, when he might have succeeded to a throne, chose rather to recall the rightful owner to his possession, than to become great by another's wrong. In the worthy Cerimon, who restored Thaisa to life, we are instructed how goodness directed by knowledge, in bestowing benefits upon mankind, approaches to the nature of the gods. It only remains to be told, that Dionysia, the wicked wife of Cleon, met with an end proportionable to her deserts; the inhabitants of Tarsus, when her cruel attempt upon Marina was known, rising in a body to revenge the daughter of their benefactor, and setting fire to the palace of Cleon, burnt both him and her, and their whole household: the gods seeming well pleased, that so foul a murder, though but intentional, and never carried into act, should be punished in a way befitting its enormity.

CYMBELINE

◆◆◆◆◆◆◆◆◆◆◆◆◆◆◆◆◆◆◆◆◆◆◆◆◆◆◆◆◆◆◆◆◆◆◆◆◆

DURING the time of Augustus Caesar, Emperor of Rome, there reigned in England (which was then called Britain) a king whose name was Cymbeline.

Cymbeline's first wife died when his three children (two sons and a daughter) were very young. Imogen, the eldest of these children, was brought up in her father's court; but by a strange chance the two sons of Cymbeline were stolen out of their nursery, when the eldest was but three years of age, and the youngest quite an infant; and Cymbeline could never discover what was become of them, or by whom they were conveyed away.

Cymbeline was twice married: his second wife was a wicked, plotting woman, and a cruel stepmother to Imogen, Cymbeline's daughter by his first wife.

The queen, though she hated Imogen, yet wished her to marry a son of her own by a former husband (she also having been twice married): for by this means she hoped upon the death of Cymbeline to place the crown of Britain upon the head of her son Cloten; for she knew that, if the king's sons were not found, the Princess Imogen must be the king's heir. But this design was prevented by Imogen herself, who married without the consent or even knowledge of her father or the queen.

Posthumus (for that was the name of Imogen's husband) was the best scholar and most accomplished gentleman of that age. His father died fighting in the wars for Cymbeline, and soon after his birth his mother died also for grief at the loss of her husband.

Cymbeline, pitying the helpless state of this orphan, took Posthumus (Cymbeline having given him that name, because he was born after his father's death), and educated him in his own court.

Imogen and Posthumus were both taught by the same masters, and were playfellows from their infancy; they loved each other tenderly when they were children, and their affection continuing to increase with their years, when they grew up they privately married.

The disappointed queen soon learned this secret, for she kept spies constantly in watch upon the actions of her daughter-in-law, and she immediately told the king of the marriage of Imogen with Posthumus.

Nothing could exceed the wrath of Cymbeline, when he heard that his daughter had been so forgetful of her high dignity as to marry a subject. He commanded Posthumus to leave Britain, and banished him from his native country for ever.

The queen, who pretended to pity Imogen for the grief she suffered at losing her husband, offered to procure them a private meeting before Posthumus set out on his journey to Rome, which place he had chosen for his residence in his banishment: this seeming kindness she showed, the better to succeed in her future designs in regard to her son Cloten; for she meant to persuade Imogen, when her husband was gone, that her marriage was not lawful, being contracted without the consent of the king.

Imogen and Posthumus took a most affectionate leave of each other. Imogen gave her husband a diamond ring, which had been her mother's, and Posthumus promised never to part with the ring; and he fastened a bracelet on the arm of his wife, which he begged she would preserve with great care, as a token of his love; they then bid each other farewell, with many vows of everlasting love and fidelity.

Imogen remained a solitary and dejected lady in her father's court, and Posthumus arrived at Rome, the place he had chosen for his banishment.

Posthumus fell into company at Rome with some gay young men of different nations, who were talking freely of ladies: each one praising the ladies of his own country, and his own mistress. Posthumus, who had ever his own dear lady in mind, affirmed that his wife, the fair Imogen, was the most virtuous, wise and constant lady in the world.

One of those gentlemen, whose name was Iachimo, being offended that a lady of Britain should be so praised above the Roman ladies, his country-women, provoked Posthumus by seeming to doubt the constancy of his so highly-praised wife; and at length, after much altercation, Posthumus consented to a proposal of Iachimo's, that he (Iachimo) should go to Britain, and endeavour to gain the love of the married Imogen. They then laid a wager, that if Iachimo did not succeed in this wicked design, he was to forfeit a large sum of money;

but if he could win Imogen's favour, and prevail upon her to give him the bracelet which Posthumus had so earnestly desired she would keep as a token of his love, then the wager was to terminate with Posthumus giving to Iachimo the ring, which was Imogen's love present when she parted with her husband. Such firm faith had Posthumus in the fidelity of Imogen, that he thought he ran no hazard in this trial of her honour.

Iachimo, on his arrival in Britain, gained admittance, and a courteous welcome from Imogen, as a friend of her husband; but when he began to make professions of love to her, she repulsed him with disdain, and he soon found that he could have no hope of succeeding in his dishonourable design.

The desire Iachimo had to win the wager made him now have recourse to a stratagem to impose upon Posthumus, and for this purpose he bribed some of Imogen's attendants, and was by them conveyed into her bedchamber, concealed in a large trunk, where he remained shut up till Imogen was retired to rest, and had fallen asleep; and then getting out of the trunk, he examined the chamber with great attention, and wrote down everything he saw there, and particularly noticed a mole which he observed upon Imogen's neck, and then softly unloosing the bracelet from her arm, which Posthumus had given to her, he retired into the chest again; and the next day he set off for Rome with great expedition, and boasted to Posthumus that Imogen had given him the bracelet, and likewise permitted him to pass a night in her chamber: and in this manner Iachimo told his false tale: 'Her bedchamber,' said he, 'was hung with tapestry of silk and silver, the story was *the proud Cleopatra when she met her Antony*, a piece of work most bravely wrought.'

'This is true,' said Posthumus; 'but this you might have heard spoken of without seeing.'

'Then the chimney,' said Iachimo, 'is south of the chamber, and the chimney-piece is *Diana bathing;* never saw I figures livelier expressed.'

'This is a thing you might have likewise heard,' said Posthumus; 'for it is much talked of.'

Iachimo as accurately described the roof of the chamber; and added, 'I had almost forgot her andirons; they were *two winking Cupids* made of silver, each on one foot standing.' He then took out the bracelet, and said, 'Know you this jewel, sir? She gave me this. She took it from her arm. I see her yet; her pretty action did outsell her gift, and yet enriched it too. She gave it me, and said, *she prized it once*.' He last of all described the mole he had observed upon her neck.

Posthumus, who had heard the whole of this artful recital in an agony of doubt, now broke out into the most passionate exclamations against Imogen. He delivered up the diamond ring to Iachimo, which he had agreed to forfeit to him, if he obtained the bracelet from Imogen.

Posthumus then in a jealous rage wrote to Pisanio, a gentleman of Britain, who was one of Imogen's attendants, and had long been a faithful friend to Posthumus; and after telling him what proof he had of his wife's disloyalty, he desired Pisanio would take Imogen to Milford-Haven, a seaport of Wales, and there kill her. And at the same time he wrote a deceitful letter to Imogen, desiring her to go with Pisanio, for that finding he could live no longer without seeing her, though he was forbidden upon pain of death to return to Britain, he would come to Milford-Haven, at which place he begged she would meet him. She, good unsuspecting lady, who loved her husband above all things, and desired more than her life to see him, hastened her departure with Pisanio, and the same night she received the letter she set out.

When their journey was nearly at an end, Pisanio, who, though faithful to Posthumus, was not faithful to serve him in an evil deed, disclosed to Imogen the cruel order he had received.

Imogen, who, instead of meeting a loving and beloved husband, found herself doomed by that husband to suffer death, was afflicted beyond measure.

Pisanio persuaded her to take comfort, and wait with patient fortitude for the time when Posthumus should see and repent his injustice: in the meantime, as she refused in her distress to return to her father's court, he advised her to dress herself in boy's clothes for more security in travelling; to which advice she agreed, and thought in that disguise she would go over to Rome, and see her husband, whom, though he had used her so barbarously, she could not forget to love.

When Pisanio had provided her with her new apparel, he left her to her uncertain fortune, being obliged to return to court, but before he departed he gave her a phial of cordial, which he said the queen had given him as a sovereign remedy in all disorders.

The queen, who hated Pisanio because he was a friend to Imogen and Posthumus, gave him this phial, which she supposed contained poison, she having ordered her physician to give her some poison, to try its effects (as she said) upon animals; but the physician, knowing her malicious disposition, would not trust her with real poison, but gave her a drug which would do no other mischief than causing a person to sleep with every appearance of death for a few hours. This mixture, which Pisanio thought a choice cordial, he gave to Imogen, desiring her, if she found herself ill upon the road, to take it; and so, with blessings and prayers for her safety and happy deliverance from her undeserved troubles, he left her.

Providence strangely directed Imogen's steps to the dwelling of her two brothers, who had been stolen away in their infancy. Bellarius, who stole them away, was a lord in the court of Cymbeline, and having been falsely accused to the king of treason, and banished from the court, in revenge he stole away the two sons of Cymbeline, and brought them up in a forest, where he lived concealed in a cave. He stole them through revenge, but he soon loved them as tenderly as if they had been his own children, educated them carefully, and they grew up into fine youths, their princely spirits leading them to bold and daring actions; and as they subsisted by hunting, they were active and hardy, and were always pressing their supposed father to let them seek their fortune in the wars.

At the cave where these youths dwelt it was Imogen's fortune to arrive. She had lost her way in a large forest, through which her road lay to Milford-Haven (from which she meant to embark for Rome); and being unable to find any place where she could purchase food, she was with weariness and hunger almost dying; for it is not merely putting on a man's apparel that will enable a young lady, tenderly brought up, to bear the fatigue of wandering about lonely forests like a man. Seeing this cave, she entered, hoping to find some one within of whom she could procure food. She found the cave empty, but looking about she discovered some cold meat, and her hunger was so pressing, that she could not wait for an invitation, but sat down and began to eat. 'Ah,' said she, talking to herself, 'I see a man's life is a tedious one; how tired am I! for two nights together I have made the ground my bed: my resolution helps me, or I should be sick. When Pisanio showed me Milford-Haven from the mountain top, how near it seemed!' Then the thoughts of her husband and his cruel mandate came across her, and she said, 'My dear Posthumus, thou art a false one!'

The two brothers of Imogen, who had been hunting with their reputed father, Bellarius, were by this time returned home. Bellarius had given them the names of Polydore and Cadwal, and they knew no better, but supposed that Bellarius was their father; but the real names of these princes were Guiderius and Arviragus.

Bellarius entered the cave first, and seeing Imogen, stopped them, saying, 'Come not in yet; it eats our victuals, or I should think it was a fairy.'

'What is the matter, sir?' said the young men. 'By Jupiter,' said Bellarius again, 'there is an angel in the cave, or if not, an earthly paragon.' So beautiful did Imogen look in her boy's apparel.

She, hearing the sound of voices, came forth from the cave, and addressed them in these words: 'Good masters, do not harm me; before I entered your cave, I had thought to have begged or bought what I have eaten. Indeed I have stolen nothing, nor would I, though I had found gold strewed on the floor. Here is money for my meat, which I would have left on the board when I had made my meal, and parted with prayers for the provider.' They refused her money with great earnestness. 'I see you are angry with me,' said the timid Imogen; 'but, sirs, if you kill me for my fault, know that I should have died if I had not made it.'

'Whither are you bound?' asked Bellarius, 'and what is your name?'

'Fidele is my name,' answered Imogen. 'I have a kinsman, who is bound for Italy; he embarked at Milford-Haven, to whom being going, almost spent with hunger, I am fallen into this offence.'

'Prithee, fair youth,' said old Bellarius, 'do not think us churls, nor measure our good minds by this rude place we live in. You are well encountered; it is almost night. You shall have better cheer before you depart, and thanks to stay and eat it. Boys, bid him welcome.'

The gentle youths, her brothers, then welcomed Imogen to their cave with many kind expressions, saying they would love her (or, as they said, *him*) as a brother, and they entered the cave, where (they having killed venison when they were hunting) Imogen delighted them with her neat housewifery, assisting them in preparing their supper; for though it is not the custom now for the young women of high birth to understand cookery, it was then, and Imogen excelled in this useful art; and, as her brothers prettily expressed it, Fidele cut their roots in characters, and sauced their broth, as if Juno had been sick, and Fidele were her dieter. 'And then,' said Polydore to his brother, 'how angel-like he sings!'

They also remarked to each other, that though Fidele smiled so sweetly, yet so sad a melancholy did overcloud his lovely face, as if grief and patience had together taken possession of him.

For these her gentle qualities (or perhaps it was their near relationship, though they knew it not) Imogen (or, as the boys called her, *Fidele*) became the doting-piece of her brothers, and she scarcely less loved them, thinking that but for the memory of her dear Posthumus, she could live and die in the cave with these wild forest youths; and she gladly consented to stay with them, till she was enough rested from the fatigue of travelling to pursue her way to Milford-Haven.

When the venison they had taken was all eaten and they were going out to hunt for more, Fidele could not accompany them because she was unwell. Sorrow, no doubt, for her husband's cruel usage, as well as the fatigue of wandering in the forest, was the cause of her illness.

They then bid her farewell, and went to their hunt, praising all the way the noble parts and graceful demeanour of the youth Fidele.

Imogen was no sooner left alone than she recollected the cordial Pisanio had given her, and drank it off, and presently fell into a sound and deathlike sleep.

When Bellarius and her brothers returned from hunting Polydore went first into the cave, and supposing her asleep, pulled off his heavy shoes, that he might tread softly and not awake her; so did true gentleness spring up in the minds of these princely foresters; but he soon discovered that she could not be awakened by any noise, and concluded her to be dead, and Polydore lamented over her with dear and brotherly regret, as if they had never from their infancy been parted.

Bellarius also proposed to carry her out into the forest, and there celebrate her funeral with songs and solemn dirges, as was then the custom.

Imogen's two brothers then carried her to a shady covert, and there laying her gently on the grass, they sang repose to her departed spirit, and covering her over with leaves and flowers, Polydore said, 'While summer lasts and I live here, Fidele, I will daily strew thy grave. The pale primrose, that flower most like thy face; the blue-bell, like thy clear veins; and the leaf of eglantine, which is not sweeter than was thy breath; all these will I strew over thee. Yea, and the furred moss in winter, when there are no flowers to cover thy sweet corse.'

When they had finished her funeral obsequies they departed very sorrowful.

Imogen had not been long left alone, when, the effect of the sleepy drug going off, she awaked, and easily shaking off the slight covering of leaves and flowers they had thrown over her, she arose, and imagining she had been dreaming, she said, 'I thought I was a cave-keeper, and cook to honest creatures; how came I here covered with flowers?' Not being able to find her way back to the cave, and seeing nothing of her new companions, she concluded it was certainly all a dream; and once more Imogen set out on her weary pilgrimage, hoping at last she should find her way to Milford-Haven, and thence get a passage in some ship bound for Italy; for all her thoughts were still with her husband Posthumus, whom she intended to seek in the disguise of a page.

But great events were happening at this time, of which Imogen knew nothing; for a war had suddenly broken out between the Roman emperor Augustus Caesar and Cymbeline, the King of Britain; and a Roman army had landed to invade Britain, and was advanced into the very forest over which Imogen was journeying. With this army came Posthumus.

Though Posthumus came over to Britain with the Roman army he did not mean to fight on their side against his own countrymen, but intended to join the army of Britain, and fight in the cause of the king who had banished him.

He still believed Imogen false to him; yet the death of her he had so fondly loved, and by his own orders too (Pisanio having written him a letter to say he had obeyed his command, and that Imogen was dead), sat heavy on his heart, and therefore he returned to Britain, desiring either to be slain in battle, or to be put to death by Cymbeline for returning home from banishment.

Imogen, before she reached Milford-Haven, fell into the hands of the Roman army; and her presence and deportment recommending her, she was made a page to Lucius, the Roman general.

Cymbeline's army now advanced to meet the enemy, and when they entered this forest, Polydore and Cadwal joined the king's army. The young men were eager to engage in acts of valour, though they little thought they were going to fight for their own royal father: and old Bellarius went with them to the battle. He had long since repented of the injury he had done to Cymbeline in carrying away his sons; and having been a warrior in his youth, he gladly joined the army to fight for the king he had so injured.

And now a great battle commenced between the two armies, and the Britons would have been defeated, and Cymbeline himself killed, but for the extraordinary valour of Posthumus and Bellarius and the two sons of Cymbeline. They rescued the king, and saved his life, and so entirely turned the fortune of the day, that the Britons gained the victory.

When the battle was over, Posthumus, who had not found the death he sought for, surrendered himself up to one of the officers of Cymbeline, willing to suffer the death which was to be his punishment if he returned from banishment.

Imogen and the master she served were taken prisoners, and brought before Cymbeline, as was also her old enemy Iachimo, who was an officer in the Roman army; and when these prisoners were before the king, Posthumus was brought in to receive his sentence of death; and at this strange juncture of time, Bellarius with Polydore and Cadwal were also brought before Cymbeline, to receive the rewards due to the great services they had by their valour done for the king. Pisanio, being one of the king's attendants, was likewise present.

Therefore there were now standing in the king's presence (but with very different hopes and fears) Posthumus and Imogen, with her new master the Roman general; the faithful servant Pisanio, and the false friend Iachimo; and likewise the two lost sons of Cymbeline, with Bellarius, who had stolen them away.

The Roman general was the first who spoke; the rest stood silent before the king, though there was many a beating heart among them.

Imogen saw Posthumus, and knew him, though he was in the disguise of a peasant; but he did not know her in her male attire: and she knew Iachimo, and she saw a ring on his finger which she perceived to be her own, but she did not know him as yet to have been the author of all her troubles: and she stood before her own father a prisoner of war.

Pisanio knew Imogen, for it was he who had dressed her in the garb of a boy. 'It is my mistress,' thought he; 'since she is living, let the time run on to good or bad.' Bellarius knew her too, and softly said to Cadwal, 'Is not this boy revived from death?' – 'One sand,' replied Cadwal, 'does not more resemble another than that sweet rosy lad is like the dead Fidele.' – 'The same dead thing alive,' said Polydore. 'Peace, peace,' said Bellarius; 'if it were he, I am sure he would have spoken to us.' – 'But we saw him dead,' again whispered Polydore. 'Be silent,' replied Bellarius.

Posthumus waited in silence to hear the welcome sentence of his own death; and he resolved not to disclose to the king that he had saved his life in the battle, lest that should move Cymbeline to pardon him.

Lucius, the Roman general, who had taken Imogen under his protection as his page, was the first (as has been before said) who spoke to the king. He was a man of high courage and noble dignity, and this was his speech to the king:

'I hear you take no ransom for your prisoners, but doom them all to death: I am a Roman, and with a Roman heart will suffer death. But there is one thing for which I would entreat.' Then bringing Imogen before the king, he said, 'This boy is a Briton born. Let him be ransomed. He is my page. Never master had a page so kind, so duteous, so diligent on all occasions, so true, so nurse-like. He hath done no Briton wrong, though he hath served a Roman. Save him, if you spare no one beside.'

Cymbeline looked earnestly on his daughter Imogen. He knew her not in that disguise; but it seemed that all-powerful Nature spake in his heart, for he said, 'I have surely seen him, his face appears familiar to me. I know not why or wherefore I say, Live, boy; but I give you your life, and ask of me what boon you will, and I will grant it you. Yea, even though it be the life of the noblest prisoner I have.'

'I humbly thank your highness,' said Imogen.

What was then called granting a boon was the same as a promise to give any one thing, whatever it might be, that the person on whom that favour was conferred chose to ask for. They all were attentive to hear what thing the page would ask for; and Lucius her master said to her, 'I do not beg my life, good lad, but I know that is what you will ask for.' – 'No, no, alas!' said Imogen, 'I have other work in hand, good master; your life I cannot ask for.'

This seeming want of gratitude in the boy astonished the Roman general.

Imogen then, fixing her eye on Iachimo, demanded no other boon than this: that Iachimo should be made to confess whence he had the ring he wore on his finger.

Cymbeline granted her this boon, and threatened Iachimo with the torture if he did not confess how he came by the diamond ring on his finger.

Iachimo then made a full acknowledgement of all his villainy, telling, as has been before related, the whole story of his wager with Posthumus, and how he had succeeded in imposing upon his credulity.

What Posthumus felt at hearing this proof of the innocence of his lady cannot be expressed. He instantly came forward, and confessed to Cymbeline the cruel sentence which he had enjoined Pisanio to execute upon the princess; exclaiming wildly, 'O Imogen, my queen, my life, my wife! O Imogen, Imogen, Imogen!'

Imogen could not see her beloved husband in this distress without discovering herself, to the unutterable joy of Posthumus, who was thus relieved from a weight of guilt and woe, and restored to the good graces of the dear lady he had so cruelly treated.

Cymbeline, almost as much overwhelmed as he with joy, at finding his lost daughter so strangely recovered, received her to her former place in his fatherly affection, and not only gave her husband Posthumus his life, but consented to acknowledge him for his son-in-law.

Bellarius chose this time of joy and reconciliation to make his confession. He presented Polydore and Cadwal to the king, telling him they were his two lost sons, Guiderius and Arviragus.

Cymbeline forgave old Bellarius; for who could think of punishments at a season of such universal happiness? To find his daughter living, and his lost sons in the persons of his young deliverers, that he had seen so bravely fight in his defence, was unlooked-for joy indeed!

Imogen was now at leisure to perform good services for her late master, the Roman general Lucius, whose life the king her father readily granted at her request; and by the mediation of the same Lucius a peace was concluded between the Romans and the Britons, which was kept inviolate many years.

How Cymbeline's wicked queen, through despair of bringing her projects to pass, and touched with remorse of conscience, sickened and died, having first lived to see her foolish son Cloten slain in a quarrel which he had provoked, are events too tragical to interrupt this happy conclusion by more than merely touching upon. It is sufficient that all were made happy who were deserving; and even the treacherous Iachimo, in consideration of his villainy having missed its final aim, was dismissed without punishment.

Histories

THE LIFE AND DEATH OF
KING JOHN

IN the palace of the Plantagenet, during the last days of the twelfth century, King John of England, a shrewd, red-haired man of some thirty-two years, sat awaiting a message from the French ambassador, Hugh de Chatillon. As usual, his mother Elinor, the Queen Dowager whom he loved and on whose counsel he depended, was close at hand; and around stood the great English lords, the Earls of Pembroke, Essex, and Salisbury, and others of high rank. When the King asked Chatillon to do his office, the ambassador, with an insolence carefully studied, began: 'Thus, after greeting, speaks the King of France to the *borrowed* majesty of England.'

Queen Elinor interposed in wrath; but her son called her gently to silence, and Chatillon went on to name the demands of his master King Philip. His King, he said, on behalf of John's young nephew, Arthur Plantagenet, made lawful claim both to the realm of England and its territories: to Ireland, Poictiers, Anjou, Touraine, Maine. Refusal of these demands could lead only to a fierce and crippling war. King John, among the approving murmurs of his court, replied with contempt; and when Chatillon said arrogantly, 'Take my King's defiance from my mouth,' John replied, 'Bear mine to him, and so depart in peace. Before you reach your King, Chatillon, France will hear our thunder. Hence! An honourable escort let him have. See to it, Pembroke.'

The ambassador, with a slight bow, turned and left the hall. Queen Elinor, leaning towards her son, reminded him that she had always said Arthur's mother, ambitious Constance, would not pause until she had brought the world to aid her child. What could have been prevented by friendly mediation must be now the cause of desperate war.

Attention was diverted from State affairs by the entrance of a sheriff's officer, saying apologetically that two men of Northamptonshire begged King John to judge their strange dispute. 'Let them approach!' said John carelessly, glad to escape from the thoughts of France and Constance. He soothed his mother: 'Our abbeys and our priories shall pay the expenses of this war.'

Two men bowed before the King. 'What are you?' he asked. It appeared that they were brothers, and that their name was Faulconbridge. One, Philip, the elder, was a tall, stalwart gallant; the second, Robert, a figure mean and puny. Each claimed to be heir to his father's land. Queen Elinor, considering the elder man closely while their stories were told, said aside to the King, 'Does he not look, my son, like your brother Richard Coeur-de-lion?' And indeed it was presently established that he was the bastard son of Richard, the last English King. Queen Elinor, attracted by his bluff, outspoken style, asked if he would prefer to remain a country squire or to be the acknowledged son of Coeur-de-lion with all that this implied. If the latter, then would he follow her to the wars in France? Philip replied warmly, 'Madam, I'll follow you unto the death'; and when the Queen said with her rasping chuckle, 'Nay, I would have you go before me there,' he bowed to her courteously: 'Our country manners give our betters way.' King John, ordering him to kneel, called for a sword, and tapping him lightly on each shoulder, said, 'From henceforth take his name whose form you bear. You knelt as Philip but arise more great. Arise Sir Philip and Plantagenet.'

It was soon after this that the supporters of the young Prince Arthur's claim to the English crown met in full array before the French town of Angiers and its massive ramparts. With Arthur and his mother Constance were King Philip of France and his son Lewis the Dauphin. Lewis and Arthur stood forward now to greet their new ally, the Archduke of Austria, a pompous elderly man who swore to prosecute the fight until England, utmost corner of the West, knew Arthur for its King. Meanwhile, said King Philip, their task was to take this town of Angiers. Constance advised him to refrain until the ambassador Chatillon had brought to them his message from King John, and, even as she said this, Chatillon arrived with the gravest tidings.

'My liege,' he cried, 'turn your forces from this paltry town and seek a mightier task. King John, refusing your just demands, is making head against you. Adverse winds held me at sea; the English army followed me to France, and already it approaches. Hear the drum! John's troops are strong, their mood is confident. With him he brings the Mother-Queen, for ever stirring him to blood and strife; with her a niece, the Lady Blanch of Spain; with them a bastard son of Lion-Heart, and many thousand daring venturers.'

Drums beat insistently close at hand. 'My liege, King John arrives to parley.' With banners flaunting before them, the English King, Queen Elinor, Lady Blanch, and the Bastard Faulconbridge entered at the head of a menacing array, and John directly challenged Philip of France. 'Peace be to France – if France permits in peace our just and honoured entry to our own. If not, bleed France! And peace ascend to heaven!' Philip, as defiantly, retorted, 'Peace be to England if your troops return from France to England, there to dwell in peace.'

There was utter silence as each army awaited its orders. From Angiers wall the citizens looked in some anxiety at the rival Kings and at the panoply of war, a thousand heraldic blazonings, the glitter of a myriad accoutrements. Then Philip, with all his self-possession, spoke again. Had not John seized the English crown unlawfully? Let him gaze on Arthur. And Arthur, a fourteen-year-old boy, stepped to Philip's side. 'Here,' said the French King, 'is dead Geoffrey's son. Geoffrey was your elder brother born. England is Arthur's right.'

John asked coldly who had moved Philip on Arthur's behalf, and when Philip replied that he stood as a guardian of the right, John said, 'You do usurp authority.' 'Pardon me,' said Philip with mock deference, 'it is to beat usurping down.' Queen Elinor snapped, 'Who is it you do call usurper, France?' Before Philip could answer, Constance said fiercely, 'I will tell you – your usurping son.'

So the insults flickered back and forth. The Bastard, looking at a lion-skin that Austria wore pompously over his armour, threatened to tear it from his shoulders. All was in unprofitable hubbub, hardly stilled when King Philip made a blunt demand: 'King John, this is the very sum of all. England and Ireland, Anjou, Touraine, Maine, in right of Arthur do I claim from you. Will you resign them and lay down your arms?'

'My life as soon!' said John. 'Arthur, yield you to me now. Out of my love I'll give you more than ever the cowardly hand of France can win.' Queen Elinor opened her arms in what she hoped was welcome: 'Come to your grandam, child,' and Constance mocked her: 'Give grandam kingdom, and its grandam will give it a plum, a cherry, and a fig.'

Arthur held her by the hand. 'Good my mother, peace. I would that I were dead; I am not worth this struggle.'

'His mother shames him so,' said Elinor, 'he weeps.'

'If he does,' cried Constance, 'your evil is the cause.'

During their wrangle King Philip was regarding the city walls. 'Trumpeters,' he said, 'summon hither the chief citizens of Angiers. Whose title do they admit, Arthur's or John's?' The spokesman of Angiers, replying to the call, demanded to know what the Kings wanted of them; and Philip advanced beneath the ramparts. 'You loving men of Angiers, Arthur's subjects, our trumpets called this parley.'

King John broke in: 'Hear us first. These Frenchmen would have besieged you without mercy. They paused on seeing us, your lawful King, and now shoot but calm words folded up in smoke. Do not believe them, friends, but let us in.'

King Philip, in his turn, said that the French meant no harm if the city paid its homage to Arthur Plantagenet, King of England. If homage were withheld, they would take Angiers by force. The first citizen returned to this that he and his fellows held Angiers for the English King; and John demanded entrance instantly. He, too, was checked with the words, 'We shall prove loyal unto the proven King: until that hour we close our gates to all the world.'

John pointed to his crown. 'Does not the crown of England prove the King? If not, then here I bring you witnesses, some thirty thousand hearts of English breed.'

The first citizen smiled: 'We do not open until you show which of you is stronger.'

In this deadlock the banners on both sides had been lowered. Now they rose again as John said, 'Then before nightfall many here must die. May God forgive their sins.' 'Amen!' responded Philip. Very soon the armies were in furious battle while the citizens watched closely from a tower of Angiers. Some hours had gone by when a French herald in full blazonry and accompanied by his trumpeters, rode up to the city wall. He cried loudly, 'You men of Angiers, open wide your gates. Victory is ours: I come now to proclaim Arthur Plantagenet England's King and yours.' At once an English herald moved up beside him. He, too, ordered a long fanfare and then proclaimed, 'Rejoice, you men of Angiers, ring your bells. Victorious John, your King and England's, doth approach. Open your gates and give the victors way.'

The first citizen shook his head. 'Heralds, we have viewed the battle, and neither side has gained the field. Here we must hold our town till one proves conqueror.'

The Kings debated again. Once more they threatened each other with high words; once more the citizens pointed to their barricaded gate. Then of a sudden the Bastard spoke. Were it not wiser, he suggested, that the armies first joined their forces against this defiant city? King John took up the cry: 'France, let us batter Angiers to the ground and fight among its ruins!'

'Let it be so,' said Philip. 'Where will you assault?'

'From the west,' said John. 'I from the north,' interrupted the Archduke of Austria. 'We from the south,' said Philip. And the Bastard chuckled to himself: 'Prudence indeed. From north to south Austria and France shoot in each other's mouth.'

At last appreciating their danger, the citizens went into earnest council. Their spokesman, coming back to the wall, said that there was a way to save Angiers and to reconcile the quarrel. Lady Blanch of Spain was niece to the King of England; Lewis, the heir to France. Both were rich in virtue, beauty, birth. Then let them wed, and by their union join the warring kingdoms.

It was a plan that pleased Queen Elinor, for – so she whispered to her son – Arthur would lose his advocates. King Philip, equally impressed but for another reason, asked King John to speak, and John said at once, 'If the Dauphin there will love my niece, she shall have the dowry of a queen: Anjou, Touraine, Maine, Poictiers, and all – except Angiers – that we do own in France.' The Dauphin had led Lady Blanch apart, and their own pact was soon agreed.

'Speak, Prince Dauphin,' invited John, 'do you love this lady?'

When the pair had given assurance, John joined their hands and said briefly, 'Then with her come Volquessen, Touraine, Maine, Poictiers and Anjou – and this besides, full thirty thousand marks of English gold.'

Promptly the citizens swung open the heavy gates of Angiers, and Philip of France ordered the marriage to take place immediately at St Mary's Chapel. Only one thought made him pause. Now Arthur's right had gone, Constance would rail. Where was she? And the Dauphin said, 'She has gone sad and passionate to your highness' tent.' Philip pursed his lips. 'This marriage will not cheer her. Brother of England, how may we help her? In her right we came.' John said carelessly, 'Fear not. We'll create young Arthur Duke of Bretagne and Earl of Richmond, and – yes – he shall be lord of this fair town of Angiers. Now summon Lady Constance. Bid her join our mirth.'

The bells rang out from Angiers, and quickly the banners and pennons of France, England, and Austria disappeared under the gate's wide arch. Only the Bastard lingered a little way outside the walls, pondering on the absurdity of the truce. To stop Arthur from gaining the whole of England, John had yielded English power in France. And Philip of France, who had come as a soldier to the field, pricked on by conscience, had forgotten his early zeal when it was to his advantage to forget.

Meanwhile, Constance, whose wrath could terrify, was raging in her pavilion against the treacherous King. 'False blood to false blood joined – Lewis and Blanch! Arthur, where are you now? France friend to England – then what becomes of me?' And, seating herself on the ground, she exclaimed, 'My grief's so great that nothing but the earth can hold it up. Here must I sit with sorrow: this my throne.' She was in tears, with Arthur trying to comfort her, when the two Kings entered from the marriage. Rising, she called down her curse upon them and upon the Archduke of Austria who had joined Arthur in seeking to pacify her. 'You wear a lion's hide! Take it off for shame, and hang a calf-skin on those recreant limbs.'

'O,' blustered Austria, 'that a man should speak those words to me!'

'And hang a calf-skin on those recreant limbs,' said the Bastard.

Austria glared at him: 'You dare not say so, villain.' Whereat the

Bastard repeated very slowly, 'And hang a calf-skin on those recreant limbs.'

This was the scene – Constance in majestic wrath, Austria bristling with rage, the Bastard mocking, King John and King Philip holding up restraining hands, and the others watching half in fear, half in laughter, when a monk, carrying a great cross, appeared at the pavilion entrance. He stood back, and there came into sight an imposing, scarlet-robed Cardinal, a train of monks behind him. King Philip knelt, saying in astonishment, 'It is the holy legate of the Pope.' The Cardinal, in an icy voice, acknowledged 'the anointed deputies of heaven'. Fixing his gaze on John, he said, 'To you I speak. I, Pandulph, Cardinal of Milan, legate of our holy father Pope Innocent, demand to know why you have spurned the Church? Why, in Canterbury, have you kept the Archbishop, Stephen Langton, from his sacred office?'

John replied in scorn that no questions could be asked of an anointed King. No Italian priest should ever rule in England. When Philip of France murmured fearfully, 'You do blaspheme in this,' John continued to revile the Pope and his deeds until Pandulph, who had listened in horror, ordered his excommunication and pronounced, with bell, book, and candle, a most solemn curse. Then he warned Philip of France, who was holding King John's hand, to sever himself from an arch-heretic.

'Do not let go your hand!' said Elinor peremptorily. Lewis the Dauphin spoke to Philip: 'But do so, father. If you have to choose between Rome's curse and the light loss of England for a friend, there is but one way to take.' Constance cried, 'Lewis, stand fast to that!' Looking round the assembly for some further aid, Philip said to Pandulph, 'What shall I do? King John's hand is newly joined with mine. We have sworn peace, amity, and true love. How can we then, upon this very marriage of our smiling peace, reject our vows?'

Pandulph was obdurate: 'All form is formless, order orderless, save what is opposite to England's love. Refuse, and the peril of our curse lights on you.'

'Father, to arms!' urged the Dauphin; but Blanch said desperately, 'Upon our wedding-day! Shall it be kept with all the noise of hell?'

The Dauphin, ignoring her, repeated his call to Philip. Still the

French King wavered until Pandulph prepared to launch the curse of Rome. Then, sadly, he released his hand, saying, 'England, I will fall from you.' With a quick-stabbed 'France, you will rue this hour!' John ordered the Bastard to assemble the English army. In the centre of the group Lady Blanch stood in helpless woe: 'Husband, I cannot pray that you will win; uncle, I needs must pray that you will lose; father, I may not wish your fortune thrive; grandam, I will not wish success to you. Whoever wins, upon that side I fall.' The Dauphin drew her to him: 'Lady, with me your fortune lies.' And Blanch said simply, 'There where my fortune lives, my hope must die.'

This time, in sustained battle, the French were forced to retreat; the Bastard slew the Archduke of Austria and took his lion-skin; and Arthur was captured. While the Bastard, at the King's command, already hurried towards the coast and to England to extort money from the Church, John spoke to his trusted officer, Hubert de Burgh, telling him that Arthur would be in his charge. 'I'll keep him so,' said Hubert, 'that he shall not offend your majesty.' And there was a swift flash between them: 'A grave?' – 'He shall not live.' As soon as Hubert breathed the words, John beckoned Arthur to him: 'For England, cousin. Hubert shall be your man, attend on you with all true duty.'

Anguish and dismay ruled the French camp. In Philip's tent Constance, overwhelmed, mourned the son she might never behold again. 'Grief takes the place now of my absent child, lies in his bed, walks up and down with me. O Lord, my boy, my Arthur, my fair son! My life, my joy, my all the world!' Unseeing, unhearing, she roamed out into the night. Pandulph, calm in defeat, began to outline a plan to the Dauphin, Lewis. John had seized Arthur, and it was not likely that he would allow the boy to live. Then Lewis, on behalf of Lady Blanch, could make every claim that Arthur had, and make them too in the knowledge that many English folk would revolt upon his side. 'For England, arm!' said Pandulph. 'I will go tell King Philip.'

John indeed was plotting against Arthur. Back in England, in a dark, heavy-walled chamber of Northampton Castle, Hubert de Burgh spoke to a pair of executioners, telling them to heat certain implements, and to station themselves just within the thick curtains by the door. When he struck his foot upon the ground they were to rush out and secure to a chair the boy Arthur they would find with him.

This done, Hubert summoned Arthur and bade him good-morning. 'You are sad, Hubert,' said the boy, 'but that should be my part. If only I were out of prison and kept sheep, I could be as happy as the day is long. Always I fear my uncle.' Hubert was preoccupied, and Arthur went on gently, 'I would to heaven I were your son, so you might love me.'

Knowing what he had to do, Hubert turned away as Arthur tried unavailingly to coax a smile from him. Then, seeking to brush from his cheeks the tears he could not hide, Hubert gave to the boy a letter that had come from the King early that morning. Trying to speak roughly, he asked if Arthur could read it, and was it not well written? Arthur had turned very pale: he looked at the paper as if he could not believe its words.

'Must you,' he said, 'with hot irons burn out both my eyes?'

'Young boy, I must,' said Hubert.

'And will you?' Arthur cried. And the heavy answer came, 'I will.'

Arthur, in deadly fear now, but also incredulous that such a thing could happen, told Hubert again of his unfaltering love. 'Will you put out my eyes? These eyes that never frowned on you, and never will.' Hubert, muttering the same answer, stamped his foot, and the two men entered with a brazier in which irons had been made red-hot. 'Do as I bid you,' said Hubert. 'Give me the irons and bind him here.'

As they tied the boy to the chair, Arthur implored Hubert to dismiss them, promising not to struggle, but to remain stone-still. After a moment's hesitation Hubert signed to the men to go. He crossed to the brazier, and Arthur ceased his frightened entreaties to exclaim, 'By my truth, the instrument is cold and would not harm me.'

'I can heat it, boy,' said Hubert.

Arthur looked down at the brazier: 'But, Hubert, see, the fire is dead with grief. There is no malice in this burning coal.' Hubert was inflexible: 'With my breath I can revive it, boy.' And Arthur made a last appeal with all the terror of the condemned: 'Hubert, all things you use to do me wrong deny their office. Fierce fire and iron are merciful. Only you are not.'

Hubert could stand no more. Sobbing without restraint, he flung the iron into a corner and embraced the boy. 'Well, see to live! I will not touch your eyes for all the treasure that your uncle owns. No more! King John's spies must hear that you are dead.' He helped Arthur towards the chamber door. 'But you, dear child, sleep fearless and secure; Hubert will never harm you.' 'O heavens,' whispered Arthur; 'I thank you.' And Hubert said sorrowfully, 'Much danger do I undergo for you.'

King John, at this hour, had chosen to be crowned for a second time to fortify his claim to the English throne: a device that his barons, who had long chafed under tyrannical rule, regarded sourly. Round him were the Earl of Pembroke, William Longsword, Earl of Salisbury, and Robert Bigot, Earl of Norfolk. Salisbury, ever downright, said bluntly that to gild refinèd gold, to paint the lily, or add new perfume to the violet, was merely wasteful and ridiculous excess. Pembroke spoke for all when he asked that Arthur should be released; but just as the King yielded, Hubert de Burgh entered the council chamber and begged a word in private. John, who had stirred nervously at Hubert's news, turned to the barons. 'Arthur,' he told them, 'is dead.' In unappeased wrath, they strode from the court; and John's woes were trebled when a messenger brought grim news. A great French army had sailed for England under the Dauphin; Queen Elinor had died in France; and Constance was also dead, in uncontrollable grief at her son Arthur's loss. John, who had long relied upon his mother, sat back in profound dejection. When the Bastard presented a wandering zealot, Peter of Pomfret, who had prophesied that before noon on the next Ascension Day the King should yield his crown, John ordered the man to be imprisoned and, upon Ascension Day, to be hanged.

Next, the King, rounding wildly upon Hubert, asked him why he had let Arthur die; and Hubert, bewildered by the sway of his master's mind, whispered that the boy was still alive. 'Then hasten to the barons,' cried John. 'Let this assure them.'

Yet, even as Hubert rode off to discover Pembroke and the rest, Arthur was dead in earnest. Having disguised himself as a ship-boy, he endeavoured to escape from the strong defences of Northampton Castle, but killed himself in leaping rashly from an upper wall. The barons, who were preparing to leave the King and to join the invading Dauphin in his camp at Bury St Edmunds, found Arthur's body and swore that the deed was Hubert's. When Hubert came hot to find them, they wheeled upon him menacingly, saying, 'Who killed this prince?' Weeping, he protested that he had honoured Arthur and loved him; not an hour earlier the boy was well.

Though the Bastard prevented the barons from doing harm to Hubert, he said after they had gone, 'I do suspect you, very grievously.' Still Hubert made anguished denial, and the Bastard put him to the test by telling him to take the dead child in his arms. 'Bear away the body and follow me with speed. I'll to the King, for heaven itself now frowns upon this land.'

With the temper of the country uncertain, and a strong French force already on English soil, King John begged forgiveness of the Pope. In his palace, as a sign of humility, he resigned the crown to Cardinal Pandulph and at once received it again as vassal of Rome. This humiliating ceremony over, John implored Pandulph to meet the French and to use all the power he could to stop the war. 'Our discontented counties,' he said, 'are in revolt; our people are swearing allegiance to the French. Pause not, or the whole land is lost.' Keeping as always arrogantly calm, Pandulph told John that his own behaviour had been the cause, but now that he had repented, the war should end on that Ascension Day. John started at the words: 'Did not the prophet tell me that before Ascension Day at noon I should lose my crown. Even so I have. But, heaven be thanked, it was but voluntary.'

Barely had Pandulph gone to treat with the French than the Bastard arrived with news for John that all Kent had yielded except Dover Castle; that London had received the Dauphin and his men; and that the barons had offered service to the French. 'Would not my lords return to me again,' cried John, 'after they had heard young Arthur was alive?' And the Bastard answered, 'They found him dead, and cast into the streets.'

'Dead? That villain Hubert told me he did live.'

'So Arthur did, for all that Hubert knew. But now, my liege, why droop? Why are you sad? Be great in act as you have been in thought! Threaten the threatener! Glitter like the god of war!'

John did not move from his throne. After a while he said, 'The Legate of the Pope has been with me. I have sworn peace with him, and he has gone to Bury St Edmunds, to the Dauphin's camp.'

'An inglorious league!' exclaimed the Bastard. 'Shall it be said that a French youth could land in England and find no check? Let us to arms, my liege. Maybe the Cardinal cannot make your peace . . . Whatever chances, let people see that we were ready with a power to fight.'

John rose. 'The command,' he said, 'is yours.'

But by now the rebel barons were in the French camp at Bury St Edmunds. Though the Dauphin had received them with barely veiled sarcasm, they swore firm faith to the invaders. Salisbury, warrior that he was, said, deeply moved, 'Is it not pitiful that we, the sons of England, should suffer so sad an hour!' The Dauphin was feigning insincerely to comfort him when Cardinal Pandulph arrived from John as a peacemaker. King John, he said, was reconciled to Rome. Therefore the war must end. But Pandulph, for once, was not allowed to manoeuvre as he wished. The Dauphin, as proud as he, thrust back at him: 'Your grace shall pardon me; I am not to be used merely as an instrument. You raised this war, and now you come to tell me King John has made his peace with Rome. What is that to me? What aid have I had from Rome, what men, what gold? Married to Blanch, I claim the crown of England. The cost is mine; I will not leave the war.'

'You look but on the outside,' said Pandulph, baffled.

'Outside or inside, I will not cease,' declared the Dauphin. And on the last word a trumpet heralded the Bastard's approach. Striding in without ceremony, he asked Pandulph how he had fared; and when the Cardinal replied that the Dauphin would not lay aside his arms, the Bastard laughed aloud: 'By all the blood that ever fury breathed, the youth says well. Now hear our English King.'

What Pandulph and the Dauphin heard was clearly not John's own speech. It was the language of the Bastard: a spirited challenge, a pledge to whip 'these pigmy arms' from England. Listening sarcastically, the Dauphin ordered a roll on the French drums. 'Indeed,' said the Bastard, 'your drums, being beaten, cry out – and, Lewis, so will you.'

Battle at first went badly for the English. Then the Bastard sent a messenger to John, telling him to leave the field, and the King, who was already sick of fever, ordered a march towards Swinstead Abbey in Lincolnshire. The Bastard's messenger had good news to bring as well. The Dauphin's reinforcements, he said, had been wrecked upon the Goodwin Sands, and the French were losing their early advantage. On the battlefield the English rebels, Salisbury, Pembroke, and Bigot, had observed this. While they waited to enter the fray again, the French Count Melun came to them, sorely wounded, warning them to fly, for they had been bought and sold. If the Dauphin won that fight, he meant to behead them on the altar at Bury St Edmunds where lately he had sworn his love. Immediately the barons vowed to return to John and to ask his pardon: tidings that reached the Dauphin just as he had learned of the crippling disaster on the Goodwin shoal.

In the darkness of night, near Swinstead Abbey, Hubert spurred to the south to meet the Bastard and to tell him that a monk had poisoned the King, who lay dangerously ill. The barons had returned; John, at the request of Prince Henry his son, had pardoned them. Grimly, the Bastard listened. Half of his men that night had fallen victim to the perilous quicksands of the Wash, and he himself had barely escaped. With Hubert now he made all speed towards the dying King.

At Swinstead where, near midnight, torches blazed in the still air of the Abbey orchard, Prince Henry waited with the silent barons. Though it was clear that John could not be saved, he believed that if he were brought into the open, it would ease the fierce burning of his fever. His mind was straying, and in his last extremity he was heard to sing. Henry marked it sadly: 'The pale, faint swan now chants a doleful hymn to his own death.'

Parchment-pale and fever-racked, John was carried forth in a chair. The Prince went to him: 'How fares your majesty?' And John answered with the frenzied imagination of a man doomed, 'Poisoned, forsaken, cast off. None of you will bid the winter cool me with its icy fingers. You will not bring the rivers of my land to cool this fever, or entreat the north wind to kiss my dry, parched lips. I do not ask you much. I beg cold comfort, yet you give me none.'

The end was near. When at last the Bastard leapt from his horse and ran up to the King, John could hardly whisper to him, 'Cousin, my heart has but one poor string. It holds until you speak – no longer.' The news was ill, but John did not know it, for his head drooped while the Bastard was speaking, and Salisbury, who stood by, said, 'You breathe your dead words in as dead an ear.' The barons knelt round the King, and the Bastard, who had loved him sincerely, rose with a clash of armour: 'I do but stay behind to revenge you, and my soul shall wait on yours to heaven.' He turned to the barons: 'Come, lords, the Dauphin rages at our very heels.'

Slowly Lord Salisbury replied, 'Not so. Within the Abbey is the Cardinal. He has brought from the Dauphin such offers as we with honour and respect can take. Already the French are marching towards their ships.'

'So be it!' said the Bastard. He sank to his knee, now before Prince Henry: 'My noble prince, with all submission I bequeath my faithful services.' Salisbury and the other barons echoed him, and the young prince bowed his head: 'I know not how to thank you but with tears.'

The Bastard was on his feet, a noble figure against the torchlight. Kissing his sword-hilt, he raised it with the words:

> 'This England never did, nor never shall,
> Lie at the proud foot of a conqueror,
> But when it first did help to wound itself.
> Now these her princes are come home again,
> Come the three corners of the world in arms,
> And we shall shock them. Nought shall make us rue,
> If England to itself do rest but true.'

In front of the barons, and behind the new King, he followed the body as it was borne with chanting towards Swinstead Abbey.

KING RICHARD II

RICHARD Plantagenet, King Richard the Second of England, was enthroned in his palace in the spring of the year 1398. He was then an elegant, effeminate young man of some thirty years, imperious and spendthrift, ruled by overwhelming pride and much influenced by the favourites who stood smiling behind his throne, Bushy, Bagot, and Green. Below the dais sat a figure venerable and white-bearded with deep-set eyes: the Duke of Lancaster, brother of the great Black Prince who was Richard's father. The King, addressing him now in a high voice that lingered mockingly on the adjectives, asked 'old John of Gaunt, time-honoured Lancaster,' whether he had summoned his son, the Duke of Hereford, Henry Bolingbroke, to make good a charge of treason against Thomas Mowbray, Duke of Norfolk.

Gaunt replied that he had; and when Richard asked whether he thought the charge was malicious or justified, answered that Bolingbroke had perceived in Mowbray the actions of a traitor. Richard ordered that the two men, known to be hasty and wrathful, should be brought to him at once to speak their minds.

Together the enemies entered the royal presence, each a man of noble bearing, each studying the other with a disdainful eye. Successively they saluted the King, the russet-bearded Bolingbroke wishing him many years of happy days, and Mowbray wishing that each day might prove better than the last. The King, thanking them with an ironical smile, said that one must assuredly be a flatterer, and he asked Bolingbroke to state his grievance against Thomas Mowbray.

Speaking with passion, Bolingbroke said that he came only as a loving subject concerned for the safety of his King. First, he warned Mowbray that what he spoke he would make good, or pay for it with his life; then, with stern emphasis, he accused his rival of being a foul traitor and a miscreant and asked for the cause to be settled by the sword.

Mowbray was as prompt to reply. If he were not in the King's presence he would thrust those treasons down his accuser's throat. As it was (and setting aside Bolingbroke's royal blood) he called him a slanderous coward and a villain: all that he could say was false.

Trembling with rage, Bolingbroke threw his gauntlet to the floor in defiance, challenging Mowbray to pick it up if guilty dread had left him so much strength. Mowbray swore at once by the sword that had knighted him that he would answer Bolingbroke in any trial of arms.

Again Richard demanded the charge. If it could persuade him of any thought of ill in Mowbray, it must be grave indeed. Bolingbroke did not hesitate. Mowbray, he said, had kept eight thousand gold pieces once given to him to pay the royal troops. Swept by an uncontrollable gust of wrath, he went on to accuse the man of plotting the Duke of Gloucester's death – Thomas of Woodstock, uncle to the King.

When Mowbray asked for the King's tolerance while he rejected Bolingbroke's foul lie, Richard said haughtily that no relationship would sway him. Though Bolingbroke was his cousin, accuser and accused were both subjects; each must speak his mind. It was then that Mowbray, putting aside reserve, charged Bolingbroke with rancorous villainy. Three parts of the money he had duly paid; the other he kept by royal consent – in settlement of a debt incurred when last he went to France to fetch the Queen. For the rest, it was the invention of a recreant and most degenerate traitor.

The King attempted to reconcile them. 'Forget, forgive, conclude, and be agreed. Uncle, we'll calm the Duke of Norfolk, you your son.'

It was useless: Mowbray, for honour's sake, insisted on facing Bolingbroke in the lists. Nor would his adversary hear of peace. And the King, stirred to anger, rose from his throne, crying that he was not born to sue but to command. They must be ready, as their lives should answer it, at Coventry upon Saint Lambert's Day. Since he could not assuage them, all must rest on sword and lance; and he called to his Lord Marshal: 'Command our officers-at-arms, be ready to direct these home alarms.'

On the afternoon appointed the King and his young Queen entered the pavilion above the lists at Coventry to the sound of a royal fanfare. When they were seated, Thomas Mowbray in full armour strode before them as defendant, preceded by a herald. In the prescribed form,

Richard told the Lord Marshal to demand Mowbray's name and the reason for his coming.

'In God's name and the King's,' cried the Marshal, 'say who thou art and why thou comest hither in knightly armour. Against whom comest thou, and what's thy quarrel? Speak truly on thy knighthood and thy oath.' Mowbray answered, 'My name is Thomas Mowbray, Duke of Norfolk. I come to defend my loyalty and my truth against the Duke of Hereford, my accuser. By God's grace and this mine arm I shall prove him a traitor to my God, my King, and me. As I truly fight, defend me heaven!'

At another blast of the trumpet, Bolingbroke, as appellant, entered the lists, and when he was asked his name, replied, 'Harry of Hereford, Lancaster, and Derby am I. I stand in arms to prove by God's grace and mine own valour that Thomas Mowbray, Duke of Norfolk, is here a traitor, foul and dangerous, to God, King Richard, and to me. As I truly fight, defend me heaven!'

There was an expectant pause. Spectators around the lists bent forward instinctively as the Lord Marshal made his last ceremonial speech. But Bolingbroke addressed the Marshal: 'Let me kiss my sovereign's hand before we fight, for Mowbray and myself are like two men that vow a long and weary pilgrimage.'

Richard said lazily, 'We will descend and embrace him.' He stepped down from the royal dais: 'Cousin, farewell. If your cause be right, so be your fortune.' Bolingbroke, a gallant figure with his helmet topped by the white swan crest, moved round the circle of nobles, bidding farewell to his cousin, the Duke of York's son, Lord Aumerle, and to John of Gaunt before whom he knelt, asking a father's blessing. 'Rouse up your youthful blood,' said Gaunt with an expression of deep melancholy. 'Be valiant, and live.'

Thomas Mowbray, no less confident, said simply that, however fortune moved, there lived or died, true to King Richard's throne, a loyal, just, and upright gentleman. He knelt to the King who said indifferently, 'Farewell, my lord. I see in you both virtue and valour.'

Each man now received his lance, and each herald uttered a formal challenge. Surveying the lists, the Lord Marshal signalled to the trumpeters: 'Sound trumpets, and set forward, combatants.' As the charge rang out, King Richard took from an attendant a gilded staff and flung it to the turf before him. A long sigh rippled across the lists; Bolingbroke and Mowbray reined back their horses; and the Lord Marshal proclaimed in a loud voice: 'Stay! the King commands!'

Richard left his seat. 'Let them lay by their helmets and their spears.' Beckoning to the nobles about him, he said, 'My lords, withdraw with us – and, Marshal, let the trumpets sound.' During a prolonged flourish, watchers observed again the grief on the face of John of Gaunt as he followed the King. Richard spoke to him, and sadly Gaunt inclined his head.

At length, reappearing on the dais, King Richard summoned the combatants who had waited in dazed astonishment. He addressed them in his imperious, distant tones. Because, he said, they had been roused to the conflict by pride and envy, and because such a struggle as this might lead to civil war, he and his council had resolved to banish them from England. Bolingbroke would be exiled for ten years. As a startled whisper, 'Banishment!', filled the lists, Richard faced Thomas Mowbray with the same detached arrogance. 'Norfolk,' he said, 'for you remains a heavier doom'; and Mowbray stood in desolate amazement while Richard sentenced him to banishment for life. He gathered himself for one shocked protest. Surely he had deserved more dearly of his King? Now the language he had known for forty years, his native English, would be lost to him for ever. What was the sentence then but speechless death?

In an intense and pitying silence he bowed to the King and strode unseeing across the grass; but Richard called him back. Taking a sword from the officer who stood by the dais, he extended the hilt towards Bolingbroke and Mowbray and ordered them, kneeling, to swear never to meet in banishment and never to contrive or join in any plot.

'I swear!' said Bolingbroke.

Mowbray looked at him. 'And I,' he said with a meaning pause, 'to keep all this.' Unremittingly stern, Bolingbroke now urged Mowbray to confess to treason before he left the land; and Mowbray replied to him in a speech of which every word was a stab, 'No, Bolingbroke, if ever I were traitor, my name be blotted from the book of life. But what you are, God, you and I do know, and all too soon I fear the King will rue.' With a last obeisance he walked firmly from the lists.

Richard waited until the lonely figure had gone, then said to John of Gaunt, 'Uncle, your grief speaks for your son.' To Bolingbroke he said, 'After six years return with welcome home from banishment'; and Bolingbroke, who had been staring into the distance after Mowbray, exclaimed in ironical gratitude, 'How long a time lives in one little word! Such is the breath of kings.'

John of Gaunt shook his head. 'My liege, I shall not see my son again. You shorten my life with sorrow, but you cannot add to it another day.' Petulantly, the King said that Gaunt had assented to the verdict; and the old man rejoined that he had spoken as a judge, not as a father. The King gestured impatiently: 'Six years we banish him, and he shall go.'

Now, with the Queen and his train, King Richard left the dais to the sound of a high, lingering trumpet-note. Certain nobles stayed hesitantly. Aumerle asked Bolingbroke to write from exile; and the Lord Marshal said, 'I will ride with you as far as land will let me.' Bolingbroke made no answer. When his father sought to comfort him, telling him to imagine that he went of his own will, not from necessity, he said with a shrug, 'Can a hungry man live on the bare imagination of a feast?' Brooding, he rode off into the afternoon on the first stage of his banishment.

King Richard had contrived this for two reasons: because he feared the strength and popularity of Bolingbroke, and because it was better that Mowbray, who had done much for him in secret, should no longer be a daily goad to his conscience. With the realm – as he thought – free at last of danger, he talked in his London palace with two insinuating favourites, Bagot and Green, and with the Duke of Aumerle, a hot-headed, fickle young man who, in the King's presence, affected hatred of Bolingbroke. But they did not speak long of the banished men. Rebellion stirred in Ireland. King Richard, resolving to travel there himself, ordained further exactions from his already oppressed realm, and he was planning these when a third of the favourites, Bushy, brought tidings of old Gaunt's grave illness. Lightly the King said that the sooner Gaunt died the better; the money he left might equip many soldiers for the Irish wars. 'Let's go visit him,' he said. 'Pray we may make haste and come too late.'

At Ely House the Duke of York sat with his dying brother. Propped among cushions in his chair, John of Gaunt awaited the King's coming in the belief that counsel from one about to die enforced attention. York was dubious. Richard, he said, was a prey to fashion and to flatterers. Wearily, Gaunt managed to raise himself, and York saw a light in his sunken eyes as the old man foretold that Richard's blaze of riot would not last. But at once sadness returned when Gaunt considered the dishonour to the realm,

> 'This royal throne of kings, this scepter'd isle,
> This earth of majesty, this seat of Mars,
> This other Eden, demi-Paradise,
> This fortress built by Nature for herself
> Against infection and the hand of war.
> This happy breed of men, this little world,
> This precious stone set in the silver sea . . .
> This blessed plot, this earth, this realm, this England . . .
> Dear for her reputation through the world . . .'

There Gaunt's voice broke. Must England be leased out like a smallholding or a trifling farm? Must England, bound in with the triumphant sea, be bound as well by shame, by inky blots and rotten parchment bonds?

York, whispering that the King had come, begged Gaunt to deal with him mildly. But when Richard spoke, Gaunt's control had vanished. These were his last moments on earth, and he spent them in attacking Richard as England's landlord, not her King; a man foolishly caught in the net of flatterers. Richard flew at him in hysterical, threatening rage; and Gaunt answered with a cold fury, 'Live in thy shame, but die not shame with thee! These words hereafter thy tormentors be!' Falling back unconscious, Gaunt was carried into the next room from which within a minute the Earl of Northumberland came to say that he was dead.

Richard accepted the news with a careless phrase and laid claim at once to the dead man's property: his plate, his goods, his money, and his lands. When the usually mild Duke of York protested in despair that the King could not behave in this way to banished Bolingbroke, Richard replied, firstly, that he intended to do so, and, secondly, that during his absence in Ireland York would act as Lord Governor of the realm.

Monks chanted in Gaunt's bedchamber and candles burned round the couch where the body lay. In an adjoining room the Earl of Northumberland, with the Lords Ross and Willoughby, pondered upon the evils of the time, the King's lack of money, and his insistence upon his favourites. Soon they spoke of Bolingbroke. Northumberland had received news that with eight ships and three thousand soldiers, Bolingbroke had already sailed from France and meant to land in England upon the Yorkshire coast. Here was a chance to save the country, to redeem the honour of the crown. 'Away with me,' he cried, 'in haste to Ravenspurgh!; and, when they had clasped hands in fellowship, Ross and Willoughby followed him to horse.

Very soon the court knew that Bolingbroke had landed at Ravenspurgh, and that many powerful nobles, including the Earl of Worcester, had fled to join him. The regent, gentle, troubled York, did not know which way to move. Richard and his forces were in Ireland; the nobles were going over to Bolingbroke, and the commoners seemed likely to revolt. York himself was divided between his duty to Richard and his love for a kinsman wronged. The favourites, Bushy, Green, and Bagot, knew that their hour was over; Bagot chose to go to Ireland to the King, and Green and Bushy to seek refuge in Bristol Castle.

It was not their refuge for long. Bolingbroke, gaining supporters every day, had marched with speed from the North to Gloucestershire. There they met Northumberland's heir, young Harry Percy, soon to be known as Hotspur, who did homage to Bolingbroke and told him that the Duke of York rested in Berkeley Castle. York himself, coming out to intercept Bolingbroke, tried to reproach him for breaking exile, but the words were not heartfelt. In offering Bolingbroke a night's lodging at Berkeley, he let it be known that he was neutral; and his nephew, realising clearly where the old man stood, both accepted the offer and said that he was marching on to Bristol Castle to weed out Bushy, Green, and their accomplices, 'the caterpillars of the commonwealth'.

Upon the next night they were at Bristol where Bolingbroke, having stormed the castle, condemned Bushy and Green to instant execution. Already he held England in everything but name. Richard had not landed from Ireland, and Lord Salisbury, who had been trying to keep together a force in Wales, heard that the superstitious Welshmen would no longer fight. The bay-trees were all withered, said a Welsh captain; meteors flashed in the sky, the moon was stained with blood, and prophets spoke of fearful change, sights presaging the death or fall of kings.

Though Richard was still alive, his reign had begun to fade. He and his forces had landed at Harlech on the coast of Wales; with him were the Duke of Aumerle and the Bishop of Carlisle, At first he cheered himself in the belief that Bolingbroke's rebellion could not succeed against an anointed king, one by divine right a monarch. This pride had sustained him throughout his life, and, standing now on the bleak Welsh shore, he gave expression to it in the words: 'For every soldier Bolingbroke has raised, God for his Richard has in heavenly pay a glorious angel. Then if angels fight, weak men must fall, for heaven still guards the right.'

His confidence waned when Salisbury rode up with the news that twelve thousand Welshmen, fearing he was dead, had either dispersed to the hills or fled to Bolingbroke. Richard, for a moment overcome, told all who wished to be safe to fly from him; but he recovered when Aumerle reminded him of his royalty. 'I had forgot myself. Am I not King?' Now Sir Stephen Scroop appeared with the worst news yet. Throughout England men, boys, even women, had risen against him; at Bristol Bushy and Green had lost their heads. Quickly despairing, Richard begged no man to speak again of comfort; it was better that they talked of graves, of worms, and epitaphs, or with their tears wrote sorrow in the dust. Now their lands and their lives were Bolingbroke's, what could they call their own but death? Nothing remained but to sit upon the ground and tell sad stories of the death of kings: some deposed, some slain in battle, some haunted by the ghosts they had deposed: 'all murdered, for within the hollow crown that rounds the mortal temples of a king, keeps Death his court.'

The Bishop of Carlisle pleaded with Richard not to lament his woes but to think how he could cure them. Alas, Scroop's tale had still to end.

The Duke of York had gone to Bolingbroke; all the northern castles had yielded, and all the southern nobles had rebelled. 'What say you now?' said Richard to Aumerle, 'What comfort have we now?' Commanding a march to Flint Castle, he cried, 'Discharge my followers! Let them hence away, from Richard's night to Bolingbroke's fair day.'

Bolingbroke himself had led his army to take Flint Castle. Learning that the King was there with Aumerle, Salisbury, Scroop, and Carlisle, he realised that this would be the final victory, though he did not claim it yet. Ordering trumpeters to sound a parley, he told Northumberland to say that Henry Bolingbroke, on both his knees, would kiss King Richard's hand. If his banishment were repealed and his lands restored, then the King should have his allegiance: if not, let war ensue. Northumberland went forward; an answering clarion echoed from the walls; and Richard, speaking for the last time in the pride of a majesty that could make men forget his weakness and his petulance, said to Northumberland, 'Tell Bolingbroke – for yonder waits the man – that every stride he takes upon my land is dangerous treason.'

Northumberland repeated Bolingbroke's message to which the King replied, 'Say that my noble cousin is right welcome hither. All his demands are granted.' As Northumberland crossed to confer with Bolingbroke, Richard turned to his friends in a wild mingling of humiliation, pride, and grief: 'What must the King do now? Must he submit? Must he lose the name of King? In God's name, let it go.' And he cried, 'I'll give my jewels for a set of beads, my gorgeous palace for a hermitage, my gay apparel for an almsman's gown, my figured goblets for a dish of wood, my sceptre for a palmer's walking staff, and my large kingdom for a little grave.' So he went on playing with word and fancy while Carlisle and Aumerle gazed at each other in despair. At Northumberland's return Richard was ironical: 'What says King Bolingbroke? Will his majesty give Richard leave to live till Richard die?'

Northumberland said that Bolingbroke sought conference below. When Richard appeared, Bolingbroke knelt to him; but the King beckoned to him to rise, pointing to the crown of England and saying, 'Up, cousin, up, your heart is up, I know – thus high at least, although your knee be low.' Seeing there was no escape, Richard had resolved to submit. He repulsed the feigned loyalty of Bolingbroke with the brief 'What you will have, I'll give, and willing too,' though his next words were 'Do we must what force will have us do.' For the first time he spoke as a virtual subject: 'We go to London, cousin? Is it so?' Slowly, Bolingbroke nodded; and the King, his reign at an end, answered, 'Then I must not say no.'

News of his capture reached the Queen while she overheard the talk of gardeners at the palace of the Duke of York where she had gone for safety. In grievous resignation she called to her ladies to make ready for London and 'London's King in woe.' Woe indeed, for on his journey from the North he understood all that Bolingbroke and the rebels intended. Bolingbroke, on a fine and stately charger, received the shouts of a multitude in London streets; Richard came behind him, wretchedly mounted and assailed by dust and rubbish flung from the upper windows. He endured everything with patience, but he had yet to find his crowning grief, the deposition in Westminister Hall before the peers.

On this solemn occasion every lord had assembled. Though the royal throne was empty, Bolingbroke sat close at hand. He had another matter to judge before Richard was brought in. Here was Bagot, one of the King's favourites, who had escaped the fate of Bushy and Green at Bristol, and Bolingbroke asked him now to say what he knew of the Duke of Gloucester's death, one of the causes of the dispute with Mowbray. Who had planned this with the King? Who finally performed the deed? Bagot, asking to be confronted with the Duke of Aumerle, said when Aumerle stood before him, 'In that dead time, when Gloucester's death was plotted, I heard you say "My arm reaches from the English court as far as Calais, to my uncle's head".' Aumerle tossed down his gauntlet in fierce denial, whereupon many lords ranged themselves on one side or the other until seven or eight gages lay on the floor of Westminster Hall. One of the lords, Fitzwater, claimed that he had learned of Aumerle's guilt from banished Norfolk: 'Two of your men, Aumerle, were sent to Calais to the noble Duke.'

'Norfolk lies!' declared Aumerle. But Bolingbroke said austerely, 'These differences shall rest until Norfolk can return. Repealed he shall be. Though mine enemy, we restore him again to all his lands, and, at a later day, against Aumerle we will enforce his trial.'

A quiet voice spoke from behind the brawling lords. It was the Bishop of Carlisle who had stood with Richard on the battlements of Flint Castle. 'That honourable day,' he said, 'can never be. Norfolk, when banished, fought on Christ's crusade against black pagans, Turks, and Saracens. Weary of war he went at last to Italy, and there at Venice died.' Bolingbroke crossed himself: 'Sweet peace conduct his sweet soul to the bosom of good old Abraham!'

Down the steps walked the Duke of York. Saluting Bolingbroke, he said that plume-plucked Richard had acknowledged him as heir and yielded the royal sceptre to his hand. Pointing to the dais beneath the canopy, York uttered the solemn words, 'Ascend his throne, descending now from him; and long live Henry, fourth of that name!'

A responsive shout, twice repeated, shook the rafters: 'Long live Henry, fourth of that name!'

Bolingbroke moved from his chair: 'In God's name I'll ascend the regal throne.' Before he could reach it the Bishop of Carlisle spoke again, not now in the quiet tones that told of Norfolk's death, but with the urgency of a just man abhorring wrong. 'Marry, God forbid!' he cried. 'Would that any here were enough noble to be upright judge of noble Richard! What subject can give sentence on his King? Who sits here that is not Richard's subject? He is the figure of God's majesty – a captain, steward, deputy-elect, anointed, crowned, and planted many years. Must he be judged by subject and inferior breath, and he himself not present?'

Carlisle's voice beat through the silence that had fallen on Westminster Hall: 'My lord of Hereford here, whom you call King, is a foul traitor to proud Hereford's King. If you crown him, let future ages groan for your dark act. Disorder, horror, fear, and mutiny shall rise in England. Our land shall be the field of Golgotha – of dead men's skulls.'

Bolingbroke, though his face remained impassive, paused by the throne and returned to his chair. Northumberland, frowning, advanced upon the Bishop: 'Well have you argued, sir, and for your pains we here arrest you.' He looked at the Abbot of Westminster: 'My lord, it is your charge to keep him safely till his trial day.'

Richard himself was now brought in, wearing only a long black velvet gown and a silver cross. With him were officers who bore the regalia. Staring first at Bolingbroke, and then at the vacant throne, he asked why he had been sent for to a King before he had learned to insinuate, flatter, bow, and bend the knee. Studying the peers with half-smiling scorn, he said, 'I remember the faces of these men. Did they not sometimes cry "All hail!" to me as Judas did to Christ? . . . To do what service am I sent for hither?' And York prompted him: 'What tired majesty made you offer: the resignation of your state and crown to Henry Bolingbroke.'

Richard told an officer to bring him the crown. Lifting it from its velvet cushion, he held it out to Bolingbroke but retained his own grasp, and the two cousins stood facing each other, the crown of England poised between them. Gruffly, Bolingbroke said, 'I thought you had been ready to resign. Are you contented now?' And Richard, drawing the crown back, answered with a sigh, 'Mark me, I will undo myself. I give this heavy weight from off my head and this unwieldy sceptre from my hand. With my own hands I give away my crown; all pomp and majesty I here forswear; my acts, decrees, and statutes I deny . . . God save King Henry, unkinged Richard says, and send him many years of sunshine days!'

At last Henry Bolingbroke, crowned and sceptred, sat enthroned. Richard turned from the sight: 'What more remains?' It was then that Northumberland, proffering a scroll, ordered him to read aloud the formal accusations against himself and his followers so that men might see he was worthily deposed. Richard, despairing, asked if it was needful – this record of his weaved-up folly. Inexorably, Northumberland held the scroll before him; and Richard, whose first apparent patience had fretted to a nervous anguish, thrust it aside and begged Bolingbroke to send for a looking-glass that he might see his face now it had lost its majesty. 'Read over this paper while the glass is coming,' insisted Northumberland; but King Henry muttered, 'Urge it no more, my lord.' An attendant brought a looking-glass in a gilded frame. Richard, seizing it eagerly and gazing long upon himself, said, 'No deeper wrinkles yet! O flattering glass, you have beguiled me. A brittle glory shineth in this face . . . As brittle as the glory *is* the face.' Dashing the glass to the stone floor where it lay shivered in a hundred pieces, he cried to Bolingbroke, 'Mark, silent King, how soon my sorrow has destroyed my face.'

Bolingbroke said curtly, 'The shadow of your sorrow has destroyed the shadow of your face.' Feverishly Richard began to play with the idea; then, looking at the pitiless faces round him, he said wearily to Bolingbroke, 'I'll beg one boon . . . Give me now leave to go.'

'Whither?' asked Bolingbroke.

'Whither you will, so I am from your sight.'

Bolingbroke called an officer, 'Go, some of you. Convey him to the Tower.' And Richard, with a last cry, strained and high-pitched, 'Convey? Conveyors are you all that rise thus nimbly by a true King's fall,' was led for ever from the men who had been his courtiers. At once Bolingbroke rose from the throne: 'Let Wednesday be our coronation. Lords, prepare yourselves.' In royal progress he passed from the darkening hall, followed by the peers. Three figures held their places for a while, the Bishop of Carlisle, Aumerle, and the Abbot of Westminster: then, talking in whispers, they moved together up the steps.

In a street leading to the Tower the Queen waited for Richard to come. When he approached her she greeted him through her tears as 'The model where old Troy did stand, the map of honour, King Richard's tomb – and not King Richard.' Embracing her and speaking very softly, her husband told her to make haste to France and think that he was dead. 'On winter nights sit by the fire with good old folks. When they have told you tales of all the woeful past, tell them of me, and that will send them weeping to their rest.' As she clung to him, Northumberland arrived with a new order from Bolingbroke that consigned the Queen to France and Richard to the remote Yorkshire keep of Pomfret. Angrily, Richard railed upon Northumberland as 'Thou ladder by which the mounting Bolingbroke ascends my throne!' and in prophecy warned him of the dangers that must follow.

Heedless, Northumberland ordered them to part forthwith. 'I towards the North,' said Richard, 'where shivering cold and sickness pines the clime; my wife to France from which she came in beauty like sweet May.' Again embracing, they parted for the last time. 'The rest let sorrow speak.'

During the spring of the next year, while Richard, more patient in adversity than in power, lay close prisoner in a dungeon at Pomfret, a few of his braver friends plotted against Bolingbroke. Twelve men, the Abbot of Westminster and Aumerle among them, took an oath to kill him at Oxford. But, before the conspiracy was ripe, the Duke of York discovered his son with a paper that revealed the secret, and he hurried at once to warn the King. The Duchess made after him to plead for her son's life.

Pardoning Aumerle magnanimously, Bolingbroke moved against the other conspirators. The plot had shown that Richard, while alive, must always be a danger; and the King said one night at court, gazing at Sir Pierce of Exton as he spoke, 'Have I no friend will rid me of this living fear?' Twice he said this with a look that Exton interpreted as 'I would you were the man that might divorce this terror from my heart.' Through the early morning a small band of horsemen galloped to the North.

At Pomfret, evilly confined, seeing no one but the gaoler who brought food to him, Richard could talk only to himself, trying to compare his prison with the world or else pondering sadly on his former state. On a spring morning, to his astonishment, the gaoler admitted to him a man in peasant dress who knelt and kissed his hand, saying, 'Hail, royal prince!' Richard rejoined, 'Thanks, noble peer! . . . Who are you? Why do you come where no man comes but the dull dog that brings me food to make misfortune live?'

The man had been a poor groom of Richard's stable. Yearning to see his master's face again, he had been given grudging leave. Now in the darkness of Pomfret he told how he had sorrowed when on Coronation Day Bolingbroke passed through the streets on Richard's horse, roan Barbary. 'How went he under Bolingbroke?' asked Richard; and the groom replied, 'So proudly as if he disdained the ground.'

'So proud that Bolingbroke was on his back? . . . Would he not stumble? Would he not fall down?'

Little more could be said; the gaoler entered with a dish and signed to the groom to leave. 'What my tongue dares not,' the man murmured, 'that my heart shall say.' Longingly Richard looked after him as the gaoler, uncovering the dish, said, 'Fall to, my lord.' Richard told him to taste it first, and the gaoler replied that he dared not do so, for Sir Pierce of Exton, who had come to Pomfret from the King, had expressly forbidden it. Richard's Plantagenet wrath flared. Hurling the dish from him, he shouted, 'The devil take Henry of Lancaster and thee!' and threw himself upon the gaoler. The man's cries for help brought to the dungeon, with torches, Sir Pierce of Exton and three of his armed men. When they encircled Richard and he saw death in their looks, he made a last wild fight, first snatching an axe from one of the men and beating him to the ground with it, then slaying another with a furious blow. Before he could lift the axe again, Pierce of Exton had stabbed him to the heart.

After a choking cry, 'Exton, your fierce hand has with the King's blood stained the King's own land,' Richard Plantagenet fell dead at the murderer's feet. Exton shuddered: 'As full of valour as of royal blood. Both have I spilled.' He signed to his men to raise the body.

Some days after this, King Henry the Fourth at Windsor Castle listened to news of failed rebellion. Northumberland and Fitzwater told him how the Oxford plot had been suppressed and its leaders executed. Then young Harry Percy entered with the Bishop of Carlisle. 'My liege,' he said, 'the Abbot of Westminster is dead; but there is Carlisle living to abide your kingly doom.' As the Bishop waited for death, Bolingbroke spoke to him chivalrously: 'Carlisle, my honourable foe, this is your doom. Find out some quiet place, some secret room more than you have, and there enjoy your days. As you have lived in peace, die free from strife.'

At the sound of a heavy measured tread all looked towards the door of the great chamber through which came four persons bearing a coffin. Behind them, wearing black, was Sir Pierce of Exton. Standing before Henry's throne, he said, 'Great King, within this coffin I present your buried fear . . . Richard of Bordeaux!' At the words he stepped aside, and Bolingbroke gazed into the face of the man before whom, one April morning, he had accused Thomas Mowbray. When he raised his head his eyes were so fierce that Exton started back dismayed.

'Exton,' said Bolingbroke in a voice that was deathly chill, 'I thank you not.'

'From your own mouth, my lord, I did this deed.'

'They love not poison that use poison most. Though I wished him dead, I love him now and hate his murderer. Hence and never let me see you more!'

Exton, pale with fear, hurried from the presence, and Bolingbroke stooped over Richard's body. 'Lords,' he said, 'lament with me; my soul is full of woe.' Reverently the coffin was borne from the audience chamber while Bolingbroke, the peers following him, paced after it, a living King to mourn the dead.

THE FIRST PART OF
KING HENRY IV

KING Henry the Fourth of England, who had been Henry Bolingbroke, was holding council in his London palace on a June night. It was a disturbed hour, for Wales was in revolt and the Scots were harrying the northern border. Though the King still held to his resolve to end these wars at home and to take an English army to a new Crusade, he found small comfort in the tidings that reached him now in London. Bolingbroke had aged quickly. The careworn King was sometimes unrecognisable as the warrior who only a few years earlier had landed from exile at Ravenspurgh and thrust his cousin Richard from the throne.

In what should have been a tranquil summer night the Earl of Westmoreland brought to him news both of Glendower's defeat of Lord Mortimer in the Welsh Marches, and of a battle in the north between young Harry Percy, known as Hotspur, and Archibald Earl of Douglas. The issue there at Holmedon, said Westmoreland, was yet unknown; but even while he gave the message to the King, Sir Walter Blunt, travel-stained with his long journey, appeared with a far happier report. Douglas had been defeated; ten thousand Scots were slain; and Hotspur had taken many noble prisoners.

'A conquest for a prince to boast of,' said Westmoreland. But the King's face was grave. While his son, Henry Prince of Wales, rioted among loose companions, the Earl of Northumberland had in Hotspur a son who was 'the theme of honour's tongue, sweet fortune's minion and her pride.' Yet even this gallant youth could offend his King: he would yield none of his prisoners but Mordake, Earl of Fife. 'It is his uncle's teaching,' cried Westmoreland. 'It is Worcester's voice, a man long disloyal to you.' King Henry rose with an imperious nod. 'And I have sent for him to answer this. For a while, Westmoreland, we must neglect our holy purpose to Jerusalem.' Heavy with care, he moved from the council.

No one, meanwhile, was apparently more carefree than Prince Hal: Henry, Prince of Wales. He seemed never to be happier than when he was with the fat knight, Sir John Falstaff, who lived by his wits with his raffish companions, and who was usually to be found lingering over his sack in an Eastcheap tavern or bent on some highly dubious enterprise. Falstaff was always reminding the youth of a time when he must become King and could bestow royal favours and make convenient laws. The two never ceased to banter each other. 'Before I knew you,' Falstaff would say, 'I knew nothing, and now am I little better than one of the wicked. I must and will give over this life; I'll be damned for never a King's son in Christendom.'

'Where shall we take a purse to-morrow, Jack?' the Prince would ask slyly, knowing that Falstaff would cry, 'Where you will, lad. I'll make one.' And when Hal said teasingly, 'I see how you are reformed – moving from prayers to purse-taking,' Falstaff retorted with his plump chuckle, 'Why, Hal, 'tis my vocation. 'Tis no sin for a man to labour in his vocation.'

Upon this particular morning they waited for their comrade Poins to tell them of a hopeful plan in Kent. On his arrival he warned them to be at Gadshill by four o'clock next morning. Pilgrims were going to Canterbury with rich offerings; traders were riding to London with fat purses. Any of these would be an easy conquest. He had already ordered supper for the next night in Eastcheap.

'Hal,' asked Falstaff, 'will you make one with us?'

'I rob? I a thief? Not I, by my faith,' said the Prince. When Falstaff grunted, 'There's neither honesty, manhood, nor good fellowship in you,' Hal laughed at him: 'Come what will, I'll stay at home.'

'By the rood, I'll be a traitor then when you are King,' swore Falstaff. But Poins put in, 'Leave the Prince alone with me, Jack. I will give him such reason for the adventure that he shall go.'

'Well, may you have the spirit of persuasion and he the means to profit by it,' rumbled Falstaff as he set off. When they were alone Poins told the Prince of his design. Falstaff and his men should be left to rob the travellers on Gadshill, and once they had secured the booty, the Prince and Poins would rush in disguised and seize it. 'The virtue of the jest,' said Poins, 'will be in the lies that Falstaff will tell us at supper; how thirty men at least he fought with; what blows, what extremities, he endured.' Hal agreed cheerfully to play his part; but when Poins had gone he said to himself, 'I bear with these rogues only as a thing of policy. The people gossip about me as a loose-living rioter who can never grace the throne. But when in time I succeed my father and pay a debt that I have never promised, then shall I seem much nobler than I am.'

Early next morning the plan prospered. Falstaff and his men, wearing masks, set upon travellers on Gadshill, bound them, and stole three hundred marks. And immediately the disguised Prince and Poins, whom Falstaff had just abused for cowardly absence, fell upon the thieves and forced them to run, leaving the gold behind them. That night, at the Boar's Head Tavern in Eastcheap, Hal and Poins talked idly while they waited for Falstaff. 'I am sworn brother to a train of potboys,' said Hal, 'and I can call them by their Christian names, Tom or Dick or Francis. They say that though I am the Prince of Wales, yet I am also the king of courtesy, no proud Jack like Falstaff but a lad of mettle, a good boy, and when I am King indeed I shall command all the lads in Eastcheap.' Poins chuckled; and Hal, stretching himself lazily, said, 'Shall we be merry? . . . I am not yet of Harry Percy's mind, the Hotspur of the north that kills some six or seven dozen of Scots at a breakfast, washes his hands, and says to his wife, "Fie on this quiet life! I want work!" "O my sweet Harry," says she, "how many have you killed to-day?" "Give my roan horse a drench!" he cries, and answers her an hour later, "O some fourteen; a trifle; a trifle." Call Falstaff, Poins: I'll play Percy, and that rogue shall play the dame his wife.'

Falstaff, accompanied by the red-faced Bardolph and his other rogues, entered glowering. With a contemptuous glance at Hal and Poins, he beckoned a potboy to bring him a cup of sack, muttering to himself: 'A plague of all cowards, I say!'

'How now, woolsack?' the Prince greeted him briskly.

'A King's son!' jeered Falstaff. 'I would beat you out of your kingdom with a toy dagger and drive all your subjects before me like wild geese . . . Are you not a coward? Answer me to that, you – and Poins there.'

'What's the matter?' said the Prince innocently. Falstaff glared: 'The matter? Four of us here took a thousand marks this morning.'

'Where is it, Jack?'

'Where is it? Why, taken from us: a hundred upon poor four of us.'

'A hundred on you?' said the Prince.

'I am a rogue,' added Falstaff hastily, 'if I were not fighting with a dozen of them for two hours together. I have escaped by a miracle: eight times thrust through the doublet, four times through the hose, my buckler bent through and through, my sword hacked like a hand-saw – behold it! . . . And what did you do? A plague of all cowards!'

The Prince asked to be told the whole story. Falstaff, calling for more sack, began by saying that though they set on some sixteen men and bound and robbed them, newcomers rushed up and he had to face at least fifty swords. Two men he killed – two in buckram suits. 'Here I stood, Hal,' he said dramatically, 'and thus I held my sword. Then four rogues in buckram let drive at me, and I took all their seven points on my shield—.'

'Seven?' said the Prince. 'There were only four just now.'

'Seven by these hilts, or I am a villain else.'

'We shall have more presently,' murmured Hal; and, surely enough, Falstaff continued, 'These nine in buckram that I told you of began to retreat, but I followed them, and, with a thought, seven of the eleven I paid.'

'O monstrous!' said the Prince. 'Eleven buckram men grown out of two.'

Falstaff did not heed: 'As the devil would have it, three misbegotten knaves in Kendal green came at my back, and let drive at me, for it was so dark, Hal, you could not see your hand.'

He stopped: the Prince and Poins were in helpless laughter. 'These lies are like their father,' said Hal, 'gross as a mountain, open, palpable.'

'Is not the truth the truth?' demanded Falstaff.

'Why,' the Prince cried, 'how could you know these men in Kendal green when it was so dark you could not see your hand? Come, Jack, tell us your reason.' And Poins insisted: 'Yes, your reason, your reason.'

Falstaff, baffled for a moment, looked from one to the other. Then he began to heave with anger. 'What, upon compulsion? Give you a reason upon compulsion? If they were as plentiful as blackberries, I'd give no man reason upon compulsion.'

Solemnly the Prince and Poins sat one upon each side of Falstaff. 'Mark now, Jack,' said Poins. And the Prince continued: 'We saw you four set on four and bind them. Then did we two set on you four, and, with a word, took your prize. Falstaff, you ran and roared for mercy. What a slave you are to hack your sword and say it was in fight!'

'What is the next trick?' asked Poins.

Falstaff remained sulkily quiet. Then he began to smile, and within a minute his great frame was shaking with laughter. 'By the Lord,' he said with ready presence of mind, 'I knew you as well as he that made you.' The idea delighted him, and he rumbled on: 'Why, was it for me to kill the heir-apparent? Should I turn upon the true Prince? I am as valiant as Hercules, but instinct is a great master, and I was a coward on instinct. I shall think the better of us during my life – I for a valiant lion, and you, Hal, for a true Prince. By the Lord, lads, I am glad you have the money. Shall we be merry? Shall we have a play?'

'Yes,' said the Prince, 'if it is about your running away.' Falstaff thrust it aside: 'No more of that, Hal, if you love me.'

Now Mistress Nell Quickly, hostess of the tavern, entered to tell the Prince that a nobleman waited for him at the door with a message from the King. 'What manner of man?' asked Falstaff. 'He is an old man,' Mistress Quickly answered; and Falstaff said to the Prince: 'What does gravity out of his bed at midnight? Shall I send him packing?'

'Prithee do!' said Hal agreeably. When Falstaff came back he said that Sir John Bracy bore the King's command for the Prince to go to the court next morning. Hotspur and Northumberland, Glendower and Mortimer and Douglas, had all joined in rebellion; and the Earl of Worcester, too, had stolen from the King. 'Are you not horribly afraid, Hal? Could the world pick you out three such enemies as that fiend Douglas, that spirit Percy, and the devil Glendower? Are you not horribly afraid – does not your blood thrill at it?'

'Not a whit,' said the Prince. 'I lack some of your instinct.'

Falstaff would have it now that they should improvise a play, one in which he would stand for the King questioning his son. Seated in a chair upon a table, with a cushion for a crown, he imitated the King's tricks of speech, and relishingly accused Hal of keeping bad company. Only one of his friends was virtuous, 'a goodly, portly man of a cheerful look, a pleasing eye, and a most noble courage. His name is Falstaff.'

The Prince pulled him down and took the King's position himself. 'Do you stand for me,' he said to Falstaff. When they had begun he asked in his father's tone who was the devil that haunted Hal in the likeness of 'an old fat man, a huge vessel of sack, a grey indignity, a father ruffian, a villainous abominable misleader of youth?' Was it not one Falstaff? To which Falstaff, in the Prince's person, replied: 'If sack and sugar be a fault, God help the wicked! If to be old and merry be a sin, then many an old host I know is damned. No, my good lord, banish Bardolph, banish Poins, but for sweet Jack Falstaff, kind Jack Falstaff, true Jack Falstaff, banish him not your Harry's company. Banish plump Jack and banish all the world.'

'I do,' said the Prince, 'I will.' He spoke with a sudden frigid resolution; but Falstaff hardly noticed it. There was no time for more; a loud knocking reverberated through the house. The sheriff and his watch had come to the Boar's Head, and Falstaff had just time to conceal himself behind the tapestries. When the sheriff entered, with one of the travellers who had been robbed that morning on Gadshill, the Prince addressed him curtly: 'Now, master sheriff?' Surprised but persistent, the sheriff explained that a hue and cry had followed certain men to the tavern, including a gross fat man well known to all. 'He is not here,' answered the Prince. 'I myself have employed him. By tomorrow, at dinner, sheriff, he will come to answer you or any man. I do entreat you, leave the house.'

The sheriff bowed, with a trace of suspicion. 'Two gentlemen in this robbery have lost three hundred marks.'

The Prince said merely, 'If he has robbed these men, he shall be answerable. So farewell.'

The night wore into morning. At two o'clock Falstaff was sleeping behind the arras, and the Prince snatched from his pocket a tavern reckoning for two gallons of sack at five and eightpence; anchovies and sack after supper, two and sixpence; and bread, one halfpenny. 'O monstrous! But one halfpennyworth of bread to this intolerable deal of sack!' He tossed back the paper. 'There let him sleep until day. I'll to court in the morning. We must all to the wars, and I'll get a place for this fat rogue. Meanwhile, the money that was taken shall be paid back, and more.' And Falstaff was left in uninterrupted sleep.

The Prince of Wales had been summoned to the palace because of dangerous rebellion. Some little time earlier, when Hotspur, with his father the Earl of Northumberland, and his uncle the Earl of Worcester, had journeyed to court, the King had dismissed Worcester angrily and turned upon Hotspur to demand the prisoners taken at Holmedon. Hotspur denied that he had refused arrogantly to send the prisoners. At the end of the battle, when he was standing breathless and faint, a certain lord, a smiling popinjay, came up to him, talking and questioning in affected terms. Among much else he demanded the Scottish prisoners on the King's behalf; and Hotspur, weary and with smarting wounds, answered impatiently he knew not what. It made him mad, he said, to see on the battlefield this man so trim and perfumed, talking like a waiting-gentlewoman of guns and swords and drums.

Sir Walter Blunt, listening with a smile to Hotspur's speech, suggested tactfully to the King that the charge might be forgotten; but Henry was in his most peremptory mood. Hotspur, he said, refused to send his prisoners unless his brother-in-law, the foolish Mortimer, was ransomed from Glendower. 'Mortimer,' exclaimed the King, 'wilfully betrayed the lives of those he led. Are we then to bring a traitor home? No: on the barren mountain tops let him starve.' Hotspur, the soul of chivalry, rushed at once to Mortimer's defence. Had he not fought for nearly an hour on the bank of Severn with great Glendower himself? 'My sovereign liege, let him not be slandered with revolt.' The King refused all word. 'Mortimer durst have met the devil alone as Owen Glendower for an enemy. Are you not ashamed? Sirrah, send me your prisoners with the speediest means, or you will hear of it.' And in rage he cut short the audience.

It was Henry's rage that fired the new rebellion. Worcester, returning to Northumberland and Hotspur to find the youth in desperate wrath, was able to heighten it by saying subtly that he could understand the King's outburst. Had not Richard the Second proclaimed Mortimer heir to the Crown? This was enough. Crying out at his father and uncle for having aided Bolingbroke to the throne, Hotspur urged them to revenge the jeering and disdained contempt of a proud King. 'All studies here I solemnly deny save how to gall and pinch this Bolingbroke and that same sword-and-buckler Prince of Wales. But that I think his father loves him not, and would be glad he met with some mischance, I'd have him poisoned with a pot of ale.'

When at last Worcester could gain silence, he proposed a way by which their forces would unite with those of the Scots, of the discontented Archbishop of York, and Glendower and Lord Mortimer. Hotspur was ready now to listen: 'It cannot choose but be a noble plot.' His father, more cautious, said simply to Worcester, 'Farewell, good brother. We shall thrive, I trust.'

Certainly it seemed at first that they must thrive. When Hotspur, Worcester, Mortimer, and Owen Glendower met at Bangor, in Wales, Mortimer agreed that the promises were fair, the parties sure, and the beginning full of prosperous hope. It did not matter that there were early differences between the high-mettled Hotspur and the flaming Welshman. 'I can call spirits from the vasty deep,' Glendower boasted. 'Why so can I, or so can any man,' retorted Hotspur, 'but will they come when you do call for them?' Mortimer swiftly made peace, and they studied the map of England as they proposed to divide it between them: England south of Trent and east of Severn to Mortimer; Wales to Glendower; and to Hotspur all land north of Trent. There was trouble here, for Hotspur, objecting to the course of the river, vowed at first to have it turned. But the others calmed him; and it was planned, once the agreements were sealed, that Hotspur, Mortimer, and Worcester should set out to meet Northumberland and the Scottish force at Shrewsbury, while Glendower and his Welshmen would be standing by later with their aid.

This settled, they sat for a time in the thickening dusk where Mortimer's wife, the daughter of Glendower, sang to them in Welsh, accompanied by the sound of music her father seemed to conjure from the air. Hotspur left his wife with a quick embrace; but Mortimer lingered until Glendower rebuked him: 'You are as slow as hot Lord Percy is on fire to go.' Very soon they had ridden south and away.

King Henry was mustering an army to answer the rebels. First, he had summoned the Prince of Wales and remonstrated with him on the life he led: 'The hope, the expectation, of your time is ruined. Every man must prophesy your fall.' The King remembered how in his own youth he had been careful not to show himself too often; when he did appear he bore himself with such modesty and grace that men would follow him and compare him with the revelling, capering Richard. Sighing, he said, 'For all the world, as you are now was Richard then, when I from France set foot at Ravenspurgh. And even as I was then is Hotspur now. What never-dying honour has he got against the Scottish Douglas! . . . And now to-day he and his father, Douglas, Mortimer – all these are leagued against me.'

Henry turned away his head: 'But wherefore do I tell this news to you? Why, Harry, do I tell you of my foes that are yourself my dearest enemy?'

At this the Prince of Wales knelt before his father: 'My liege, I shall redeem myself on Percy's head. An hour will come when I shall make this northern youth exchange his glorious deeds for my indignities. I will call him to such a strict account that he shall render every glory up.'

The King rose and embraced him; and when Sir Walter Blunt entered to report the rebel assembly at Shrewsbury, he found father and son together, planning the stratagems of the war. Soon the royal drums were beating and the first of the King's armies sped towards the west.

The Prince had not forgotten Falstaff, who was sitting in the Boar's Head, grumbling, 'Company, villainous company, has spoiled me.' Seeing Hal, he asked what had happened about the robbery upon Gadshill, and the Prince reassured him: the money had been paid back. 'I do not like that paying back,' Falstaff said. 'It is a double labour.' The Prince checked him; there was no time for jest. Falstaff had been given the command of a company, and he must leave at once for the war, recruiting as he went. With this, Hal hurried from the tavern, and Falstaff beat an impatient tattoo on his plate, crying, 'Rare words! brave world! Hostess, my breakfast, come! O I could wish this tavern were my drum.'

For some days the rebels and the King's force, each encamped near Shrewsbury, waited while messengers passed between them. The rebels had an early discouragement when letters came from Northumberland to say that, because of grievous sickness, he could not gather his men to join the army. The Earl of Worcester, brooding upon the news, feared that some might say Northumberland had stayed at home for his own reasons; but Hotspur said impulsively that his father's absence would lend glory to their enterprise, for all would think they must be great indeed if, unaided, they still pressed against the King. Sir Richard Vernon appeared next to describe the King's assembly and its 'mighty preparation.' Hotspur asked one question: 'Where is the madcap Prince of Wales?' And Vernon answered, 'As full of spirit as the month of May, and gorgeous as the sun at midsummer. I saw young Harry, with his armour on, leap from the ground like feathered Mercury – vaulting with such grace upon his steed that an angel might have dropped down from the clouds to show the world some noble horsemanship.'

Hotspur exclaimed ardently, 'Let them come. I wait to take my horse which is to bear me like a thunderbolt against the bosom of the Prince of Wales . . . O that Glendower were here!' Vernon hesitated. 'There is more news, my lord. Glendower—'

'Yes, what of him?'

'He cannot raise his men for fourteen days.'

The bold Scot, Lord Douglas, not easily discomfited, said, 'That's the worst tidings I have heard of yet.' But Hotspur rallied them: 'What is the number of the King's army?' he asked, and, on the reply, 'Thirty thousand,' exclaimed, 'Then forty let it be. Even without my father and Glendower, our powers will serve to meet so great a day . . . Die all, die merrily!'

All the while, Falstaff was gathering his troops as he marched through the Midlands. His method of recruiting was his own. He took only such men as he knew could buy themselves out, so though the soldiers that remained with him were pitiful rascals, his purse was full and his spirit contented. He arrived at Shrewsbury a happy man.

In the rebel camp, Hotspur, Douglas, and Worcester received a royal envoy. Sir Walter Blunt said that the King was ready to meet their reasonable demands and to proclaim a general pardon. But Hotspur answered by reciting the history of the past years: how the members of the House of Percy had welcomed Bolingbroke back to England; how they had helped him to gain his demands; and how, once Richard had been deposed and killed, Henry had turned upon his helpers, sent Worcester from the council, dismissed Northumberland from court, disgraced Hotspur in his victories, and driven them at last to rise against the royal state. Early next day, said Hotspur, Worcester would bring their reply. 'I would you had accepted grace and love,' said Blunt. 'Maybe,' said Hotspur, 'so we shall.'

But they did not. In a windy summer daybreak, with the sun rising red and ominous over the eastern plain, the Earl of Worcester and Sir Richard Vernon brought to the King the defiance of the rebel party. When Worcester had spoken, Prince Henry stood out before the royal array: 'My lord, the Prince of Wales does join with all the world in praise of Harry Percy. For me – and I speak it to my shame – I have long stood apart from chivalry. But now, before my father, I am ready – to save the loss of blood on either side – to meet this Hotspur in a single fight.'

King Henry, pride in his face, shook his head. No, he answered, Worcester should bear once more a message that if the rebels accepted his offer, all would yet be well. If they did not yield, battle was certain. The royal party retired to its tents, and Worcester and Vernon galloped to the rebel camp. Falstaff, who had been listening aside, mused wryly that honour was but a word and one that could do no service to the dead.

Worcester and Vernon had agreed not to tell Hotspur the King's reply. If it were accepted, the rebels would be punished in time for other faults. Their one hope was battle. When Hotspur asked for the news, they said only that the King would take the field. But they did add that the Prince of Wales had stepped forth to challenge Hotspur to single combat. As he listened, a messenger brought letters that he thrust aside without reading. 'I cannot stay for these . . . Let each man do his best. Here now I draw my sword. Cry "*Esperance*! Percy!" and set on!' A full-throated answering shout of '*Esperance!* Percy!' rang across the town of Shrewsbury, and every rebel trumpet spoke.

On the plain between the camps the armies met. In the fury of the first battle, Lord Douglas came face to face with Sir Walter Blunt. Like certain other nobles, Blunt had put on armour bearing the royal insignia so that he might be mistaken for his King and lead the fight away from Henry. 'What honour do you seek upon my helm?' he cried now; and the Scot, his sword raised, challenged him: 'My name is Douglas. I follow you because some tell me that you are a King.'

'They tell you true,' said Blunt.

'Then yield my prisoner!'

'I was not born a yielder, you proud Scot!' Their swords met, and Blunt was slain. Hotspur, who saw the last moments, cried in salute, 'Douglas, if you had fought thus at Holmedon, I had never triumphed.' Douglas pointed to his victim: 'Harry, all's done. Here breathless lies the King.'

'No,' said Hotspur, 'I knew him well. A gallant knight, his armour furnished like the King's.'

Douglas gazed down at Blunt: 'A borrowed title have you bought too dear. Why did you tell me that you were a King?'

'The King,' said Hotspur, 'has many marching in his coats.' Douglas replied furiously, 'Now, by my sword, I will kill all his coats; I'll murder all his wardrobe, piece by piece, until the King confronts me.'

Later, among the alarums, Falstaff found himself isolated by Sir Walter's body. 'Sir Walter Blunt!' he mused; 'There's honour for you. Give me life. If I can save it, so much the better. If not, honour comes unlooked-for, and there's an end.'

Through the long day the Prince of Wales fought with a bravery to amaze all that watched him. During the broil he saw his father seeking to hold off Douglas, and in high peril. Rushing between them, he cried, 'Hold up your head, vile Scot! It is the Prince of Wales that threatens now!' Desperately he repulsed Douglas, only to find, when the Scot had retreated and his father had hastened across the battlefield, that he was in the presence of Hotspur himself, armour dinted, face blood-stained.

Jubilantly, Hotspur spoke: 'If I mistake not, you are Prince Henry!'

'You speak as if I would deny myself,' said the Prince. Hotspur said merely, pointing to his shield, 'My name is Harry Percy'; and, with a cry of exultation, the Prince answered, 'Why then, I see a very valiant rebel of that name. Do not think to share with me in glory any more. Our England cannot bear a double rule of Harry Percy and the Prince of Wales.'

'Nor shall it!' threatened Hotspur. 'The hour has come to end the one of us. Would to God your fame in arms were now as great as mine!' Exclaiming 'I'll make it greater ere I part from you,' Prince Henry lunged at Hotspur who caught the blow on his shield. The battle was thick about them while they fought. Douglas, in wild career, had stabbed at Falstaff who fell as if he were dead.

After a prolonged and bitter conflict, Hotspur tired at last. He stumbled, the Prince gave him the death-blow, and he sank upon his knee, gasping, 'O Harry, you have robbed me of my youth.' Then he fell forward dead, and the Prince bent to cover his face: 'Fare you well, great heart. Take your praise to heaven.' Looking up, he spied Falstaff on the ground: 'What, old acquaintance! Poor Jack, adieu . . . I could have better spared a better man.' Sorrowfully, he walked away; and, as soon as he had gone, Falstaff struggled uneasily to his feet. 'I was wise to sham death, or that furious Scot would have had me. The better part of valour is discretion.'

He went towards Hotspur's body: 'I am afraid of this gunpowder Percy, even though he be dead. I'll make sure, and then swear that I killed him.' Stabbing Hotspur in the thigh and painfully lowering himself and hoisting the body on his back, he was about to go when Prince Hal strode back with his brother, Prince John of Lancaster.

'Did you not tell me,' said John, startled, 'that this fat man was dead?'

'Are you alive?' asked Prince Henry, 'or is this sight a fantasy?'

'I am alive,' said Falstaff in his most dignified tone. 'There is Percy.' He threw the body down. 'I look to be either an earl or a duke, I assure you.'

'Why,' said the Prince, 'I killed Percy myself and saw you dead.'

Falstaff looked innocently hurt. 'Lord, lord, how this world is given to lying! I grant you, I was down and out of breath, and so was he; but we both rose and fought a long hour by Shrewsbury clock.'

Prince John laughed in amazement. 'This is the strangest tale that ever I heard'; and his brother said resignedly, 'This is the strangest fellow. Come, Falstaff, I'll do my best for you . . . But listen! The trumpet sounds retreat. The day is ours.'

Presently, beneath the royal standard, King Henry stood with his nobles. Worcester and Sir Richard Vernon were brought in bare-headed, their hands bound. 'This is the end of rebellion,' said the King. 'Ill-spirited Worcester, did I not send grace, pardon, and terms of love to all of you?'

Steadily Worcester answered, 'I accept my fortune.'

'Then,' said the King, 'bear these men to death.' When they were gone, the Prince knelt to his father: 'At my tent Lord Douglas lies; and I beseech your grace I may dispose of him.'

'With all my heart,' King Henry said; and the Prince called to his brother, 'Then, John of Lancaster, go to the valiant Douglas and tell him he is ransomless and free.'

Nothing remained but to crush rebellion finally. The King despatched Prince John to march upon Northumberland and the Archbishop of York. He and the Prince of Wales would move against Glendower: 'Since this business so fair is done, let us not leave till all our task be won.' By sunset, only the wind that had blown all day still fretted above the littered field of Shrewsbury.

THE SECOND PART OF

KING HENRY IV

AFTER the battle of Shrewsbury conflicting rumours sped to the north. Some of them said that Hotspur had slain the young Prince, and that King Henry himself had fallen to Douglas. The Lord Bardolph, one of the Earl of Northumberland's trusted allies, believed that the news he heard was true, and he rode hard with it to the strong and remote castle of Warkworth where Northumberland, recovering from sickness, was walking beneath his orchard trees. 'Noble earl,' cried Bardolph, 'I bring you certain news from Shrewsbury. The King is wounded almost to the death; Prince Henry slain outright; and young Prince John, with Westmoreland and Stafford, fly the field.'

Northumberland asked at once how Bardolph had heard this. Had he come from Shrewsbury? Bardolph admitted that he had not: 'a gentleman, well-bred and of good name,' had given him the news. 'We shall know soon,' said the Earl, listening to a ring of hooves at the gate. 'This is my servant Travers whom days ago I sent for tidings.' Bardolph scoffed, 'Travers? My lord, I passed him on the way. He can tell you no more than I do.' But Northumberland, ignoring him, turned to the newcomer and knew at once that rumour was denied. Travers had spoken with a fugitive from Shrewsbury: 'He told me that rebellion had ill luck, and that young Harry Percy's spur was cold.'

Lord Bardolph said impatiently, 'If my young lord, your son, have not the day, I'll yield my title. Never talk of it.'

But another rider galloped in, a second retainer of Northumberland, one Morton. He looked profoundly grieved, and when the Earl questioned him, he could barely speak, 'I ran from Shrewsbury, my noble lord.'

'My son—?' asked Northumberland. 'My brother—?' He stopped, for Morton seemed about to fall. 'Even such a man, so faint, so spiritless, so woe-begone, drew Priam's curtain in the dead of night and would have told him half his Troy was burned.'

Morton spoke tonelessly: 'My lord, your son—.' And Northumberland finished the sentence: 'My son is dead.'

'I cannot think so,' Lord Bardolph protested. But now Morton found his voice and he told them the fatal tale of Shrewsbury; how the Prince had beaten down the never-daunted Hotspur; how the news of his loss caused Hotspur's men to despair and retreat; how Worcester and Douglas both were taken; and how King Henry had now despatched his forces to the rebellious north.

At first, on hearing this, Northumberland was overborne by passionate rage; but he grew quiet when he was told that it was time not to mourn but again to venture; the Archbishop of York had already raised an army, and the north was strong against the King. 'Go in with me,' said the Earl, 'and show to every man the surest way to safety and revenge.'

Down in London Sir John Falstaff, not only witty in himself, but (as he said) the cause of wit in other men, was walking with his page, wondering where he could raise money. He was so lost in thought that he did not observe the approach of the Lord Chief Justice, an upright judge who had once committed the Prince of Wales himself to prison for striking him. Falstaff turned to avoid being seen; but, of all men, he could not hope to escape. The Justice's servant called to him, and Falstaff's page Robin said, 'You must speak louder; my master is deaf.'

The Lord Chief Justice corrected him: 'I am sure he is deaf to anything good. Pluck him by the elbow . . . Sir John, a word with you.' Falstaff moved across in obsequious salutation; and the Justice, after telling him that he lived in great infamy and had misled the Prince of Wales, said that his day's service on the field of Shrewsbury had atoned a little for the night's exploit on Gadshill. But now that all was well, he had better keep it so and not awaken a sleeping wolf. 'God send the Prince a better companion!' To which Falstaff replied, 'God send the companion a better Prince!'

'Well, the King has severed you and Prince Henry,' said the Lord Chief Justice. 'I hear you are going with Lord John of Lancaster against the Archbishop and the Earl of Northumberland.'

'I would my name were not so terrible to the enemy as it is,' answered Falstaff. 'Will your worship lend me a thousand pounds to furnish my expedition?'

The old Justice had amusement in his eyes though his voice was stern. 'Not a penny, not a penny. Fare you well, Sir John. Commend me to my cousin Westmoreland.' He walked on with dignity, and Falstaff spoke to his page: 'What money is in my purse?'

'Seven groats and two pence, sir.'

'I can find no remedy against this consumption of the purse,' said Falstaff. 'Borrowing serves for a while, but the disease is incurable. Bear now these letters for me, this to my lord of Lancaster, this to the Prince, this to the Earl of Westmoreland, and this to old Mistress Ursula whom I have weekly sworn to marry since I perceived the first white hairs on my chin. Away! You know where to find me.'

Other people wished to know where to find him. One, a few days later, was Mistress Quickly, hostess of the Boar's Head Tavern, who had engaged two sheriff's officers, Fang and Snare, to arrest him for debt. She was with them when they met Falstaff in the street. A brawl ensued that was stopped only by the entrance of the Lord Chief Justice asking what the matter was. 'Why, are you brawling here, Sir John!' he exclaimed; 'You should have been well on your way to York.'

'My most worshipful lord,' pleaded Mistress Quickly, 'I am a poor widow of Eastcheap, and he is arrested at my suit.'

'For what sum?' the Justice asked; and Mistress Quickly said it was for all she had: he had eaten her out of house and home. When Falstaff demanded the exact sum he owed her, she replied that if he were honest, it was himself and the money as well. And she went off into a detailed description of the precise evening on which he had sworn to marry her: a Wednesday in Whitsun week as he was sitting at a round table by a sea-coal fire in the Dolphin chamber of her tavern. Falstaff tried to say that she was a poor mad soul distracted by poverty, but the Justice ordered him to pay the debt, one part of it with money, the other with repentance. 'Come hither, hostess,' said Falstaff, sighing, and within a minute he had persuaded her both to pawn her plate to get ten pounds for him, and to invite him back to supper where, she promised, Doll Tearsheet would be waiting.

That day the Prince of Wales, back in London, received a letter that was signed 'Jack Falstaff with my familiars, John with my brothers and sisters, and Sir John with all Europe.' Hearing that he proposed to sup that night at the tavern with Mistress Quickly and Doll Tearsheet, the Prince and Poins resolved to disguise themselves in leather jerkins and aprons and attend upon Falstaff as potboys. When they reached the Boar's Head it was plain that it had already been a merry night. Doll Tearsheet had drunk too much wine; Mistress Quickly was more talkative than ever; and one of Falstaff's followers, the swaggering Pistol, had already quarrelled with Doll until the tavern rang with their taunts and with the muddled snatches from old plays that Pistol would bellow at the top of his voice:

'Shall pack-horses,
And hollow pampered jades of Asia,
Which cannot go but thirty miles a day,
Compare with Caesars, and with cannibals,
And Trojan Greeks?'

'Pistol,' said Falstaff, 'I would be quiet.'

When the fellow shouted louder than ever, Falstaff, with unwonted decision, drew his sword and drove the man before him down the stairs. Hired musicians began to play; and Doll, under the influence of wine and music and in the most sentimental mood, sat upon Falstaff's knee and said to him, as she embraced him, 'When will you begin to patch up your old body for heaven?' Falstaff was suddenly very still. 'Peace, good Doll, do not speak like a death's head. Do not bid me remember my end.' But Doll was off now in another vein; neither she nor Falstaff noticed the appearance behind them of the Prince and Poins in their potboys' aprons.

'What is the Prince like?' Doll was asking.

'Oh, a good shallow young fellow,' Falstaff told her. 'He would have made a good pantry-boy, chipping the bread-crusts.'

'They say Poins has a good wit.'

'He a good wit! 'Tis as thick as Tewkesbury mustard.'

So they went on talking while Poins and the Prince, half-frowning half-laughing, listened to them unseen. Doll's head was on Falstaff's shoulder, and she drew him to her. 'I kiss you,' she said, 'with a most constant heart.'

Falstaff said with a melancholy sigh, 'I am old, I am old. You will forget me when I have gone.'

'If you say so,' answered Doll, 'you will set me weeping.' Falstaff, without looking up, called for sack, and with a shout of 'Anon, anon, sir!', the Prince and Poins left the shadows and stood beside him at the fire. 'What a life you lead!' cried the Prince. 'A better than yours,' retaliated Falstaff, unabashed at their presence. 'I am a gentleman. You are a potboy.'

Knocking battered at the door. It was a messenger to say that the King was at Westminster; that news was arriving from the north; and that captains were calling at the taverns and asking for Falstaff. 'By heavens, Poins,' said the Prince, 'I am to blame for spending time so idly. My sword and cloak! Falstaff, good night!' More knocking now: Falstaff was summoned, and with a reluctant look at Doll, at the bright fire, and at the tankard by his side, he climbed heavily from his chair. 'Pay the musicians!' he said to little Robin who bore his purse. 'Farewell, hostess! Farewell, Doll! You see how men of merit are sought after. The undeserving sleep, but the man of action is called.'

Doll was in helpless tears. 'I cannot speak . . . Well, my sweet Jack, have a care of yourself.' A draught from the open door fluttered the candles; cries of 'Farewell!' disturbed the midnight gloom of Eastcheap.

In the Palace of Westminster King Henry, ill and huddled in a chair, was remembering how many thousands of his honest subjects were at that hour asleep. His mind was thick with fancies. Shifting uneasily among the cushions, he asked why upon some night of storm a ship-boy could find sleep upon his high and giddy mast, while on the calmest and most tranquil night a King must fret awake. 'Uneasy lies the head that wears a crown.'

It was past one o'clock when the Earls of Surrey and Warwick discovered him there, brooding over the land's present dangers. He remembered how King Richard, once calling Northumberland 'the ladder by which my cousin Bolingbroke ascends my throne,' had prophesied the breaking of their friendship and this dire rebellion. Warwick soothed the King's troubled mind. Rumour, he said, had falsely doubled the numbers of the northern rebels; Prince John and Westmoreland would easily subdue them. Moreover, he had learned from Wales that Owen Glendower was dead. The King's face lightened a little but conscience still beset him. As he tried to rest, he mused longingly, 'Were these wars at an end, we would, dear lords, unto the Holy Land.'

The King would have slept more surely that night if he had known that Northumberland had already withdrawn from the war and taken refuge in Scotland at the insistence of his wife and of Hotspur's widow. The rebellion, indeed, was in its last weeks. When, at length, the rebels, under the Archbishop of York, Lord Mowbray (the Duke of Norfolk's son), and Lord Hastings, took stand in the Yorkshire forest of Gaultree, the Earl of Westmoreland came from Prince John to offer a parley and the satisfaction of their reasonable demands. The rebels agreeing to this, midway between the armies the leaders met. There Prince John promised that rebel grievances should be speedily redressed: 'If it please you, discharge your powers. We will likewise dismiss our men and drink to friendship here.'

While they stood talking, Lord Hastings went to discharge the rebel army and came back presently to say that it had already dispersed to every compass-point. The rebels were aware of a sudden that a ring of armed men had been marshalled round them. As they looked at this guard in dismay, the Earl of Westmoreland struck Hastings upon the shoulder, crying, 'I do arrest you, traitor, of high treason. You, too, Lord Archbishop, and you, Lord Mowbray – of capital treason I arrest you both.'

'Is this proceeding just and honourable?' demanded Mowbray; but Westmoreland rebuked him: 'Is your assembly so?' The Archbishop cried in agony, 'Will you thus break your faith?' only to be answered in blunt terms by Prince John, 'I offered none, merely the redress of those grievances of which you did complain. This, I promise you, I will perform . . . But, for yourselves, look only to meet the fate due to all rebels.' Sharply he ordered, 'Guards, bring these traitors to the block of death!', and the wretched men were led forthwith to doom.

When Prince John prepared to march back to London, Falstaff, who was in his troop, obtained leave to go on a roundabout journey through Gloucestershire. He had been there very recently on a recruiting expedition, and he had seen possibilities in the garrulous and kindly Cotswold Justice of the Peace with whom he had stayed. Shallow, who was a small, frail, bearded man, living talkatively in the past, had once been a student in London, at Clement's Inn, and he loved to imagine that he had been called 'lusty Shallow' and 'mad Shallow'. Nothing pleased him more than to remember, and to exaggerate, his deeds, at a time when Jack Falstaff was a boy and a page to the Duke of Norfolk. His talk flickered like his flickering mind.

'To see how many of my old acquaintance are dead!' he mused to his admiring and laconic fellow-Justice and cousin, Silence.

'We shall all follow,' Silence said.

'Certain,' said Shallow, ' 'tis certain, very sure, very sure, death, as the Psalmist saith, is certain to all, all must die . . . How much for a good yoke of bullocks at Stamford Fair?'

'I was not there myself,' answered Silence, and Shallow went on, 'Death is certain . . . Is old Double of your town living yet?'

'Dead, sir.'

'Dead? . . . He drew a good bow . . . and dead! . . . He shot a fine shoot. John of Gaunt loved him well and betted much money on his head. Dead! . . . What for a score of ewes now?'

'Thereafter as they be,' said Silence stolidly, adding, 'A score of good ewes may be worth ten pounds.'

It was then that Falstaff had arrived, greeting the Justices jovially, and, in the hot summer weather, preparing to recruit the men Shallow had assembled. The two most likely were the glum Ralph Mouldy and the craven Peter Bullcalf, but they duly paid to be released. Falstaff took instead the cadaverous Simon Shadow, explaining that he presented no mark to the foe who might just as well aim at the edge of a penknife, and the gallant Francis Feeble, a woman's tailor, who said simply, 'A man can die but once. We owe God a death.'

While this was going on, Shallow had babbled eagerly to his visitor. Saying, 'We have heard the chimes at midnight, Master Shallow,' Falstaff humoured the old man's talk of fifty-five years before and his fantasies about 'the mad days we have seen,' In fact, they had met at

Clement's Inn when young Shallow looked like nothing more than 'a man made after supper of a cheese-paring.' Now he had become a simple prattling squire who talked as familiarly of John of Gaunt as if he had been Gaunt's sworn brother. 'Lord, lord,' murmured Falstaff, 'how subject we old men are to this vice of lying!' For all this it had been a profitable day in the Cotswold remoteness; and as Falstaff rode down from Yorkshire after the rebels had been dispersed in Gaultree Forest, he was eager to make good use of Shallow's garrulous fellowship.

In London King Henry was now very ill. Awaiting news from the north, he lay at Westminster in the room that was called the Jerusalem Chamber, with two of his youngest sons, the Princes Thomas of Clarence and Humphrey of Gloucester, and certain of his lords, notably Warwick, standing about the bed. He was still thinking of the crusade to the Holy Land that he would never make, and he told himself that he would go upon it as soon as he was stronger and rebellion had been crushed. Peering now at the faces by his bedside, he asked for the Prince of Wales: 'Humphrey, my son of Gloucester, where is the Prince your brother?' 'I think,' Gloucester replied, 'that he has gone to hunt, my lord, at Windsor.'

'Is not his brother Thomas of Clarence with him?'

'No, my good lord,' said Gloucester, 'he is in presence here'; and Clarence asked gently, 'What would my lord and father?' The King said affectionately, 'Nothing but well to thee, Thomas . . . but why are you not with the Prince of Wales? He loves you more than any of his brothers. Then cherish him, my boy, and when I am dead, make what peace you can between his greatness and my other sons. Do not seem cold or careless, for he is gracious if he is observed; he has a tear for pity, though in anger he is flint. So watch his temper, Thomas; chide his faults only when you see he is inclined to mirth. When he is moody, give him time and scope . . . Learn this, and be a shelter to your friends, a hoop of gold to bind your brothers.'

'I shall observe him,' promised Clarence, 'with all care and love.'

'Why are you not at Windsor with him?' the King repeated; and Clarence said hesitantly, 'He is not there to-day: he dines in London with Poins and his constant followers.'

The King brooded before he spoke his thoughts; he dreaded to look beyond his death, to a time when Prince Henry's headstrong riot had no curb. Then he stirred as Westmoreland knelt beside his bed to tell him that the fighting was over: 'Peace puts forth her olive everywhere.' In a voice louder and clearer than he had used since his illness began, the King said, 'O Westmoreland, you are a summer bird that ever in the heart of winter sings the lifting-up of day.'

More good news followed, and again from Yorkshire. There the Sheriff had routed the Earl of Northumberland and Lord Bardolph as they marched southward with a great army of Scots and English. But King Henry's momentary strength had waned; crying out, he lay inert, weakened by a stroke. Upon opening his eyes he demanded to be borne into some other chamber, and he was carried to an inner room where he asked for gentle music, and for the crown to be set beside his pillow on its cushion of cloth-of-gold. He closed his eyes and seemed disposed to sleep, while Warwick whispered, 'Less noise, less noise!'

Unknowing, the Prince of Wales had come into the room, saying loudly, 'Has he heard the good news yet? Tell it to him.'

'He altered much when he heard it,' said Gloucester; and the Prince laughed: 'If he be sick with joy, he'll recover without physic.' Warwick implored again, 'Not so much noise, my lord! Sweet prince, I beg you to speak low.' The Prince nodded: 'I will sit here and watch beside the King.'

They left him; and the Prince gazed curiously at the Crown of England on the pillow by his father's head. It had caused much pain and many sleepless nights. Why should it lie there now? By the crown a small feather had drifted from somewhere to the pillow; Henry, studying it idly, his mind on other things, realised that it did not move, as move it must if the King were breathing. Suddenly appalled, he drew back the coverlet and bent over the rigid form. 'My gracious lord!' he said; then, more loudly, 'My father!' There was no sound, no movement; and he knelt crossing himself: 'Dear father, your right from me is tears, which I shall pay. My right from you is this imperial crown.' Reaching for it, he placed it on his head. 'See where it sits. Nothing shall take this lineal honour from me.' Still wearing the crown, he walked slowly from the chamber.

Now, feebly, the King stirred. He called, 'Warwick! Gloucester! Clarence!' And as they entered by another door, 'Warwick! Gloucester! why did you leave me?' Clarence, surprised, said that they had left the Prince of Wales to sit and watch by him. Warwick pointed to the second door, which stood open: 'He has gone that way.'

The King, for all his illness, was in anger: 'Where is the crown? Who has taken it from my pillow?' Then: 'The Prince has taken it. Is he so hasty that he supposes my sleep my death? Find him, my lord of Warwick.' In the far room Warwick at once discovered the Prince who was weeping still when he returned with the crown. As the others hurried from the presence, he went to his father's side: 'I never thought to hear you speak again.'

There was no gentleness in the King's reply: 'Your wish was father, Harry, to that thought. I stay too long by you, I weary you. Do you so hunger for my empty chair?' He was using his last strength. 'Henry the fifth is crowned! Up, vanity! Down, royal state! O, my poor kingdom, sick with civil blows, here you must be a wilderness again, peopled with wolves – your old inhabitants!'

Exhausted, he lay back. Replacing the crown upon the pillow, the Prince knelt in sorrow and tried to explain his act. In grief at seeing, as he thought, his father dead, he had taken the crown and upbraided it as though it had been an enemy, one that destroyed its wearer. 'If it did infect my blood with joy, or swell my thoughts to any strain of pride, then let God forever keep it from me.'

The King's wrath had ebbed. He was now in his final extremity. In a whisper scarcely audible, he gave his last dying counsel, remembering how indirectly he had reached the crown; how he had fought to bear its burden; how even yet it was not safely held. And he urged his son to turn all minds from it and to distract them with foreign quarrels. Barely able to speak, he said as Henry leant over him, 'How I came by this crown, O God forgive; and grant it may with you in true peace live.'

Prince John and others had come in to their father. Faintly he asked if the room where he had first swooned had any name, and Warwick replied that it was called Jerusalem. Hearing this, the King uttered his last words: 'There my life must end. They told me I should die but in

Jerusalem, which vainly I supposed the Holy Land . . . Now bear me to that chamber. There I'll lie. In that Jerusalem shall Harry die.'

Far off, in the quiet afternoon sunshine of Gloucestershire, Justice Shallow had insisted that Falstaff, whom he was proud to meet again, should stay for the night. 'I will not excuse you,' he said. 'You shall not be excused, excuse shall not be admitted, there is no excuse shall serve. Why, Davy!' His servant entered. 'Let me see, let me see . . . yea, marry – William cook, bid him come hither. Are there no young pigeons? . . . You shall not be excused, Sir John.'

Davy, used to his master's rambling, waited stolidly: 'Yes, sir, but here is now the smith's note for shoeing and plough-irons.'

'Let it be checked and paid . . . Sir John, you shall not be excused.'

Davy went on solemnly, 'Now, sir, a new link to the bucket must needs be had. And, sir, do you mean to stop any of William's wages about the sack he lost the other day at Hinckley fair?'

'Yes, yes,' said Shallow testily, 'he shall answer it. And now, some pigeons, Davy, a couple of short-legged hens, a joint of mutton, and any pretty little tiny kickshaws, tell William cook.'

Davy turned to look at Falstaff. 'Does the man of war stay all night, sir?'

Shallow beckoned him aside. 'Yea, Davy, I will use him well. A friend in court is better than a penny in the purse. About your business, Davy . . . Now where are you, Sir John? Come, come, come, off with your boots . . . Come, Sir John.' He bustled off while Falstaff, saying, 'I'll follow you, good Master Robert Shallow,' chuckled to himself: 'I will get matter enough out of this Shallow to keep Prince Henry in continual laughter. He shall laugh till his face be like a wet cloak ill laid up.' And Falstaff followed the old Justice into the house.

That evening, after supper, in the long serene twilight, they sat under an arbour in Shallow's orchard while Davy put a dish of apples on the table, Shallow chattered unceasingly ('I have drunk too much sack at supper'), and Silence, who had been with them and who was in a mood as mellow as the night, sang to himself, ' 'Tis merry in hall when beards wag all. And welcome, merry Shrove-tide!'

Davy went round with the wine; Shallow gave his busy, clucking orders; Silence said with some difficulty 'We shall be merry. Now comes in the sweet of the night.' It was a very long way from Eastcheap, thought Falstaff as he said, 'Health and long life to you, Master Silence!', and Silence sang unexpectedly, 'Fill the cup, and let it come; I'll pledge you a mile to the bottom.'

While they sat peacefully, they heard from across the orchard a thunderous banging at the house-door. Silence and Falstaff, who were pledging each other, took no notice, but Shallow called fussily, 'Look who's at the door there!' and Davy, still unhurried, went away beneath the trees. In a moment he returned: 'An it please your worship, there's one Pistol, come from the court with news.' Falstaff looked up in sharp excitement: 'From the court? Let him come in.' And into the orchard, a strange sight in this rural world, came the flamboyant figure of Pistol, travel-stained, his beard and moustaches bristling, and a scarlet cloak swung about him. Gazing at him with mild interest, Silence said, 'I think he be but Goodman Puff of Barson.'

'Puff!' boomed Pistol. He stared at Silence who stared back at him benignly. 'Puff in thy teeth, most recreant coward base!' He stalked across to Falstaff: 'Sweet knight, thou art now one of the greatest men in the realm. Tidings do I bring, and lucky joys, and golden times, and happy news of price!'

'I pray you now,' said Falstaff, 'deliver this like a man of this world.' Then, listening to another of Pistol's flourishes, he shrugged and replied in the same vein: 'O base Assyrian knight, what is thy news? Let King Cophetua know the truth thereof!' Silence, his eyes closed, was singing to himself about Robin Hood, Scarlet, and John; and Pistol, glaring at him, roared, 'Shall good news be baffled?'

Shallow, who had been observing him in some surprise, now spoke with dignity: 'Give me pardon, sir. If, sir, you come with news from the court, I take it there's but two ways, either to utter them or conceal them.' He drew himself up: 'I am, sir, under the King, in some authority.'

'Under which King, Besonian?' cried Pistol. 'Speak, or die!'

'Under King Harry!' said Shallow; whereupon Pistol, in a voice that set the doves fluttering from their cote and the dogs barking on the orchard fringe, cried, 'Harry the fourth – or fifth?'

'Harry the fourth.'

Pistol snapped his fingers. 'That for thy office! . . . Sir John, thy tender lambkin now is King. Harry the Fifth's the man. I speak the truth.'

Falstaff was looking into the distance. 'What, Pistol, is the old King dead?'

'As nail in door,' said Pistol. 'The things I speak are just.'

Falstaff came briskly to himself. 'Then saddle my horse! Master Robert Shallow, choose what office you will in the land, it is yours.'

Beside them a plump figure had slipped down under the table; he lay there, breathing heavily and contentedly. Falstaff beckoned. 'Carry Master Silence to bed . . . Now, Master Shallow, my lord Shallow, be what you will, I am fortune's steward. Get on your boots; we'll ride all night.' As they hurried over the turf, Shallow twittering in front and Pistol storming away behind, Falstaff exclaimed, 'I know the young King is sick for me. Let us take any man's horses, the laws of England are at my commandment. Blessed are they that have been my friends . . . and woe to the Lord Chief Justice!'

Within less than an hour, hooves were clattering along the lonely Cotswold roads as John Falstaff and his troop, Shallow still bewildered, flaming Pistol, red-nosed Bardolph, and the youthful page, headed at a trot towards the new promise of Henry the Fifth's London.

In Westminster there had been both grief and fear. How would the young King deal with those who had opposed his youthful riot? It looked ill for his brothers; for the Lord Chief Justice who had once sent him to prison; and for the grave lords of Henry the Fourth. Clarence said sadly to the Lord Chief Justice, 'Well, you must now speak Sir John Falstaff fair.'

But all doubts were resolved when the King entered. 'Let me but bear your love,' he said to his brothers, 'I'll bear your cares.' And though he seemed to look coldly at first upon the Lord Chief Justice, the old man's wise and dignified words brought from the King a royal response: 'You shall be as a father to my youth. As you prompt me I shall speak, humbling myself to you and to your counsel.' The reveller of Eastcheap had gone; in his place was a young and sombre monarch.

Unknowing, Falstaff was riding on through the summer night. When at last he and Shallow had reached their London lodging, he planned to take his place close to Westminster on the day of the Coronation and to make himself prominent among the crowd as the King passed by.

At the time appointed he duly took his stand with his party round him. 'Come here by me, Master Robert Shallow,' he said, 'I will make the King do you grace. Mark his expression when I speak to him.' He was not at all dismayed when he learned from the roar that with Pistol served for a whisper, that Doll Tearsheet had been taken to prison. 'I will deliver her,' he said confidently. Now the bells were swinging and the royal trumpets pealing; and the vast crowd shouted as Henry the Fifth, crowned and robed, and followed by his lords, the Chief Justice among them, moved in procession from the Abbey. As they approached him, Falstaff pushed out before the front rank of the crowd and cried, 'God save your grace, King Hal, my royal Hal!' Pistol exhorted, 'The heavens thee guard and keep, most royal imp of fame!'; and Falstaff again took up the cry, 'God save you, my sweet boy!'

The crowd listened in astonished speculation. This, then, was Sir John Falstaff; this was the King's companion in the days of riot. Everywhere a whispered hiss of 'Falstaff'; everywhere faces turned to the King. Henry showed no recognition. 'My Lord Chief Justice,' he said, 'speak to that vain man'; and the Justice called to Falstaff, 'Have you your wits? Know what it is you speak?' Falstaff, unheeding, kept up his confident shout, 'My King, my Jove! I speak to you, my heart!' Old Shallow, trembling with hope beside him, waited for the miracle.

There was no miracle. Henry, still in the same cold, impersonal voice, addressed himself to Falstaff who stood like one stricken. 'I know you not, old man; fall to your prayers. How ill white hairs become a fool and jester! I have long dreamed of such a man as you, but, being awake, I do despise my dream . . . Know that the grave doth gape for you, thrice wider than for other men.' Falstaff began to smile. Surely it was the Boar's Head humour – Hal at his tricks? The crowd saw the last hint of the old Falstaff, a kindling of the eye and a swing of the body as he prepared to launch an answering quip. Then hope was cruelly quenched: 'Reply not to me with a fool-born jest!' The spark died; and Falstaff faded into a man tired and old as Henry went on inexorably, 'Presume not that I am the thing I was, for as I have turned away my former self, so I banish those that kept me company. Do not come near our person by ten miles.'

He spoke to the Lord Chief Justice and turned to look at Falstaff for the last time: 'Such means I will allow you that poverty enforce you not to evil . . . Be it your charge, my lord, to see this done . . . Set on!'

The glittering procession rolled forward; the crowd scattered with curious looks at Falstaff, and he was left with Shallow and his followers, a broken man. The King had killed his heart, and what was left to do? 'Master Shallow,' he said, 'I owe you a thousand pounds.' Shallow piped despondently, 'Yea, marry, Sir John, which I beseech you to let me bear home with me.'

Falstaff, squaring his shoulders, tried miserably to look unconcerned. 'Do not grieve, Master Shallow. I shall be sent for in private, for, look you, he must be seen thus to the world. I will yet be the man that shall make you great.' Shallow gave his quick headshake and said in the thin voice that now crackled with disbelief, 'I beseech you, good Sir John, let me have five hundred of my thousand.'

'I will be as good as my word,' repeated Falstaff. 'The King's saying was but a ruse. Go with me to dinner. I shall be sent for soon at night.'

It was not so, for the Lord Chief Justice reappeared with his officers. 'Go,' he said, 'bear Sir John Falstaff to the Fleet Prison, and all his company along with him.'

'My lord, my lord—!' pleaded Falstaff.

The Lord Chief Justice waved him aside. 'I cannot speak now. I will hear you soon. Take them away!' The officers advanced; and there, in the bright afternoon, Falstaff and Shallow, Pistol and Bardolph were hustled across the rush-strewn cobbles. Over all still pealed the bells of Westminster, and, far off, London was shouting for its King.

THE LIFE OF
KING HENRY V

Outside the Presence Chamber of Henry the Fifth, King of England, who had been Henry Prince of Wales, envoys from the French Dauphin, Lewis, waited for audience. It was a summer afternoon in the year 1415. Within the chamber the King, then twenty-seven years of age, a man with dark smooth hair and bright eyes, in speech firm and composed, in bearing regal, addressed two venerable Churchmen, the Archbishop of Canterbury and the Bishop of Ely, demanding to know from them the facts of his claim to the throne of France: 'May I with right and conscience make it?'

In a long and intricate speech to which Henry listened with patience, the Archbishop established to his own satisfaction the justice of the claim. Then the Bishop of Ely, rising emotionally, urged the King to remember his mighty ancestors: 'You are their heir, you sit upon their throne. And my thrice-puissant liege is in the very May-morn of his youth, ripe for exploits and mighty enterprises.'

Now the lords of England added their appeal. 'Your brother Kings,' said the Duke of Exeter, 'all expect that you should rouse yourself as did the former lions of your blood.' The Earl of Westmoreland said, 'They know your grace has cause, and means, and right.' The King replied to this that they must arm not only against the French but prepare also to defend the northern borders against the Scots. Westmoreland quoted the saying, very old and true: 'If that you will France win, then with Scotland first begin.' And the Archbishop rejoined that if the King took one quarter of his powers into France, those left at home would be enough to defend their own doors from assault.

Henry, having considered this, beckoned to his attendants. 'Call in the messengers sent from the Dauphin. Now are we well resolved.'

The principal ambassador faced the King with a demeanour that contrived to be at once respectful and arrogant. England, he said, had lately sent to France a claim for certain dukedoms. In reply the Dauphin bade them say, 'You speak too like a youth. No game can win you any part of France; you cannot revel into dukedoms there. He sends then, as a gift more fitting, this chest of treasure.' And two officers brought down the chamber a chest, gilded, barred, and emblazoned with the fleur-de-lys. Bowing to the King, they placed it before the throne; and the ambassador proceeded, 'Then let the dukedoms that you claim hear nothing more of you. So the Dauphin speaks.'

With unchanging countenance, King Henry said to Exeter who stood by him, 'What treasure, uncle?' Exeter lifted the lid of the chest and let it fall again with an angry clash: 'Tennis-balls, my liege.'

There was so long a silence that even the arrogant ambassador shifted nervously. At length Henry spoke, slowly at first but rising into a passionate warning: 'We are glad the Dauphin is so pleasant with us . . . But tell him now this jest of his has turned these balls to gun-stones: we are coming to revenge us as we may. Now get you hence and say so. This will seem a thing of shallow wit when thousands weep more than have laughed at it.' To his attendants Henry said, 'Convey them with safe conduct. So farewell.'

'This was a merry message,' said Exeter, frowning at the Dauphin's gift.

Henry smiled for the first time that afternoon. 'We hope, uncle, to make the sender blush. Come, lords . . . We have no thought in us but France.'

During the ensuing weeks of swift preparation, three treacherous nobles, Richard Earl of Cambridge, Henry Lord Scroop of Masham, and Sir Thomas Grey, a Northumbrian knight, vowed for a French reward to kill King Henry before he took ship from Southampton. Meanwhile the fleet assembled, and from all over the land soldiers, veterans or newly recruited, marched to take ship. Three veterans were Sir John Falstaff's old followers, Pistol, who was now married to the former Mistress Nell Quickly of the Boar's Head; Bardolph, and Nym. Pistol was still his old flamboyant self. To Bardolph's greeting, 'Mine host, Pistol!' he replied, 'Base tyke, call'st thou me host! Now by this hand I swear I scorn the title!' And when Nym said, 'You'll pay me the eight shillings I won of you at betting,' back came the thrust, 'Base is the knave that pays.' But the departure for France was sad. Falstaff had died, and Bardolph said wistfully, 'Would I were with him, wherever he be, in heaven or in hell.'

'Nay,' said the former Nell Quickly, 'he's in Arthur's bosom, if ever a man went to Arthur's bosom. He went away as if he had been a babe in arms. It was just between twelve and one, at the turning of the tide. After I saw him fumble with the bedclothes, and play with flowers, and smile at his finger-tips, I knew there was no way but one; for his nose was as sharp as a pen and he babbled of green fields. "How now, Sir John?" said I. "What, man, be of good cheer?" He cried out "God!" three or four times; to comfort him I hoped there was no need for him to trouble himself with any such thoughts yet. So he bade me lay more clothes on his feet. I put my hand into the bed and felt them, and they were as cold as any stone, and so upward and upward, and all was cold as any stone.'

'They say he cried out for sack,' said Nym.

'Ay, that he did,' said Nell.

'And of women,' put in Bardolph.

'Nay,' said Nell, 'that he did not!' but when Falstaff's page corrected her, she said gloomily, 'He did so, and he said they were devils incarnate. He could never abide carnation; it was a colour he never liked.'

'Shall we move?' insisted Nym. 'The King will be gone from Southampton.' And the little party tramped off down the street while Nell, weeping, waved after them from the tavern door until they had turned the corner out of her sight.

At Southampton, with the wind fair for France, King Henry prepared to sail. But first he had to deal with the three traitors of whose treachery he had been kept informed. Flattering, they gathered round him. When he told Exeter to release a man who had abused him on the previous day, the traitors each swore that the offender must be punished. Ironically, the King answered, 'We'll yet forgive him, though Cambridge, Scroop, and Grey, in their dear care and tender preservation of our person, would have him punished.' Saying this, he handed to the three men documents which they assumed to be the letters of appointment for which they had asked: 'Read them, and know we know your worthiness.'

One by one, as the men read, they paled and dropped to their knees to beg mercy of the King. 'By your own counsel,' he said implacably, 'it is suppressed and killed. Your faults are open.' Exeter formally charged them with high treason, and Henry sentenced them at once to death. Under guard they were swiftly removed. When they had vanished the King stepped out upon the windy quay to take boat to his ship, *The Trinity*, in Southampton Water. 'Cheerly to sea!' he cried, 'The signs of war advance! No King of England if not King of France!'

Like a moving city, the majestic fleet sailed in the August weather across the Channel to Harfleur. In Paris Charles the Sixth, the French King, a man who, though under fifty, was prematurely aged and unstable in intellect, held council with the Dauphin, the Dukes of Berri and Bretagne, Charles Delabreth who was Constable of France, and other lords of the realm. The Dauphin made light of the threatened English invasion. What was Henry, he said, but a shallow, wayward youth? The Constable of France, more clear-sighted, strongly disagreed, and King Charles remembered with haunted fear the tale of the battle of Crécy and that fearful name, Edward the Black Prince of Wales: 'This is a stem of that victorious stock.'

Outside the English ambassadors had waited. Immediately they entered, the Duke of Exeter handed to Charles a paper that set out King Henry's claim to France. 'If we do not resign, what follows?' asked Charles; and Exeter replied, 'If you hide the crown even in your hearts, there he will rake for it.' For the Dauphin Exeter brought a message of 'scorn and defiance, slight regard, contempt.' Though Charles, dreading the inevitable war, sought to defer his answer until the following day, it was plain what this must be.

Henry had already made his first conquest in France, the capture of Harfleur, urging on his men with an eloquent oration:

> 'Once more unto the breach, dear friends, once more;
> Or close the wall up with our English dead.
> In peace there's nothing so becomes a man
> As modest stillness, and humility:
> But when the blast of war blows in our ears
> Then imitate the action of the tiger . . .'

And at the last, just before the scaling-ladders were placed against the walls, and the English prepared for a rush that would bear down all before them, Henry cried,

> 'I see you stand like greyhounds in the slips,
> Straining upon the start. The game's afoot:
> Follow your spirit; and upon this charge
> Cry 'God for Harry, England, and Saint George!'

With Harfleur taken after much loss, and safely under the English banner, King Henry sought to retire to Calais for a time with his weakened army. But the enemy was in anxious expectation. Princess Katharine, the French King's daughter, resourcefully took English lessons from her gentlewoman Alice, who had been in England and who could teach her such useful words as 'hand' and 'fingers' and 'nails,' 'elbow' (which she called 'de bilbow') and 'chin' and 'foot'. Elsewhere in the palace her father, her brother, and the lords discussed sterner things. Should they attack the English who had crossed the River Somme? Angrily, the lords asked themselves how the barbarous English could show such mettle, bred as they were in a raw and foggy island, and raised upon the barley-broth they knew as ale. King Charles spoke suddenly in one of his outbursts of angry desperation. Montjoy, the herald, must greet Henry with their sharp defiance. By name – Bourbon and Berri, Alençon and Brabant, Bar and Burgundy – he summoned the muster-roll of French chivalry, commanding his high dukes, great princes, barons, lords, and knights to fall upon Henry as the melted Alpine snow into the valleys: 'Go down upon him, you have power enough, and make him prisoner.'

Henry's army was fighting its way through Picardy. Fluellen, a voluble and gallant Welsh captain, had conceived great admiration for the bearing of a man named Pistol; but his admiration faded when this Pistol, no other than Falstaff's former lieutenant, asked him to intercede with the Duke of Exeter for the life of Bardolph. It seemed that Bardolph had stolen a sacred vessel from a church. 'Let not hemp his windpipe suffocate,' said Pistol in language that was new to Fluellen. 'Exeter has given the doom of death for a pyx of little price.' Upon Fluellen's refusal to help, Pistol stormed at him in such phrases that the little Welshman said in astonishment to his friend Captain Gower, 'Cannot you hear it lighten and thunder?' Gower remembered Pistol now: 'He is an arrogant counterfeit rascal that goes now and then to the wars so that he may fare well when he returns to London under the guise of a soldier. These fellows learn the great commanders' names and where service was done at such-and-such a place; who came off bravely, who was shot, and who was disgraced; and they dress all this up in the phrases of war, with the latest military oaths to garnish it. What a beard cut like a general's, and a soldier's suit, will do among foaming bottles and ale-washed wits, is wonderful to think about. You must learn, Fluellen, to know these tricksters, or one day you may be marvellously mistaken.'

It was then that King Henry approached and asked Fluellen what had happened in the latest skirmish. Fluellen answered that the Duke of Exeter had lost no men except one that was likely to be executed for robbing a church. He was called Bardolph.

Henry, making no sign at the once familiar name, said simply that he desired all similar offenders to be condemned. At this moment, ushered in by the sound of a trumpet, the French herald Montjoy appeared with a defiant challenge: 'This from my King. Say to Henry of England: "Though we seemed dead, we did but slumber. Advantage is a better soldier than rashness. Now our voice is imperial: England shall repent its folly, see its weakness, and admire our clemency." '

King Henry responded that, weakened by sickness as his army was, he had not sought a battle. Yet, though the few men he had were now almost no better than so many French, they would continue to advance even if the enemy's strength was double what it was.

'I hope they will not come upon us now,' said the Duke of Gloucester as Montjoy galloped away; and the King replied, 'We are in God's hand, brother, not in theirs.'

That night, October 24, 1415, Saint Crispin's Eve, the rival armies encamped near the village of Maisoncelles and the castle of Agincourt. The French spent the night, gambling, drinking, and bragging of feats they would do upon the morrow. 'Alas, poor Harry of England!' said the Constable of France, 'he longs not for the morning as we do.'

The armies were just fifteen hundred paces from each other. Camp fires flared or sparkled through the chilly darkness; each army heard the distant sounds of preparation as well as those among its own tents. Horses neighed, and armour clashed as the armourers made their rounds long after midnight. In the early hours of St Crispin's Day the ominous noises spoke to each other across the bare plain. It was three in the morning when King Henry, concealed in a cloak he had borrowed from old Sir Thomas Erpingham, walked out to survey the camp and to ponder on the task before them. His soldiers, sadly sparse against the great army of the French, clustered round braziers of glowing wood. A few, unable to sleep, moved about restlessly, and one of these was the first personage the King met. '*Qui va là?*' exclaimed Pistol. When the King replied 'A friend,' Pistol said in resolute suspicion, 'Are you officer, or are you base, common, and popular?'

'I am a gentleman of a company,' replied the King. 'What are you?'

'As good a gentleman as the Emperor.'

'Then you are a better than the King?'

'The King?' said Pistol. 'The King's a heart of gold, a lad of life, an imp of fame, of parents good, of fist most valiant. I love the lovely bully . . . What's your name?'

'Harry Le Roy.'

Pistol was dubious: 'Le Roy? A Cornish name. Are you of Cornish crew?'

'No,' said Henry, 'I am a Welshman.'

Pistol blazed. 'Know you Fluellen? Tell him I'll knock his leek about his pate upon St Davy's Day.'

'You should wear your dagger in your cap that day,' said Henry. 'I am his kinsman.'

'I scorn you then!' roared Pistol. He moved hastily into the night, hissing over his shoulder, 'My name is Pistol called.'

As Henry moved back into the shadows, Fluellen passed him, recommending Captain Gower to speak lower and to examine what happened in the wars of Pompey the Great. 'The enemy is loud,' remonstrated Gower. 'You hear him all night.' Fluellen took him by the arm. 'If the enemy is an ass, and a fool, and a prating coxcomb, is it meet, think you, that we should also be an ass and a fool and a prating coxcomb. In your conscience now?' They, too, disappeared into the darkness, and Henry walked over to a brazier where three soldiers named John Bates, Alexander Court, and Michael Williams sat huddled together dismally. Dawn was just beginning to flake in the eastern sky, and Williams pointed to it: 'We see the beginning of the day, but I think we shall never see its end.' He turned at Henry's tread: 'Who goes there?' And when the King answered that he served under Sir Thomas Erpingham, Williams asked, 'What does he think of our chances?'

'Even,' said Henry, 'as if we were men wrecked upon a sandbank and looking to be washed off by the next tide.'

'He has not told that to the King?' asked Bates. It was not right, Henry responded, that he should, for the King was but a man as they were, and no one should disclose any fear to him lest, by showing it himself, he might dishearten his army.

Round the brazier, under the slowly paling sky, the four debated the King's responsibility to his men for venturing them in battle. Henry spoke here with a personal anxiety that the others did not discern. At the last he was exclaiming, 'I myself heard the King say he would not be ransomed,' when the blunt soldier, Williams, inflexible in argument, suddenly interrupted: 'Ay, he said so! To make us fight cheerfully. But when our throats are cut, he may be ransomed, and we shall be none the wiser.'

'If I live to see it,' the King said, 'I will never trust his word afterwards.'

Williams laughed in contempt. 'Who can you be? Your poor displeasure against a monarch's! You as may well try to turn the sun to ice by fanning it with a peacock's feather. "You'll never trust his word afterwards!" Come, that's a foolish saying.'

'You speak too fiercely,' said the King in his quietest voice, one with an edge his court would have recognised. 'At another time I would be angry with you.'

Williams said promptly, 'Then let it be a quarrel between us—if we live. But how shall I know you again?' They exchanged gloves, vowing to wear them in their caps. 'If ever I live to see your glove,' said Henry, 'I will challenge it, even though I take you in the King's company.'

'Keep your word!' said Williams gruffly. 'Fare you well.' Rising from his place by the now smouldering brazier, he strode off into the morning while John Bates, as he stretched sleepily, murmured, 'Be friends, you English fools, be friends. We have French quarrels enough on our hands.' Bidding Bates and Court farewell, the King walked on through the camp until he reached a place, away from the now mustering men and the line of the fires, where for a moment he was unobserved. There he halted, saying to himself, 'Upon the King! . . . Our lives, our souls, our debts, our wives and children, even our sins, lay all upon the King! He must bear all!' And he reflected upon the burden that a King must shoulder with nothing for his reward but ceremony and empty pomp. How infinitely happier was the private man!

He was pondering this when Sir Thomas Erpingham hurried to him to say that his nobles, made anxious by his absence, were seeking him through the camp. 'Good old knight,' said the King, 'I pray you collect them at my tent'; and as Erpingham went from him, he fell upon his knees, praying, 'O god of battles, steel my soldiers' hearts, possess them not with fear!' His brother Gloucester called to him, and Henry, rising and looking towards the east where a pale sun gleamed above the field of Agincourt, said simply, 'The day, my friends, and all things, stay for me!' He hastened towards his tent through a camp now fully astir.

Among the French, astir also, the Constable and the Dauphin listened to a mocking report of the English army, ragged and hopeless: 'The knavish crows fly overhead, impatient for their hour.' The Dauphin exclaimed, 'Let us go send the English dinners and fresh suits, and after fight with them.' Laughing together, the lords hurried out to a battle that seemed to be won already, for the French outnumbered the weary English by five to one.

At that moment, in the English camp, the Earl of Westmoreland was wishing, 'O, that we now had here but one ten thousand of those men in England that do no work to-day!' It was on these words that the King entered the circle of his lords. 'Who's he that wishes so? My cousin Westmoreland? No, my fair cousin, if we are marked to die, we are enough to do our country loss; and if we live, the fewer men, the greater share of honour. No, do not wish one more! If any man fears to fight with us to-day, let him go home: we would not die in that man's company.' He looked proudly round his friends. 'This day is called the feast of Crispian. He that outlives it and makes safe return will stand up proudly when this day is named and glory in the thought of Crispian. Yearly he will greet his friends and say "Tomorrow is Saint Crispian" ... All of us, familiar to him then as household words, Harry the King, Bedford and Exeter, Warwick and Talbot, Salisbury and Gloucester, will be remembered as the wine goes round and ushers in the feast of Crispian.' His voice rang across the camp:

> 'We few, we happy few, we band of brothers;
> For he today that sheds his blood with me
> Shall be my brother.'

He cried 'God be with you all!' and the answering cheer was taken up along the English lines. It still hung in the air when Montjoy, the French herald, bore to the King a message from the Constable of France, again urging Henry to yield. The King replied that the English were warriors for a working-day. They had neither gilt nor plume; they were draggled by long marching in the painful field. 'But, by the mass, our hearts are in the trim. So save your labour, Montjoy! Come no more for ransom!'

Montjoy rode back to the glitter of the French army as it waited, beneath its billowing standards, in line of battle. The English archers stood ready to launch their first arrow-flight across the plain.

Very soon the battle raged, and the furious morning was not spent before the Frenchmen knew that these despised English held the field. Over-confidence vanished in the bitter realities of the fray; but the French fought on blindly, seeking to redeem their early losses and their pressing shame. Some of those that fled pounced upon the boys left in charge of the English baggage and slew them: an offence against the law of arms that roused King Henry to immediate and unsparing revenge. 'Until now,' he said, 'I have not known anger since I came to France.'

At length, in the waning of St Crispin's Day, the herald Montjoy, his face strained and sad, stood once more before King Henry. Now he asked only that the French might have leave to cross the field to take and bury their dead. Henry replied, 'I tell you, Montjoy, I know not if the day be ours or no'; and Montjoy bowed his head: 'The day is yours.'

'Praised be God, and not our strength for it!' said the King. 'What is the castle called that stands hard by?'

'We call it Agincourt.'

'Then,' ordained the King, 'call we this the field of Agincourt, fought upon the day of Crispin Crispianus.'

The English soldiers, tired but jubilant, gathered while Montjoy, with the English heralds, returned to the strewn battlefield. Henry, noticing a burly figure standing apart, whispered to Exeter who called imperatively, 'Soldier, come to the King!'

Michael Williams saluted Henry. 'Soldier,' the King said to him, 'why do you wear that glove in your cap?' And Williams answered stoutly, 'It belongs to a man I should fight with if he were alive; a rascal that swaggered with me last night. If I see my glove in his cap, I have sworn to take him a box of the ear.'

'Keep that vow when you meet him,' said the King; and Williams promised, 'So I will, my liege, as I live.' He saluted and moved off. The King, taking from beneath his cloak the glove that Williams had given to him in the daybreak, motioned to Fluellen the Welshman: 'Here, Fluellen, wear this favour for me and stick it in your cap. When Alençon and myself were down together in battle, I plucked this glove from his helm. If any man challenge this, he is a friend to Alençon and an enemy to us.' In his delight Fluellen's Welsh accent was stronger than ever. 'Your grace does me the greatest honour that can be desired in the heart of his subjects. I would fain see the man that shall find himself aggriefed at this glove.' Like a cheerful cockerel he strutted off into the camp, and he had not gone far when Michael Williams barred his way.

'Sir,' said Williams, pointing to his own cap, 'do you know this glove?'

'Know it? I know it is a glove,' said Fluellen.

'I know this one,' cried Williams, staring at Fluellen's cap and touching the glove the King had placed there. 'Thus I challenge it.' He hit Fluellen in the face.

The Welshman bristled with anger. 'As arrant a traitor as any is in the universal world, or in France, or in England! I charge you, in his majesty's name, apprehend this man, he's a friend of the Duke of Alençon's. A most contagious treason as you shall find in a summer's day . . . But, look you, here is his majesty.'

'What is the quarrel?' said Henry gravely.

'My liege,' Williams said. 'This was my glove. Here is its fellow. He that I gave it to promised to wear it in his cap. I promised to strike him if he did, and I have been as good as my word.'

While Fluellen spluttered angrily, the King took his own glove from Williams and placed beside it its companion. 'Look, soldier, here! I am the man you promised to strike . . . How can you make me satisfaction?'

Williams, amazed, said with his stern directness, 'My liege, all offence comes from the heart. None came from mine to offend your majesty. You appeared to me as a common man. Witness the night, your garments, your lowliness. Whatever you received under that disguise, I beseech your majesty to call it your own fault, not mine. You came not like yourself. Therefore I ask your grace to pardon me.'

Henry was smiling now. 'Here, uncle Exeter, fill this glove with crowns and give it to the man. Keep it, fellow, and wear it for an honour in your cap until I challenge you. Fluellen, you must needs be friends with him.'

'By this day and this light,' said Fluellen, 'the fellow has mettle enough. Hold, there is twelve pence for you; and I pray you to keep out of brawls and prabbles and quarrels and dissensions, and it will be the better for you.'

They broke off, for a herald had entered with a paper. 'My liege, here is the number of the slaughtered French.' Henry read it aloud. That day the French had lost ten thousand men. The High Constable was dead; with him, Jaques of Chatillon, Admiral of France; the Great Master of France, Sir Guichard Dolphin; the master of the cross-bows Lord Rambures; the Dukes of Alençon, Brabant, and Bar; the lords Grandpré, Roussi, Fauconberg, and Foix, Beaumont and Marle, Vaudemont and Lestrale . . .

Henry lifted his head: 'Here was a royal fellowship of death! Where is the number of our English dead?' And when the herald handed him another paper, he read from it slowly: 'Edward the Duke of York, the Earl of Suffolk, Sir Richard Ketley, Davy Gam, esquire: none else of name, and of all other men but five and twenty. O God, Thine arm was here, and not to us but to Thine arm alone, ascribe we praise!'

Presently, when the victorious army streamed from the field, the peasants heard the soldiers singing as they marched down towards the village of Maisoncelles:

> 'Our King went forth to Normandy,
> With grace and might of chivalry;
> The God for him wrought marvellously,
> Wherefore England may call and cry,
> *Deo gratias! . . .*'

King Henry, 'star of England', and his men, returned home to a magnificent welcome. In the spring they were once more in France for the King to make a final settlement. And it was there among the English tents on a March morning immediately after St David's Day, that Fluellen had his private revenge upon Pistol. The braggart had come to him upon St David's Day itself, offering bread and salt and desiring him to eat the leek that he wore in his Welsh cap. Now Fluellen intercepted Pistol, cudgelled him heartily, and obliged him to eat the leek to the last morsel. 'When you take occasions to see leeks hereafter, I pray you mock not at them, that is all.'

Pistol, left alone, reflected wearily that he was growing old, and that he had no one now to turn to, for his wife in England was dead. Still, a rogue could find some way to live. He dragged himself to his feet: 'A cutpurse I will be . . . and patches I will find for all my cudgelled scars, and swear I got them in the Frenchmen's wars.'

Now, at the city of Troyes in Champagne, the Kings of France and England met for both a treaty of peace and, as a further union between their countries, the betrothal of King Henry to the Princess Katharine. Henry, more skilled as soldier than wooer, struggled to address her in French while she and her gentlewoman laughed without malice at his attempts.

'Your majestee,' said Katharine, ' 'ave fausse French enough to deceive de most sage demoiselle dat is en France.' Henry addressed her in his plainest English. 'By my honour, I love you, Kate. Though my stubborn outside, my aspect of iron, may frighten a lady when I come to woo her, yet in faith, Kate, the older I grow, the better I shall appear. So put off your maiden blushes. Take me by the hand, and say "Harry of England, I am yours," and no sooner have I heard this than I will tell you aloud, "England is yours, Ireland is yours, France is yours, and Harry Plantagenet is yours" – one who, if he be not fellow with the best king, you shall find the best king of good fellows.' He took her hand: 'Come, your answer in broken music; for your voice is music, and your English broken: therefore, queen of all, Katharine, break your mind to me in broken English. Will you have me?'

Katharine hesitated: 'Dat is as it sall please de roi, mon père.'

'Nay,' declared Henry, 'it will please him well, Kate; it shall please him.'

'Den,' Katharine said, 'it sall also content me'; and Henry cried, 'Upon that, I call you my queen.'

On returning to the chamber, the French King and Queen and the French and English lords found Henry embracing the Princess. 'My royal cousin,' said the Duke of Burgundy, 'teach you our Princess English?'

'I would have her learn, my fair cousin,' said Henry, 'how perfectly I love her – and that is good English.' To the King of France he said merely, 'Shall Kate be my wife?' And, upon Charles's reply, 'Take her, fair son,' the King led Katharine forward, and, to a royal trumpet-flourish, saluted her as his sovereign queen.

Queen Isabel of France spoke the last words: 'God, the best maker of all marriages, combine your hearts in one, your realms in one. Let Englishmen be French, French Englishmen.'

An answering 'Amen!' filled the hall; and Henry of England, as he stood there with Katharine of France, remembered another afternoon beyond the gulf of war, and heard his voice saying in his own Presence Chamber, 'May I with right and conscience make this claim?'

THE WARS OF THE ROSES

(KING HENRY VI AND KING RICHARD III)

HENRY the Fifth was dead; and round his coffin in Westminster Abbey the peers, led by his brothers, Humphrey Duke of Gloucester, now Protector of the realm, and the Duke of Bedford, now Regent of France, stood in deepest mourning: 'King Henry the Fifth, too famous to live long. England never lost a King of so much worth.' Their solemnities were interrupted by three messengers with grievous news. Nearly the whole of France had revolted from the English; Charles the Dauphin had been crowned King at Rheims; and the English army in Orleans was heavily besieged.

At once the Duke of Bedford travelled with all speed back to France. Before he arrived there, the enemy, freshly inspired by Joan La Pucelle, a shepherd's daughter from Lorraine, had captured Orleans. But Bedford, with Lord Talbot, the renowned English soldier so feared by the French, reclaimed the town; and again the English began to make head, though Bedford did not live to see it.

In England meantime the great peers fought for power. Henry the Sixth as yet was a mere youth, and round him ambitious factions were seeking to rule. One summer day John Beaufort, the Earl of Somerset, and Richard Plantagenet quarrelled fiercely in the riverside gardens of the Temple. Each of them plucked a rose as his badge – Somerset a red rose, Plantagenet a white one, and their supporters did likewise. It was the beginning of what would be known as the long-drawn Wars of the Roses.

In France, after much fierce and complex fighting, Lord Talbot was cornered, defeated, and killed by the French army under the Dauphin and Joan La Pucelle. Talbot's son John fell in the same battle, and the old warrior, embracing the body before his own death, said with a last proud effort, 'Poor boy! he smiles, methinks, as who should say, "Had death been French, then death had died to-day!"' It was not long before the English, under the brave and stubborn Richard Plantagenet, now created Duke of York, revenged themselves by capturing Joan and sending her to her death at Rouen. For a time the war came to a halt. Under a truce the Dauphin consented for the sake of policy to reign in France as viceroy for the English, knowing that he would soon get supreme power.

During the fighting the Earl of Suffolk (later to be Duke) had taken prisoner the beautiful Princess Margaret, daughter of the Duke of Anjou who called himself the King of Naples. For his own purposes Suffolk undertook to achieve a marriage between this strange and wilful girl and his own master, King Henry the Sixth. 'Margaret shall now be Queen and rule the King; but I will rule both her, the King and realm.'

Suffolk, bland man of the world, was overweeningly confident. Nobody could rule Margaret, a deadly foe to anyone who crossed her. Henry's Queen would always mean far more than her gentle heavy-eyed husband in his long gown, a man who, as he grew older, was fitted better for a hermitage than for the complex affairs of state. During his long reign the land was in continual turmoil, with the factions of the Red Rose (espoused by the King's party) and of the White Rose (that of the Yorkists) passing in and out of power during a sequence of ferocious battles. France was neglected and lost. In the midst of the wars at home came the brief rebellion of the Kentishmen under a roaring braggart Jack Cade, who was killed at last, as a fugitive, by a Kentish squire at Ashford.

To be near the throne in those years was to court death, and many such redoubtable figures as Humphrey of Gloucester and the Duke of Suffolk – who was captured and beheaded by Channel pirates – lost their lives before the wars were sharpened to a conflict between Margaret and the Duke of York, who claimed the throne. She killed him savagely after the battle of Wakefield; and his sons, the very tall, flaxen-haired Edward, the petulant George, and the hunchbacked Richard, took their father's place as Margaret's inexorable enemies. Among all this, poor Henry the Sixth, harried from place to place, battle to battle, longed only for peace as he did upon the field of Towton. Momentarily alone in the twilight, he meditated: 'Is not the shepherd happier beneath his hawthorn-bush than a King beneath his canopy of state? Better the shepherd's homely meal of curds and water than a royal banquet and a golden cup; better his sleep beneath a spreading tree than the royal couch where care and treason wait.'

In the varying fortunes of the war Henry would be imprisoned in the Tower of London. The growing power in the realm was the young Richard of York, who had been newly created Duke of Gloucester, just as his brother George, whom Margaret called 'a quicksand of deceit,' was now Duke of Clarence. Deformed though Richard was, with a hump on his back, a withered arm, and a club foot, he had a piercing, ruthless intellect and a plausible charm. Very early he set his mind on the throne. He said to himself, 'Why, I can smile, and murder as I smile, and cry "Content" to that which grieves my heart, and wet my cheeks with artificial tears, and frame my face to all occasions.'

First, he had to dispose of those who stood between him and the crown. His elder brother, the Earl of March, had become King Edward IV. The civil wars appeared to have ended when Margaret, valiant in decline, was defeated at Tewkesbury after a desperate oration to her soldiers: 'Courage! what cannot be avoided 'twere childish weakness to lament or fear.' She was captured; her son, the Prince of Wales, was slain; and Richard of Gloucester hurried to London to kill the gentle Henry in the Tower. 'For this, among the rest, was I ordained,' said Richard, thrusting home his dagger; and Henry said with his dying voice, 'Ay, and for much more slaughter after this.' Richard, standing by the body, said softly to himself, 'I have neither pity, love, nor fear. King Henry and the prince, his son, are gone. My brother Clarence, your time is next – and then the rest must follow.'

For a while there might be peace that the troubled land needed sorely, though one man desired it less. Richard, as he walked down a street near the Tower of London, said thoughtfully to himself, 'Now is the winter of our discontent made glorious summer by this sun of

York.' But he cared nothing for a 'weak, piping time of peace': that very day it must be ended. Determined, he said, to prove a villain, he had devised a curious plot to snare his elder brother George of Clarence. King Edward had already received a prophecy that an unnamed 'G' would be the murderer of his heirs, and the hint should be enough for the superstitious King.

An armed guard now clanked through the street towards the Tower. In its midst was Clarence, a prisoner; and Richard went up to him with the innocent inquiry, 'Brother, what means this?' When Clarence replied that the King had committed him because of some foolish prophecy, Richard said with a great show of anger that all this was the Queen's doing. The imprisonment, he promised, should be brief; but after his brother had passed from sight, he said softly, 'Go, take your path, but ne'er return by it. Clarence, I do love you so that I will shortly send your soul to heaven.' King Edward had been taken seriously ill. Richard pondered the possibilities: Clarence, he decided, must die first, and he limped purposefully away.

Before finally silencing Clarence, he fulfilled another plan dear to his heart. He had resolved to wed no less a person than the daughter-in-law of Henry the Sixth, Lady Anne Neville as she was known, whose husband, the young heir to the throne, he had stabbed at Tewkesbury. It was bravado that made Richard attempt this extraordinary wooing. He stopped the hearse of Henry the Sixth as it was borne through London, with Lady Anne following it, and after listening in smiling patience to her fierce outcries, offered her his love. On being repulsed with furious scorn, he handed her his sword, laid open his breast, and invited her to kill him. 'Nay, do not pause; 'twas I that killed your husband, but 'twas your beauty that provoked me thus . . . Nay, come, dispatch; 'twas I that killed King Henry, but 'twas your heavenly face that set me on.' Twice she prepared for the stroke; twice, looking into his smiling eyes, she drew back. Finally, she dropped the sword. Richard knew that, incredibly, his peace was made and that he would have his wish. When, equally incredulous, she had left him, he stood a while, reflecting, 'Was ever woman in this humour wooed? Was ever woman in this humour won?' He chuckled: 'She finds I am a marvellous proper man . . . Then here I needs must buy a looking-glass.'

Later, when Clarence was imprisoned and King Edward lay very sick, Richard stormed into the palace, crying that the Queen and her relatives had complained about him to the King and that they had caused his brother to be committed to the Tower. The Queen was seeking wearily to reply to him when a figure in black, the former Queen Margaret, her hair dishevelled and her eyes blazing, suddenly confronted her with the bitter exclamation, 'Your honour, state, and seat are due to me.' Raging, she called down her curses upon them all, and especially upon Richard of Gloucester, the 'rag of honour' and the 'son of hell': 'If the heavens have any grievous plague in store, exceeding those that I can wish upon you, O let them keep it till your sins be ripe!' She and Richard were still at defiance when a King's messenger summoned the Queen and the lords. Richard, contemplating his plans with quiet relish, stayed behind to receive a pair of ruffians whom he dispatched presently with a warrant to murder Clarence.

In the Tower Clarence was relating to the Keeper, Sir Robert Brakenbury, his night's fearful dream: one in which, upon a voyage to France, it seemed that his brother Richard had struck him overboard so that he was drowned in 'the slimy bottom of the deep'. Thence he had passed to the regions after death, a kingdom of perpetual night haunted by the ghosts of those he had abandoned or had slain. Brakenbury was leaving him to rest when the murderers arrived from Richard with their warrant. One of these men was merciless, one troubled by his conscience; but they proceeded together with their task, awakened Clarence, and in spite of his entreaties stabbed him to death and carried his body to be drowned in a butt of wine in the adjoining room.

The news, brought by the first murderer, for the second had repented and run away, reached Richard at his town house while King Edward, now at the point of death, was urging the rival factions of his court to settle their quarrel and to live in amity. Peace was being made, as the King desired, when Richard entered and added his own assurances of friendship. But in a moment, while the Queen entreated her husband to restore Clarence to favour, Richard cried in well-simulated grief, 'Who knows not that the noble Duke is dead? You do him injury to scorn him thus.' The King, deeply disstressed, exclaimed that a first order for Clarence's death had been reversed; but Richard said sternly, 'He, poor soul, by your first order died.'

The shock caused a stroke from which the King did not recover. Very soon Richard found himself Protector of the realm, able – with the help of the Duke of Buckingham – to send the Queen's relatives, Rivers and Grey, to execution at Pomfret Castle, and to commit to the Tower, for apparent safety, the child Prince of Wales and his brother the child Duke of York. The Prince had been brought up from Ludlow Castle in the West, and York taken from his mother to meet him. Innocent and doomed, the children greeted each other with all ceremony. 'Richard of York!' said the Prince, 'How fares our loving brother?' And York answered, 'Well, my dread lord – so must I call you now.' It was dark as they stood hesitantly in the torchlight among the peers outside the gate of the Tower.

'What, will you go into the Tower, my lord?' said little York to his brother, who replied, 'My Lord Protector will have it so.' York shook his head: 'I shall not sleep in quiet at the Tower; I fear my uncle Clarence's angry ghost.'

'I fear no uncles dead,' said the Prince.

Richard put his arm round him: 'Nor none that live, I hope.'

'If they live,' said the boy, 'I hope I need not fear . . . But come, my brother, with a heavy heart I go into the Tower.' The little procession moved forward beneath the arch, and the gate closed.

The subtle Duke of Buckingham, with hope of favours ahead, was working in Richard's cause. He now asked Sir William Catesby, Richard's most loyal follower, whether the influential Lord Hastings and Lord Stanley would be willing to support Richard in a claim to the throne. Hastings was an easy-going man whose association with a notorious woman of the town named Jane Shore had caused much scandal. Though Catesby doubted whether his mission would succeed, he went at once to Hastings on the pretext of summoning him to a council meeting. 'What shall we do,' asked Buckingham of Richard, 'if we perceive that he will not yield?' And Richard, with an evil glance that chilled even Buckingham, replied, 'Chop off his head, man! Somewhat will we do.' He added suddenly, 'When I am King, claim from me the earldom of Hereford that was my brother's.'

Catesby chose to call upon Hastings just after daybreak. But before he got there, Hastings had been roused already by a message in which the Earl of Derby urged that they should ride together to the north and escape from pressing danger. Though he turned this away with a laugh, even his easy mind was troubled for a moment when Catesby entered. 'What news in this our tottering state?' asked Hastings; and Catesby answered in a low voice, 'A reeling world indeed, my lord . . . It will not stand upright till Richard wear the crown.'

'I'll have this crown of mine cut from my shoulders,' said Hastings, 'before I see the English crown so misplaced.' But Catesby was grave: 'My lord, Richard hopes to find you in his party. He sends you word that this very morning Rivers and Grey, your enemies, the kindred of the Queen, will die at Pomfret.'

'I do not mourn for that,' said Hastings, 'but I cannot give my voice to Richard to bar King Edward's heirs in true descent.'

Catesby appeared to be thinking aloud: 'It is terrible for men to die quite unprepared.'

'O monstrous, monstrous!' said Hastings lightly. 'So it has fallen out with Grey and Rivers. It will be so, no doubt, with some who think themselves as safe as we are – men as dear to princely Richard and to Buckingham.' Catesby, smiling, said softly, 'They love you well.'

In the clear morning Hastings rode to the Tower where, presently, the Protector's Council gathered to plan the coronation of the boy Edward the Fifth. It was a strange meeting. Richard, apparently in a good humour, arrived late and at once asked the Bishop of Ely to send for some fine strawberries that grew in his Holborn garden at Ely Place. Then he withdrew for some minutes with Buckingham, leaving the other councillors around the table. When he re-entered he was in a cold rage. Bending across the table, he asked malevolently, 'What do they deserve that conspire my doom with plots of deadly witchcraft?' After a shocked pause, Hastings answered, 'Death, my gracious lord.' And Richard held out his arm: 'Behold! my arm is like a sapling that is withered up. And who has done this thing but Edward's Queen – ' and he turned his gaze full upon Hastings – 'in league with that abhorrèd witch, Jane Shore.'

Hastings faltered, 'If they have done this thing, my noble lord—.' And Richard stormed back, 'If? You, the protector of this wretched Shore – you dare to speak of "ifs"! You are a traitor!' Without looking at the condemned man, he cried, 'Off with his head! Until I see his head I will not dine to-day.' He strode from the room; and while Hastings sat dazed, Catesby touched his arm: 'Dispatch, my lord! The Duke would be at dinner.' Hastings stumbled to his feet among the guards that closed in on him: 'Then lead me to the block. Bear him my head . . . They smile at me that shortly shall be dead.'

Nothing but the children in the Tower stood now between Richard and the throne. Neither he nor Buckingham intended this to be a bar. First, Buckingham went to the Lord Mayor and leading citizens of London, suggesting that the children were illegitimate and that Richard must be the rightful heir. Though at first he could get no response from the City worthies, he summoned them to Baynard's Castle, Richard's house beside the Thames, where its owner took care to be found on the walls, meditating on a devotional book with a bishop on each side of him. By now the Lord Mayor and citizens were in a more responsive mood, and when Buckingham entreated Richard to assume the government of the realm, not as Protector but as King by right of birth, the cheering behind him grew louder.

Very humbly, Richard refused the high request. Aided by the protestations of Buckingham and Catesby, the citizens repeated it, and Richard, carefully calculating his time, said once more, 'Take it not amiss I cannot and I will not yield to you.' Buckingham made as if to go in angry impatience, drawing the citizens with him; and, as they streamed away, Richard mouthed to Catesby, 'Call them back!' When they returned, staring up at this picture of piety on the sunlit walls, he addressed them with all modesty: 'Since you will buckle fortune on my back, to bear its burden whether I will or not, I must have patience to endure the load.'

Swinging round, Buckingham cried, 'Then I salute you with this kingly title, "Long live King Richard, England's royal King!"' And the citizens repeated the shout, 'Long live King Richard!'

'To-morrow will it please you to be crowned?' said Buckingham hastily, to which Richard, his eyes again on the prayer-book, responded in great meekness: 'Even when you will, since you will have it so . . . Come, let us to our holy task again.'

In excitement the citizens dispersed. Buckingham looked up triumphantly as Richard, tossing the prayer-book in the air, caught it again as it fell.

Next day, when Elizabeth the Queen-Mother came to the Tower to visit her children, she met Richard's mother – the old Duchess of York – and his wife, the Lady Anne, arriving for the same purpose. But the Lieutenant of the Tower approached them, saying that the King had refused to permit their visit.

'The King?' exclaimed the Queen-Mother. 'Who is that?' Upon the Lieutenant's reply, 'I mean the Lord Protector,' she said fervently, 'Protect him from the kingly title!' She turned to greet Lord Stanley; but, bowing low to her and to the Duchess, he passed them and went straight up to Lady Anne: 'Come, Madam, you must go with me to Westminster, there to be crowned as Richard's lawful Queen.' To all three women the news was terrifying, but especially to Anne who cried out, 'Let me be anointed with deadly poison, and die ere men can say "God save the Queen!"' She had no remedy; Stanley waited in silence, and within the hour, standing dejectedly at Richard's side, she was crowned with him in the Abbey.

Hypocrisy had had its day. Richard had gained the crown, and he had now to keep it. As soon as he was enthroned in the pomp he had long coveted, he summoned Buckingham to him and said meaningly that the Princes in the Tower still lived. Buckingham, who had done enough, would not stir even when Richard flared out at him, 'Shall I be plain? I wish the children dead.' Asking for time to consider, he left the throne-room, and when he had gone the King muttered, 'The deep-revolving, witty Buckingham shall be no more my private counsellor.' Calling Catesby, he told him to let it be rumoured that Anne, the Queen, was sick and likely to die. To himself he said, 'I must be married to my brother Edward's daughter, or else my kingdom stands on brittle glass. But, first, murder her brothers!' And he ordered the daring and discontented James Tyrrel, who had just bowed before him, to dispatch the children in the Tower.

Now Buckingham came back to say that he had thought about

Richard's demand. But the King would not hear him speak; and when Buckingham, daring greatly at such a time as this, asked for fulfilment of the royal promise to give to him the earldom of Hereford, Richard swooped round with a furious 'I am not in the giving vein today.' No longer suavely sure, Buckingham watched the tyrant as, crowned and robed, he walked between the bowing courtiers. 'Is it even so?' he said. 'Does he think of me with such contempt? Was it for this that I made Richard King? . . . O let me remember Hastings, and be gone.' And he galloped away through the night towards his castle in Wales.

Tyrrel, that same night, returned with the tidings that the children in the Tower were dead. He had sent two men, Dighton and Forrest, to do the task, and as he repeated to himself what the men had said, he felt the terror of the deed as strongly as they had done. 'Here,' Forrest had told him, 'they lay in each other's arms, asleep. Their lips were four red roses on a stalk which in their summer beauty kissed each other.' Dighton could hardly bear to recall how the children were smothered. Though he felt as they did, Tyrrel concealed his feelings before Richard and said merely, 'My liege, the thing is done.'

Already Richard's Queen, Lady Anne, was dead. Now, all round, the usurper was threatened. Buckingham was in the field with a rebel force. More important, Henry Tudor, Earl of Richmond, was planning an invasion from Brittany. Long in exile, this stern warrior, then nearly thirty-eight years old, had become the head of the House of Lancaster; and, at a council of refugees in Brittany, he had promised, if he gained the crown, to marry Elizabeth of York, daughter of Edward the Fourth.

Such a marriage as this would unite the rival factions and bring the long conflict of the Roses to its end. But in England Richard sought Elizabeth for himself; first of all, he attempted to gain her mother's favour with the insolent confidence that had served him once with Lady Anne. Here the Queen-Mother would not respond. While she seemed to yield to Richard, she gave glad consent to Elizabeth's union with Richmond when the crown was won.

On every side the usurper was environed by bad news. Told that Richmond was on the sea, the King, swirling his great cloak around him, limped back to his throne with the wrathful cry, 'Is the chair empty? Is the sword unswayed? Is the King dead, the empire left to fall?' In Devon Sir William Courtenay and the Bishop of Exeter were in arms; in Kent, the Guildfords. Then good news came after bad: Buckingham had been captured, and Richard at once ordered his execution at Salisbury.

Relief was short, for no sooner had the King taken comfort from this quick revenge than Henry, Earl of Richmond, landed in his native Wales at Milford Haven, and pressed his march towards London. Immediately Richard's army moved out to meet him.

It came about, then, that on the night of August 21, 1485, the rival armies were encamped close to each other near the plain of Bosworth Field in Leicestershire. Half a mile from Richard lay the troops of the Earl of Derby whose son, George Lord Stanley, the King held as a hostage. If Derby did not join the royal army in the coming battle, Stanley's head was forfeit.

The evening was raw and windy. After ordering Sir Richard Ratcliff to come to his tent at midnight, the King sank into an uneasy sleep. Meanwhile Lord Derby had gone in secret to Richmond, promising that at the most convenient time next day he would give his aid. When Derby had been given a safe guard through the lines to his own camp, Richmond also fell to slumber.

It seemed both to him and to Richard that, as they slept, a group of phantoms flitted from tent to tent across the expanse of Bosworth Field. The first ghost was that of Prince Edward, Henry the Sixth's son, who said as he stood by the restlessly-stirring King, 'Let me sit heavy on your soul to-morrow! Think how you stabbed me in my prime of youth at Tewkesbury. Richard, despair and die.' But by Richmond he said, 'Be cheerful, for the souls of murdered princes fight on your behalf.'

Next came the ghost of Henry the Sixth, who said to Richard, 'Think on the Tower and think on Henry's end. Richard, despair and die!' and to Richmond, 'Virtuous and holy, conquer in the fight!' So the strange procession passed: Clarence, Rivers and Grey, the two young Princes, Hastings, Lady Anne, and, at the last, Buckingham. His ghost paused by Richard's couch: 'The first was I that helped you to the crown, the last was I that felt your tyranny. O, in the battle think of Buckingham, and die in terror of your guiltiness.' Beside Richmond the same ghostly voice breathed into the darkness: 'I died for hope e'er

I could lend you aid; but cheer your heart and be not now dismayed: God and good angels fight on Richmond's side, and Richard fall in height of all his pride.'

Now only silence and the night held Bosworth Field. Richard started from his dream with a sudden 'Give me another horse, bind up my wounds!' and then realised that he was awake, the lights burning blue, the sky starless, the next day's battle before him. He sank down again, still haunted. 'I shall despair,' he muttered to himself; 'There is no creature loves me, and if I die no soul will pity me . . . But wherefore should they? I find no pity for myself.' As he sat, burdened by conscience and fear, Sir Richard Ratcliff came to his tent to rouse him: 'Be not afraid of shadows, good my lord.' And Richard said wearily, 'Shadows have struck more terror to my soul than can ten thousand men.'

Henry of Richmond, on being roused upon the stroke of four, was telling his lords of the sweetest sleep, the fairest dream, that he had ever known. In the grey summer dawning he walked before his assembled army, saying that all good fought upon their side. 'What is Richard? One raised in blood, and one in blood established. Then sound trumpets, boldly, cheerfully. God and Saint George! Richmond and victory!'

The morning was still grey when Richard appeared before his troops. 'The sun,' he said sadly to Ratcliff and Catesby, 'will not be seen; the sky frowns upon our army . . . Well, what is that to me more than to Richmond?' As he planned the disposition of his forces, drawing out their lines upon the grass with his sword-point, the Duke of Norfolk brought a paper to him: 'This found I in my tent this morning.' Richard read the rhyme: 'Jockey of Norfolk, be not so bold, for Dickon your master is bought and sold,' and then crumpled the paper in disdain as a thing devised by the enemy. Going forward, he spoke to his soldiers: 'Whom do you fight with? They are vagabonds, rascals, and runaways, a scum of Bretons and base lackey peasants! And who leads them but a petty fellow, long kept in Brittany at our mother's cost?' Across the plain a drum was throbbing. 'Hark! I hear their drum. Fight, gentlemen of England! Fight, bold yeomen! And, archers, draw your arrows to the head!'

Now a messenger flung himself down before the King.

'What says Lord Derby?' cried Richard. 'Will he bring his power?'

'My lord,' said the messenger, 'he will not come.'

Richard shouted in wrath, 'Off with his son George's head!' But Norfolk restrained him: 'My lord, the enemy is past the marsh. Let George Stanley die when the battle is over.' Richard turned on his heel with a look of desperate resolution: 'Advance our standards! Victory stays for us!'

That day, wearing the crown upon his helmet, he fought like the gallant demon he was. His horse White Surrey was killed under him, but he continued to fight unmounted, brandishing a heavy spiked mace and calling upon Richmond, while his standard-bearer bravely kept the lions of England overhead. Slowly his forces were driven back, battling all the way, until Richard, weary at last and feeling that the devilish strength that sustained him had begun to ebb, cried, 'I think there be six Richmonds in the field. Five have I slain to-day instead of him. A horse! A horse! My kingdom for a horse!'

Suddenly the surge of battle brought him before Richmond and, with a harsh cry, he leapt upon his enemy. It was a prolonged and savage duel. Once Richmond was down, but he pulled himself clear, and in a final rally, blow upon blow, he beat in Richard's shield, forced him, struggling, to the earth, and ended all with a fierce dagger-stroke.

Richmond stood panting. 'God and your arms be praised, victorious friends! The day is ours!' Lord Derby, taking the crown from the dead man's helmet, placed it upon Richmond's head, crying, 'Long live King Henry the Seventh!' As his army doubled its cheering, Richmond said very slowly, 'God say Amen to all!' Then he asked anxiously, 'Is George Stanley living?' and received the answer, 'He is, my lord, and safe in Leicester town – whither, if it please you, we will now withdraw.'

'Proclaim it so!' said Richmond. He looked sad-faced across Bosworth Field: 'England has long been mad and scarred herself . . . But now let Richmond and Elizabeth resolve these wars of York and Lancaster, give smiling plenty and fair prosperous days!' As the bells struck noon on August 22, 1485, Henry, Earl of Richmond, King Henry the Seventh of England, turned his horse from the battlefield and rode beneath the stone-grey sky towards the town of Leicester.

The original Preface of 1807
by Charles & Mary Lamb

THE following Tales are meant to be submitted to the young reader as an introduction to the study of Shakespeare, for which purpose his words are used whenever it seemed possible to bring them in; and in whatever has been added to give them the regular form of a connected story, diligent care has been taken to select such words as might least interrupt the effect of the beautiful English tongue in which he wrote: therefore, words introduced into our language since his time have been as far as possible avoided.

In those tales which have been taken from the Tragedies, the young readers will perceive, when they come to see the source from which these stories are derived, that Shakespeare's own words, with little alteration, recur very frequently in the narrative as well as in the dialogue; but in those made from the Comedies the writers found themselves scarcely ever able to turn his words into the narrative form: therefore it is feared that, in them, dialogue has been made use of too frequently for young people not accustomed to the dramatic form of writing. But this fault, if it be a fault, has been caused by an earnest wish to give as much of Shakespeare's own words as possible: and if the *He said*, and *She said*, the question and the reply, should sometimes seem tedious to their young ears, they must pardon it, because it was the only way in which could be given to them a few hints and little foretastes of the great pleasure which awaits them in their elder years, when they come to the rich treasures from which these small and valueless coins are extracted; pretending to no other merit than as faint and imperfect stamps of Shakespeare's matchless image. Faint and imperfect images they must be called, because the beauty of his language is too frequently destroyed by the necessity of changing many of his excellent words into words far less expressive of his true sense, to make it read something like prose; and even in some few places, where his blank verse is given unaltered, as hoping from its simple plainness to cheat the young readers into the belief that they are reading prose, yet still his language being transplanted from its own natural soil and wild poetic garden, it must want much of its native beauty.

It has been wished to make these Tales easy reading for very young children. To the utmost of their ability the writers have constantly kept this in mind; but the subject of most of them made this a very difficult task. It was no easy matter to give the histories of men and women in terms familiar to the apprehension of a very young mind. For young ladies too, it has been the intention chiefly to write; because boys being generally permitted the use of their fathers' libraries at a much earlier age than girls are, they frequently have the best scenes of Shakespeare by heart, before their sisters are permitted to look into this manly book; and, therefore, instead of recommending these Tales to the perusal of young gentlemen who can read them so much better in the originals, their kind assistance is rather requested in explaining to their sisters such parts as are hardest for them to understand: and when they have helped them to get over the difficulties, then perhaps they will read to them (carefully selecting what is proper for a young sister's ear) some passage which has pleased them in one of these stories, in the very words of the scene from which it is taken; and it is hoped they will find that the beautiful extracts, the select passages, they may choose to give their sisters in this way will be much better relished and understood from their having some notion of the general story from one of these imperfect abridgments – which if they be fortunately so done as to prove delightful to any of the young readers, it is hoped that no worse effect will result than to make them wish themselves a little older, that they may be allowed to read the Plays at full length (such a wish will be neither peevish nor irrational). When the time and leave of judicious friends shall put them into their hands, they will discover in such of them as are here abridged (not to mention almost as many more, which are left untouched) many surprising events and turns of fortune, which for their infinite variety could not be contained in this little book, besides a world of sprightly and cheerful characters, both men and women, the humour of which it was feared would be lost if it were attempted to reduce the length of them.

What these Tales shall have been to the *young* readers, that, and much more it is the writers' wish that the true Plays of Shakespeare may prove to them in older years – enrichers of the fancy, strengtheners of virtue, a withdrawing from all selfish and mercenary thoughts, a lesson of all sweet and honourable thoughts and actions, to teach courtesy, benignity, generosity, humanity: for of examples, teaching these virtues, his pages are full.